Coronation Hymns

No. 1. All Hail the Power of Jesus' Name.

Edward Perronet. Oliver Holden.

1. All hail the pow'r of Je - sus' name, Let an - gels pros-trate fall;
2. Crown Him, ye morn-ing stars of light, Who fixed this earth-ly ball;
3. Sin - ners, whose love can ne'er for - get The wormwood and the gall,
4. Let ev - 'ry kin-dred, ev - 'ry tribe, On this ter-res-trial ball,
5. O that with yon-der sa-cred throng We at His feet may fall;

Bring forth the roy - al di - a - dem, And crown Him Lord of all;
Now hail the strength of Is-rael's might, And crown Him Lord of all;
Go, spread your tro-phies at His feet, And crown Him Lord of all;
To Him all maj - es - ty as - cribe, And crown Him Lord of all;
We'll join the ev - er - last-ing song, And crown Him Lord of all;

Bring forth the roy - al di - a - dem, And crown Him Lord of all.
Now hail the strength of Is-rael's might, And crown Him Lord of all.
Go, spread your tro-phies at His feet, And crown Him Lord of all.
To Him all maj - es - ty as - cribe, And crown Him Lord of all.
We'll join the ev - er - last-ing song, And crown Him Lord of all.

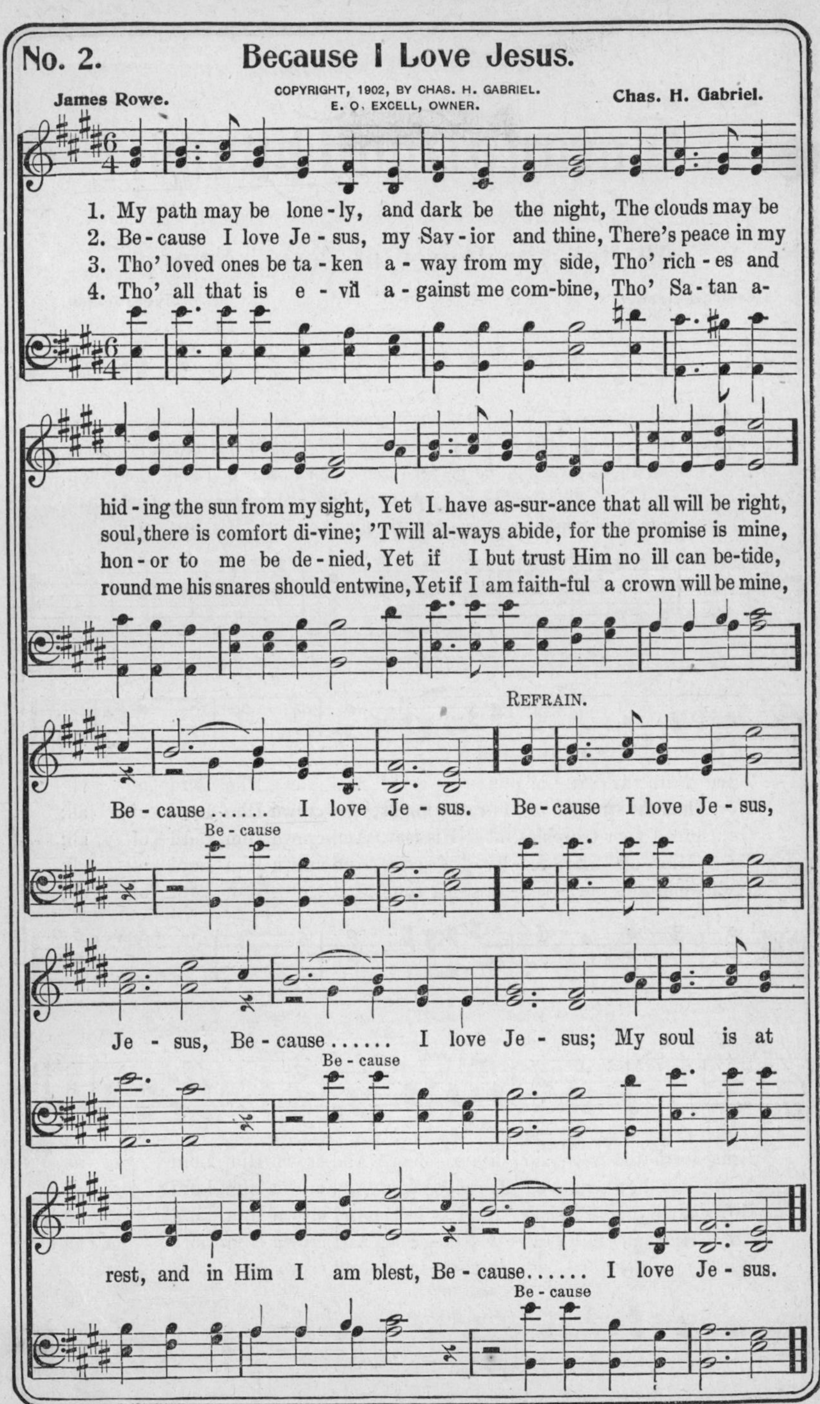
No. 2. Because I Love Jesus.
James Rowe.
COPYRIGHT, 1902, BY CHAS. H. GABRIEL.
E. O. EXCELL, OWNER.
Chas. H. Gabriel.
1. My path may be lone-ly, and dark be the night, The clouds may be hid-ing the sun from my sight, Yet I have as-sur-ance that all will be right,
2. Be-cause I love Je-sus, my Sav-ior and thine, There's peace in my soul, there is comfort di-vine; 'Twill al-ways abide, for the promise is mine,
3. Tho' loved ones be ta-ken a-way from my side, Tho' rich-es and hon-or to me be de-nied, Yet if I but trust Him no ill can be-tide,
4. Tho' all that is e-vil a-gainst me com-bine, Tho' Sa-tan a-round me his snares should entwine, Yet if I am faith-ful a crown will be mine,
REFRAIN.
Be-cause...... I love Je-sus. Be-cause I love Je-sus,
Be-cause
Je-sus, Be-cause...... I love Je-sus; My soul is at
Be-cause
rest, and in Him I am blest, Be-cause...... I love Je-sus.
Be-cause

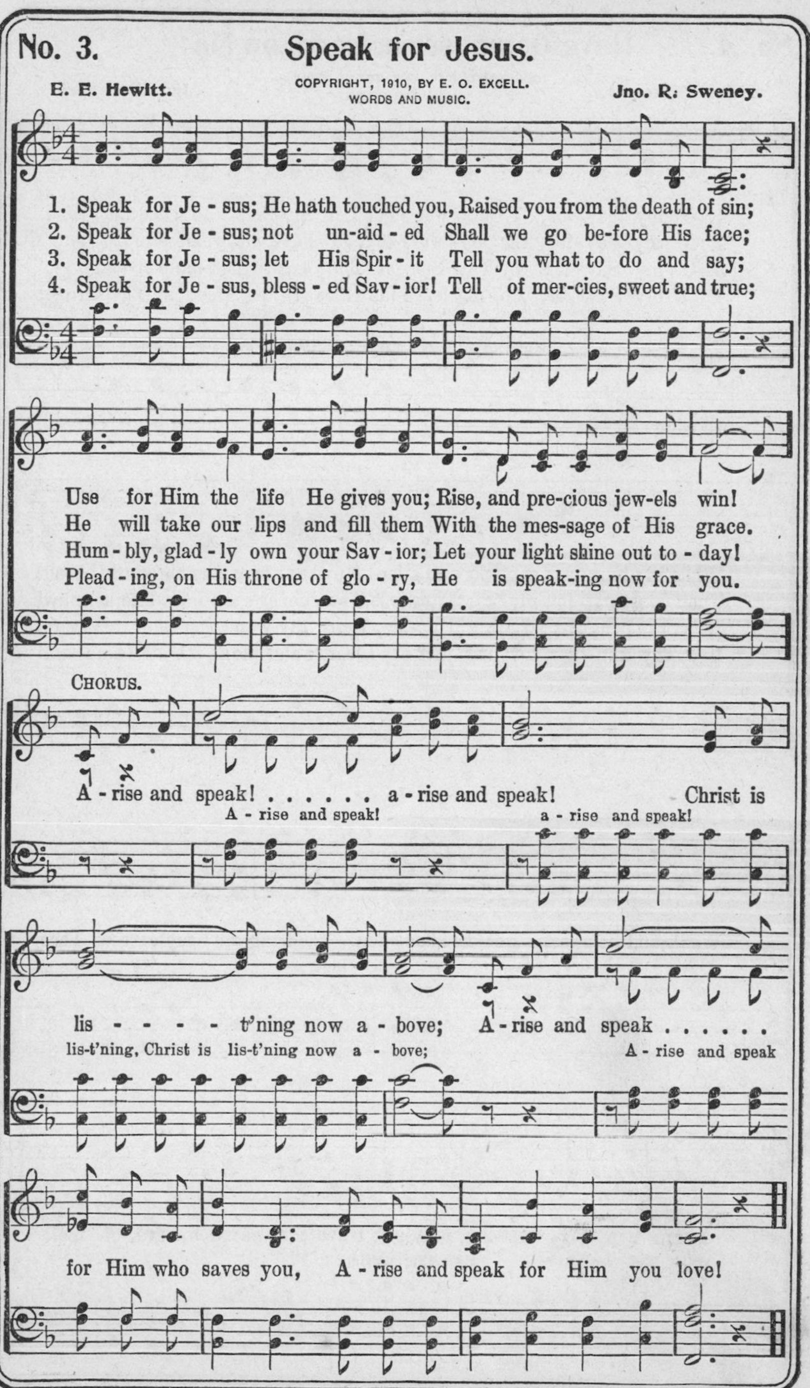
No. 3.
Speak for Jesus.
E. E. Hewitt.
COPYRIGHT, 1910, BY E. O. EXCELL. WORDS AND MUSIC.
Jno. R. Sweney.
1. Speak for Je - sus; He hath touched you, Raised you from the death of sin;
2. Speak for Je - sus; not un-aid - ed Shall we go be-fore His face;
3. Speak for Je - sus; let His Spir - it Tell you what to do and say;
4. Speak for Je - sus, bless - ed Sav - ior! Tell of mer-cies, sweet and true;
Use for Him the life He gives you; Rise, and pre-cious jew-els win!
He will take our lips and fill them With the mes-sage of His grace.
Hum - bly, glad - ly own your Sav - ior; Let your light shine out to - day!
Plead - ing, on His throne of glo - ry, He is speak-ing now for you.
CHORUS.
A - rise and speak! . . . . . . a - rise and speak! Christ is
A - rise and speak! a - rise and speak!
lis - - - - t'ning now a - bove; A - rise and speak . . . . . .
lis-t'ning, Christ is lis-t'ning now a - bove; A - rise and speak
for Him who saves you, A - rise and speak for Him you love!

No. 4. Have Compassion, Lord, on Me!
COPYRIGHT, 1907, 1909, BY E. O. EXCELL.
WORDS AND MUSIC.
Lizzie Edwards.
Jno. R. Sweney.
1. O my Sav-ior, I am wea-ry! Let my cry to Thee as-cend
2. O my Sav-ior, tho' un-wor-thy, I have no where else to go;
3. O my Sav-ior, by Thy Spir-it Thou hast called me o'er and o'er;
4. O my Sav-ior, do not leave me Here to per-ish at Thy throne;
While in hum-ble sup-pli-ca-tion Now be-fore Thy throne I bend!
Thou canst par-don my trans-gressions,Thou canst wash me white as snow!
Now re-pent-ant I am com-ing; Lord, my wand'ring soul re-store!
In Thy ten-der, lov-ing mer-cy Cleanse and make me all Thine own!
CHORUS
Weak and help-less, yet be-liev-ing, Cast-ing all my care on Thee,
Weak and helpless, yet be-liev-ing,
ad lib.
I am hop-ing, trust-ing, pray-ing; Have com-pass-ion,Lord, on me!
I am hop-ing, trusting, praying;

Coronation Hymns

for

THE CHURCH AND
SUNDAY-SCHOOL

EDITED *and* COMPILED
BY E. O. EXCELL

CHURCH HYMNS
SUNDAY-SCHOOL SONGS
RESPONSIVE READINGS
SOLOS *and* CHORUSES

Regular Edition

PRICES: Full Cloth Boards, $30.00 the hundred, express not prepaid; Single copies, 35 cents, post-paid.

Economy Edition

PRICES: Cloth, Limp, $20.00 the hundred, express not prepaid; Single copies, 25 cents, post-paid.

E. O. EXCELL, PUBLISHER
CHICAGO
The Fine Arts Building

A PSALM OF PRAISE

Praise ye the Lord. Praise God in his sanctuary: praise him in the firmament of his power.

Praise him for his mighty acts: praise him according to his excellent greatness.

Praise him with the sound of the trumpet: praise him with the psaltery and harp:

Praise him with the timbrel and dance: praise him with stringed instruments and organs.

Praise him upon the loud cymbals: praise him upon the high sounding cymbals.

Let everything that hath breath praise the Lord.

Praise ye the Lord.

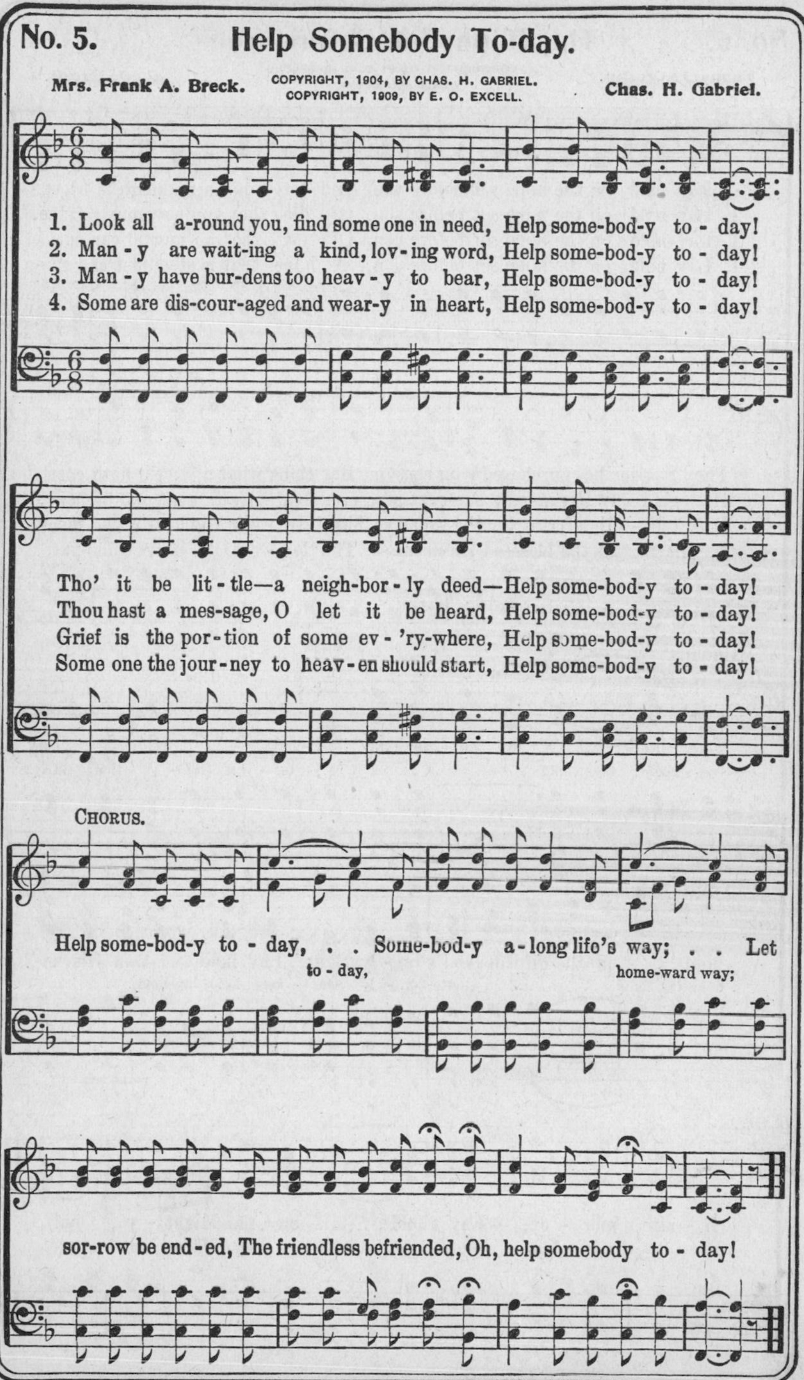
No. 5. Help Somebody To-day.
Mrs. Frank A. Breck.
COPYRIGHT, 1904, BY CHAS. H. GABRIEL.
COPYRIGHT, 1909, BY E. O. EXCELL.
Chas. H. Gabriel.
1. Look all a-round you, find some one in need, Help some-bod-y to - day!
2. Man - y are wait-ing a kind, lov-ing word, Help some-bod-y to - day!
3. Man - y have bur-dens too heav - y to bear, Help some-bod-y to - day!
4. Some are dis-cour-aged and wear-y in heart, Help some-bod-y to - day!
Tho' it be lit-tle—a neigh-bor-ly deed—Help some-bod-y to - day!
Thou hast a mes-sage, O let it be heard, Help some-bod-y to - day!
Grief is the por-tion of some ev-'ry-where, Help some-bod-y to - day!
Some one the jour-ney to heav-en should start, Help some-bod-y to - day!
CHORUS.
Help some-bod-y to - day, . . Some-bod-y a-long life's way; . . Let
to - day,
home-ward way;
sor-row be end-ed, The friendless befriended, Oh, help somebody to - day!

No. 6. The Hope Set Before You.
Fanny J. Crosby.
COPYRIGHT, 1910, BY E. O. EXCELL.
WORDS AND MUSIC.
E. O. Excell.
1. Lay hold on the hope set before you, And let not a moment be lost,
2. Lay hold on the hope set before you, Of life that you now may receive,
3. Lay hold on the hope set before you, Of joy that no mortal can speak;
4. Lay hold on the hope set before you, A hope that is steadfast and sure;
The Sav-ior has purchased your ransom, But think what a price it hath cost!
If, glad - ly His mer-cy ac - cept-ing, You tru - ly re-pent and be-lieve.
It tell - eth of rest for the wear-y, Thro' Je - sus, the low-ly and meek.
O haste to the bless-ed Re-deem-er, The lov - ing, the perfect and pure.
CHORUS.
Lay hold . . . . . . on e - ter - nal sal - va - - tion, Lay
Lay hold, lay hold . . . . on e - ter - nal sal - va - tion, Lay
hold . . . . on the gift of God's on - ly Son; Lay hold . . . . on His in-
hold, lay hold . . . . on God's on - ly Son; Lay hold, lay hold . . . .
fi - nite mer - cy, Lay hold . . . . . on the Might - y One!
on His mer - cy, Lay hold, lay hold on the Might - y One!

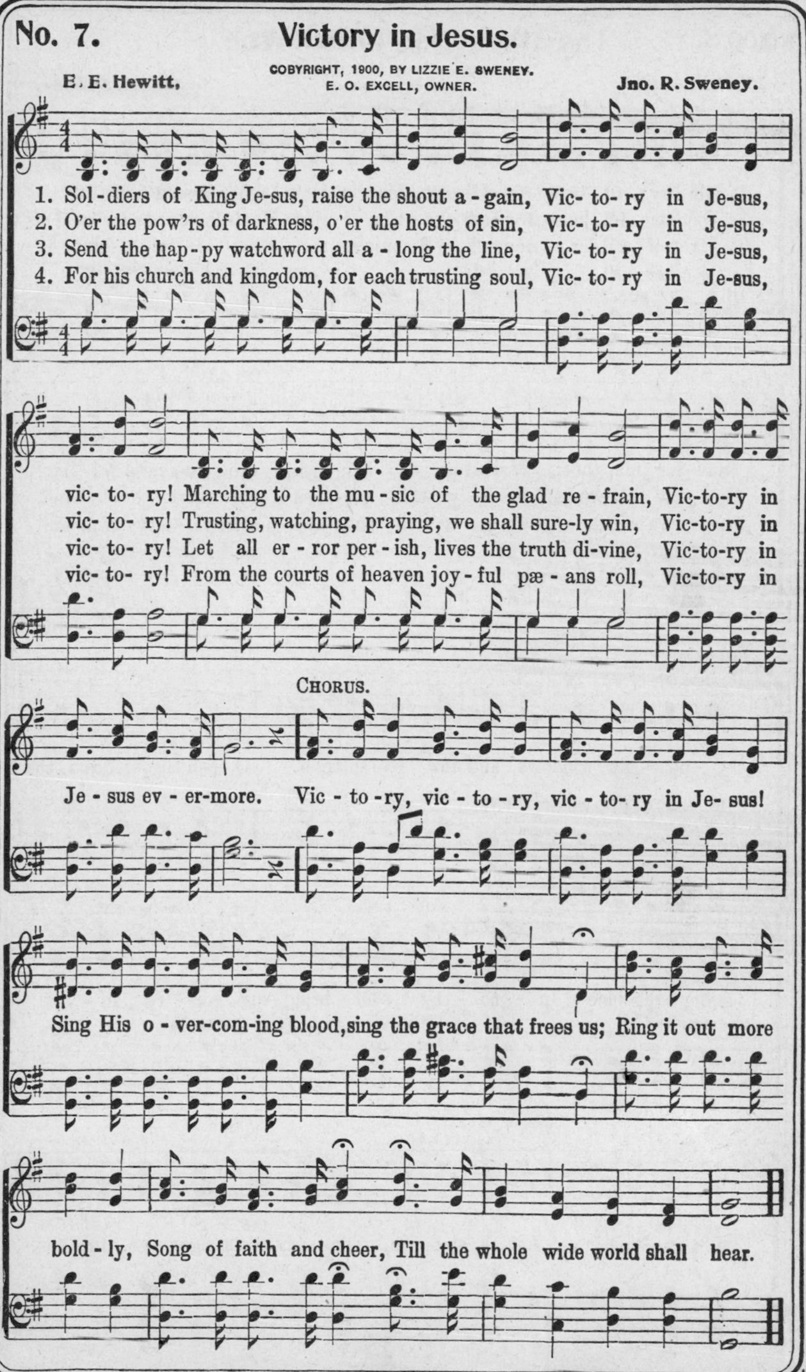
No. 7. Victory in Jesus.
COBYRIGHT, 1900, BY LIZZIE E. SWENEY.
E. O. EXCELL, OWNER.
E. E. Hewitt,
Jno. R. Sweney.
1. Sol-diers of King Je-sus, raise the shout a-gain, Vic-to-ry in Je-sus,
2. O'er the pow'rs of darkness, o'er the hosts of sin, Vic-to-ry in Je-sus,
3. Send the hap-py watchword all a-long the line, Vic-to-ry in Je-sus,
4. For his church and kingdom, for each trusting soul, Vic-to-ry in Je-sus,
vic-to-ry! Marching to the mu-sic of the glad re-frain, Vic-to-ry in
vic-to-ry! Trusting, watching, praying, we shall sure-ly win, Vic-to-ry in
vic-to-ry! Let all er-ror per-ish, lives the truth di-vine, Vic-to-ry in
vic-to-ry! From the courts of heaven joy-ful pæ-ans roll, Vic-to-ry in
CHORUS.
Je-sus ev-er-more. Vic-to-ry, vic-to-ry, vic-to-ry in Je-sus!
Sing His o-ver-com-ing blood, sing the grace that frees us; Ring it out more
bold-ly, Song of faith and cheer, Till the whole wide world shall hear.

No. 8.
Open Thy Windows.
COPYRIGHT, 1908, BY E. O. EXCELL,
WORDS AND MUSIC.
E. E. Hewitt.
John R. Sweney.
1. Glo - ry to God for His sun-shine is free, Light, blessed light in the
2. Won-der - ful light, for sal - va - tion it brings, Heal - ing and peace from its
3. Light of sal - va - tion, oh, wel-come its ray, Beau - ti - ful to-ken of
Sav - ior for thee; Wait - ing to ban - ish the dark-ness of sin,
life - giv - ing wings; Read - y this mo-ment its work to be - gin,
heav-en's bright day; O - ver all shad-ows the vic - t'ry 'twill win,
O - pen thy windows and let it shine in.
CHORUS.
O - pen thy windows, the
light will shine In - to thy soul bring - ing glo - ry di - vine;
Let it shine in, Let it shine in, The sav - ing light of Je - sus.

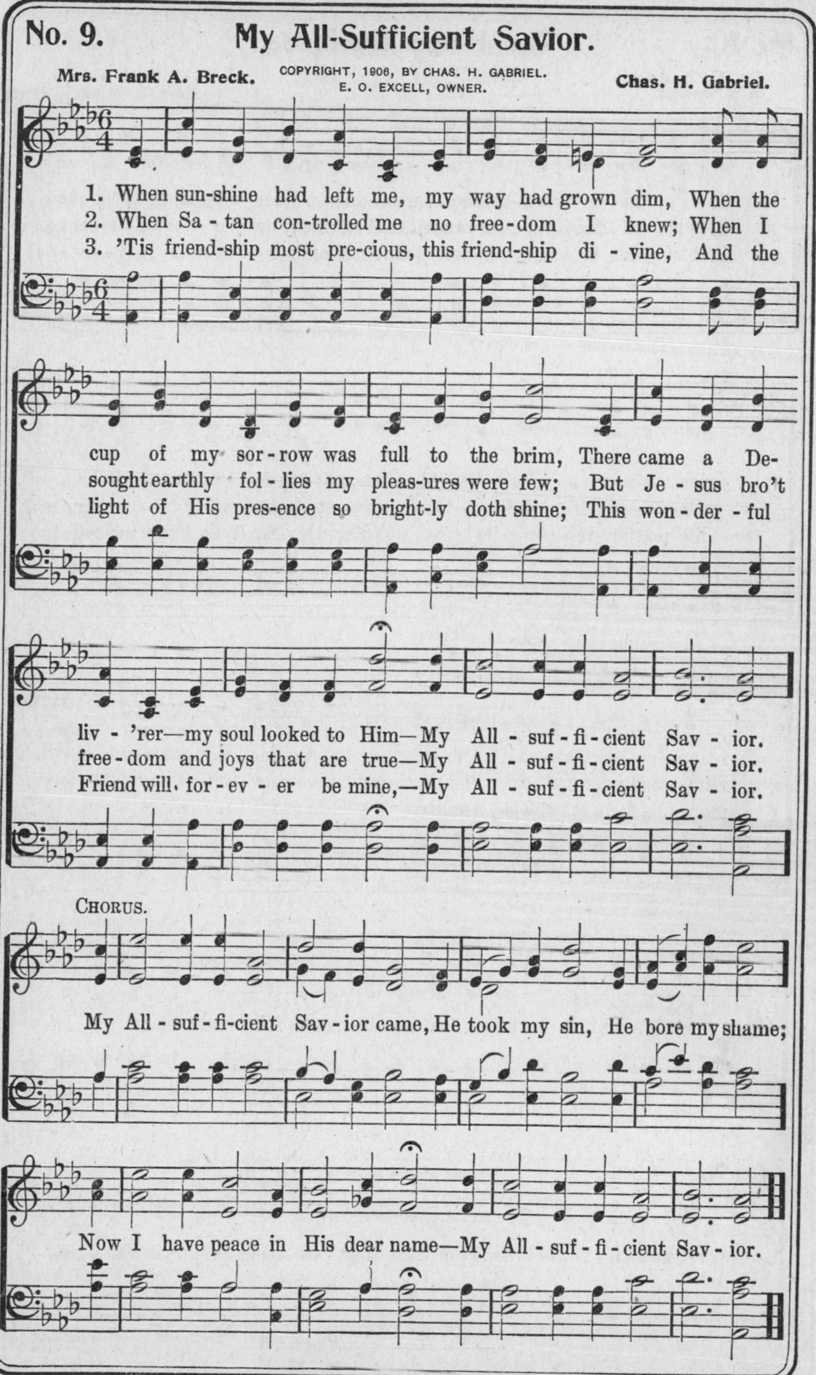
No. 9. My All-Sufficient Savior.
Mrs. Frank A. Breck.
COPYRIGHT, 1906, BY CHAS. H. GABRIEL. E. O. EXCELL, OWNER.
Chas. H. Gabriel.
1. When sun-shine had left me, my way had grown dim, When the cup of my sor-row was full to the brim, There came a De-liv-'rer—my soul looked to Him—My All-suf-fi-cient Sav-ior.
2. When Sa-tan con-trolled me no free-dom I knew; When I sought earthly fol-lies my pleas-ures were few; But Je-sus bro't free-dom and joys that are true—My All-suf-fi-cient Sav-ior.
3. 'Tis friend-ship most pre-cious, this friend-ship di-vine, And the light of His pres-ence so bright-ly doth shine; This won-der-ful Friend will for-ev-er be mine,—My All-suf-fi-cient Sav-ior.
CHORUS.
My All-suf-fi-cient Sav-ior came, He took my sin, He bore my shame; Now I have peace in His dear name—My All-suf-fi-cient Sav-ior.

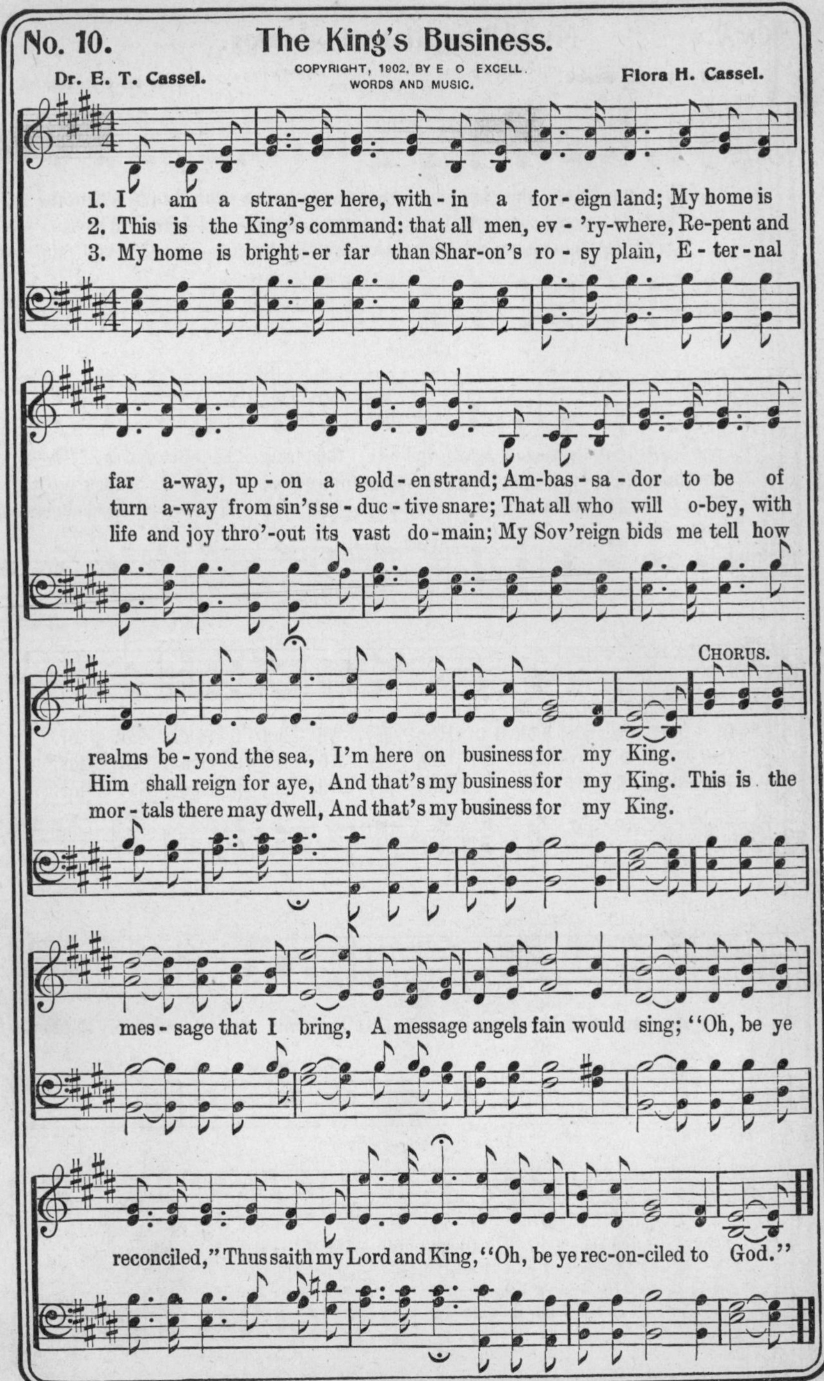
No. 10. The King's Business.
Dr. E. T. Cassel.
COPYRIGHT, 1902, BY E O EXCELL.
WORDS AND MUSIC.
Flora H. Cassel.
1. I am a stran-ger here, with - in a for - eign land; My home is
2. This is the King's command: that all men, ev - 'ry-where, Re-pent and
3. My home is bright - er far than Shar-on's ro - sy plain, E - ter - nal
far a-way, up - on a gold - en strand; Am-bas - sa - dor to be of
turn a-way from sin's se - duc - tive snare; That all who will o-bey, with
life and joy thro'-out its vast do - main; My Sov'reign bids me tell how
realms be - yond the sea, I'm here on business for my King.
Him shall reign for aye, And that's my business for my King. This is the
mor - tals there may dwell, And that's my business for my King.
CHORUS.
mes - sage that I bring, A message angels fain would sing; "Oh, be ye
reconciled," Thus saith my Lord and King, "Oh, be ye rec-on-ciled to God."

No. 11. He Knoweth the Way.
Rev. W. R. Fitch.
COPYRIGHT, 1908, BY CHAS H. GABRIEL.
E. O. EXCELL, OWNER.
Chas. H. Gabriel.
1. I know not the field where the Mas-ter to-day Would have me to glean, and the sheaves gath-er in; But this I do know, He will show me the way To gar-ner the souls I am striv-ing to win.
2. A prayer, or a tear, or a glance of the eye, May soft-en a heart that is care-less or cold; The Spir-it will help me, if on-ly I try To lead a lost sin-ner back in-to the fold.
3. I can-not quite tell where to-day He will lead, Or say on what er-rand He'll ask me to go; And yet I am sure that what-ev-er my need, His wis-dom and grace He will free-ly be-stow.
CHORUS.
He knoweth the way, ... His will I o-bey, ... What-ev-er be-fall, I can trust Him for all; He knoweth, He knoweth the way.
He knoweth the way, His will I o-bey,

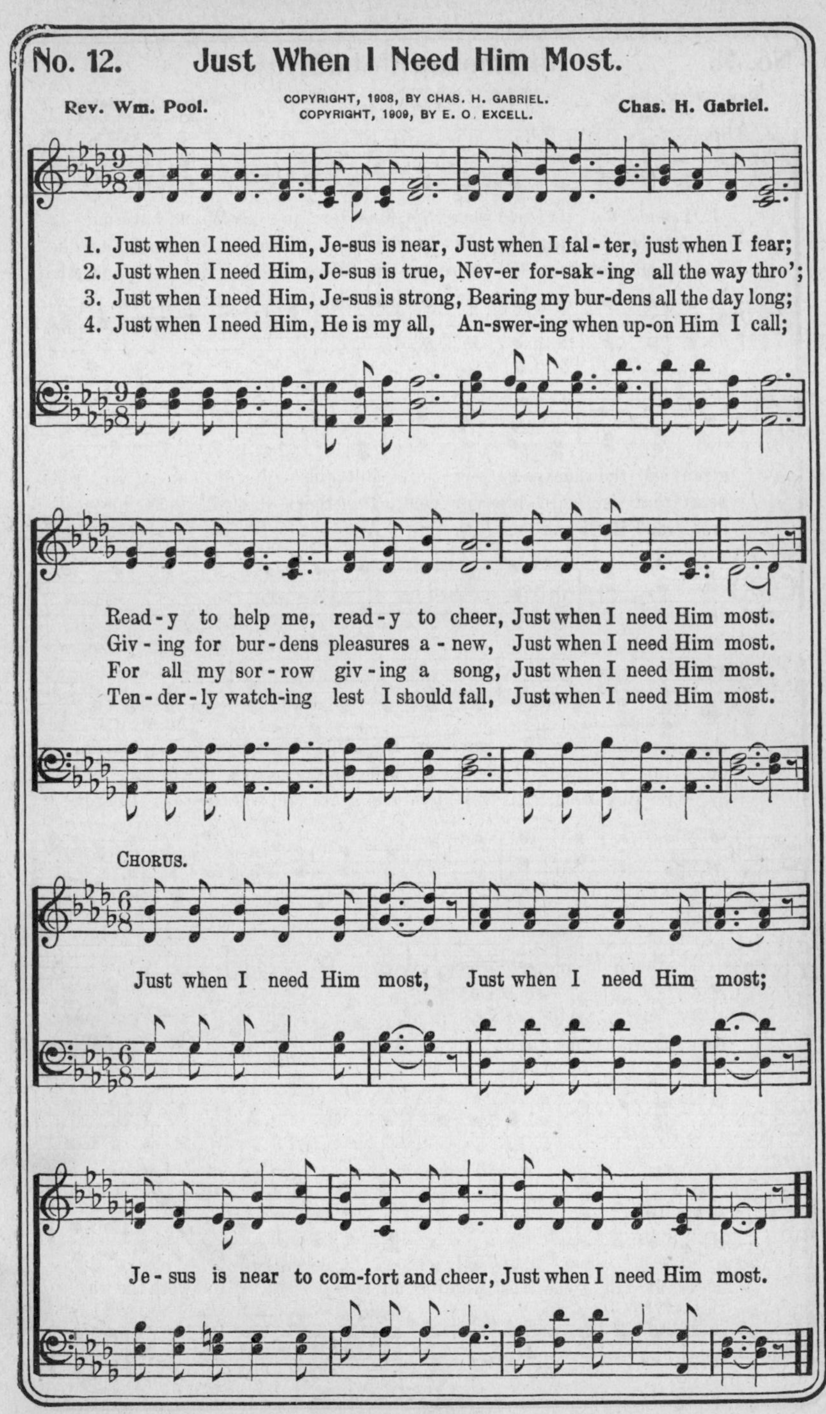
No. 12. Just When I Need Him Most.
Rev. Wm. Pool.
COPYRIGHT, 1908, BY CHAS. H. GABRIEL.
COPYRIGHT, 1909, BY E. O. EXCELL.
Chas. H. Gabriel.
1. Just when I need Him, Je-sus is near, Just when I fal - ter, just when I fear;
2. Just when I need Him, Je-sus is true, Nev-er for-sak - ing all the way thro';
3. Just when I need Him, Je-sus is strong, Bearing my bur-dens all the day long;
4. Just when I need Him, He is my all, An-swer-ing when up-on Him I call;
Read - y to help me, read - y to cheer, Just when I need Him most.
Giv - ing for bur - dens pleasures a - new, Just when I need Him most.
For all my sor - row giv - ing a song, Just when I need Him most.
Ten - der - ly watch-ing lest I should fall, Just when I need Him most.
CHORUS.
Just when I need Him most, Just when I need Him most;
Je - sus is near to com-fort and cheer, Just when I need Him most.

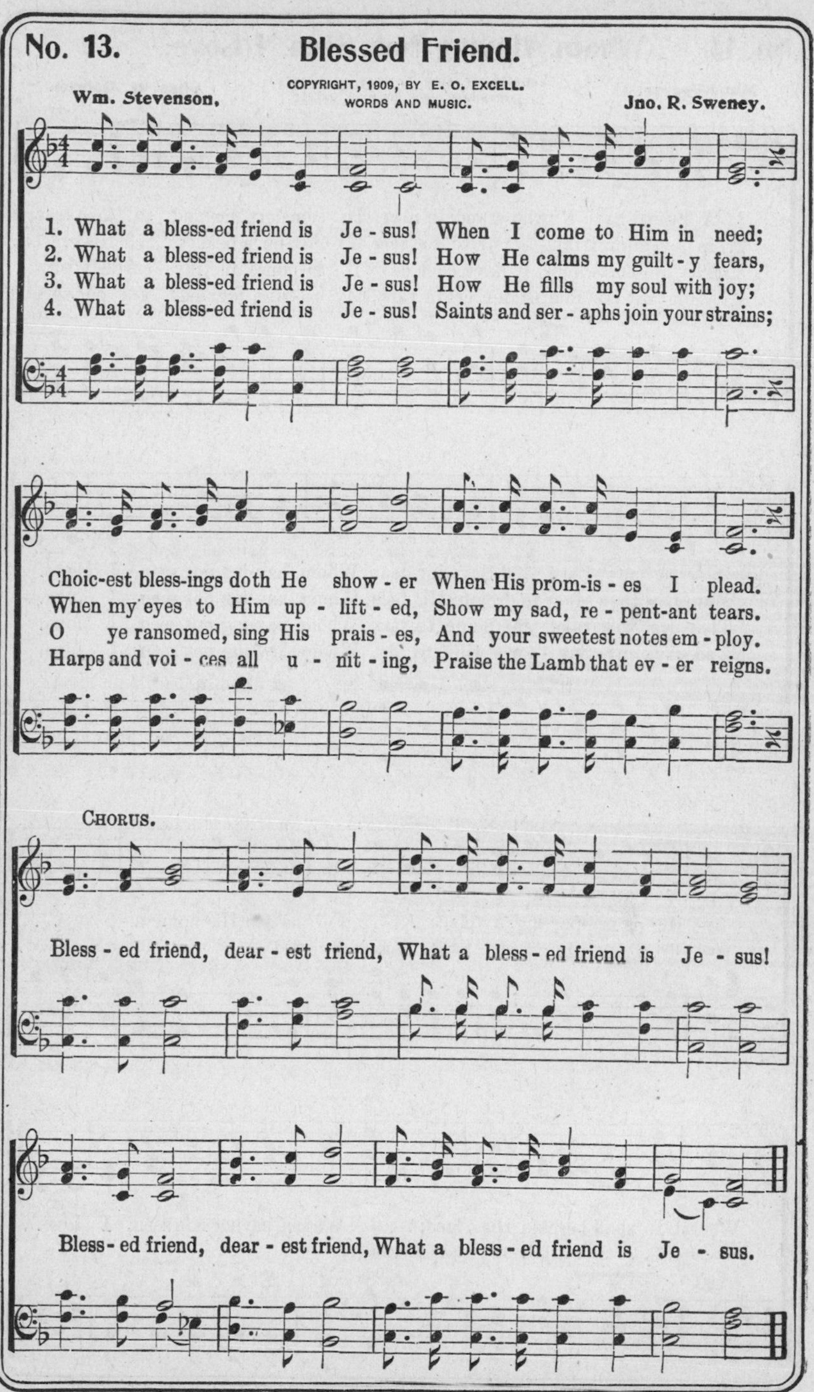
No. 13.
Blessed Friend.
COPYRIGHT, 1909, BY E. O. EXCELL.
WORDS AND MUSIC.
Wm. Stevenson.
Jno. R. Sweney.
1. What a bless-ed friend is Je - sus! When I come to Him in need;
2. What a bless-ed friend is Je - sus! How He calms my guilt - y fears,
3. What a bless-ed friend is Je - sus! How He fills my soul with joy;
4. What a bless-ed friend is Je - sus! Saints and ser - aphs join your strains;
Choic-est bless-ings doth He show - er When His prom-is - es I plead.
When my eyes to Him up - lift - ed, Show my sad, re - pent-ant tears.
O ye ransomed, sing His prais - es, And your sweetest notes em - ploy.
Harps and voi - ces all u - nit - ing, Praise the Lamb that ev - er reigns.
CHORUS.
Bless - ed friend, dear - est friend, What a bless - ed friend is Je - sus!
Bless - ed friend, dear - est friend, What a bless - ed friend is Je - sus.

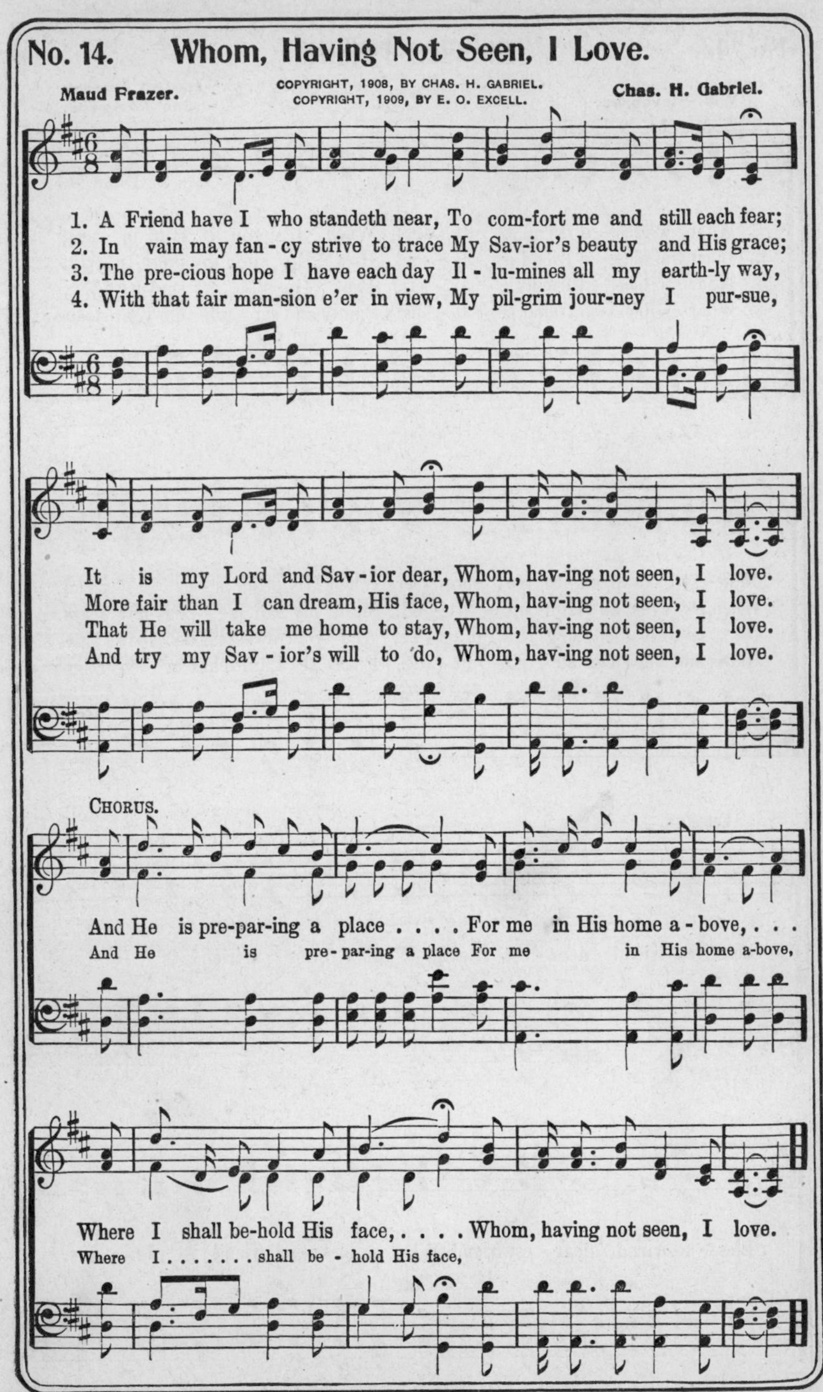
No. 14. Whom, Having Not Seen, I Love.
Maud Frazer.
COPYRIGHT, 1908, BY CHAS. H. GABRIEL.
COPYRIGHT, 1909, BY E. O. EXCELL.
Chas. H. Gabriel.
1. A Friend have I who standeth near, To com-fort me and still each fear;
2. In vain may fan-cy strive to trace My Sav-ior's beauty and His grace;
3. The pre-cious hope I have each day Il - lu-mines all my earth-ly way,
4. With that fair man-sion e'er in view, My pil-grim jour-ney I pur-sue,
It is my Lord and Sav-ior dear, Whom, hav-ing not seen, I love.
More fair than I can dream, His face, Whom, hav-ing not seen, I love.
That He will take me home to stay, Whom, hav-ing not seen, I love.
And try my Sav-ior's will to do, Whom, hav-ing not seen, I love.
CHORUS.
And He is pre-par-ing a place . . . . For me in His home a-bove, . . .
And He is pre-par-ing a place For me in His home a-bove,
Where I shall be-hold His face, ... Whom, having not seen, I love.
Where I . . . . . . shall be - hold His face,

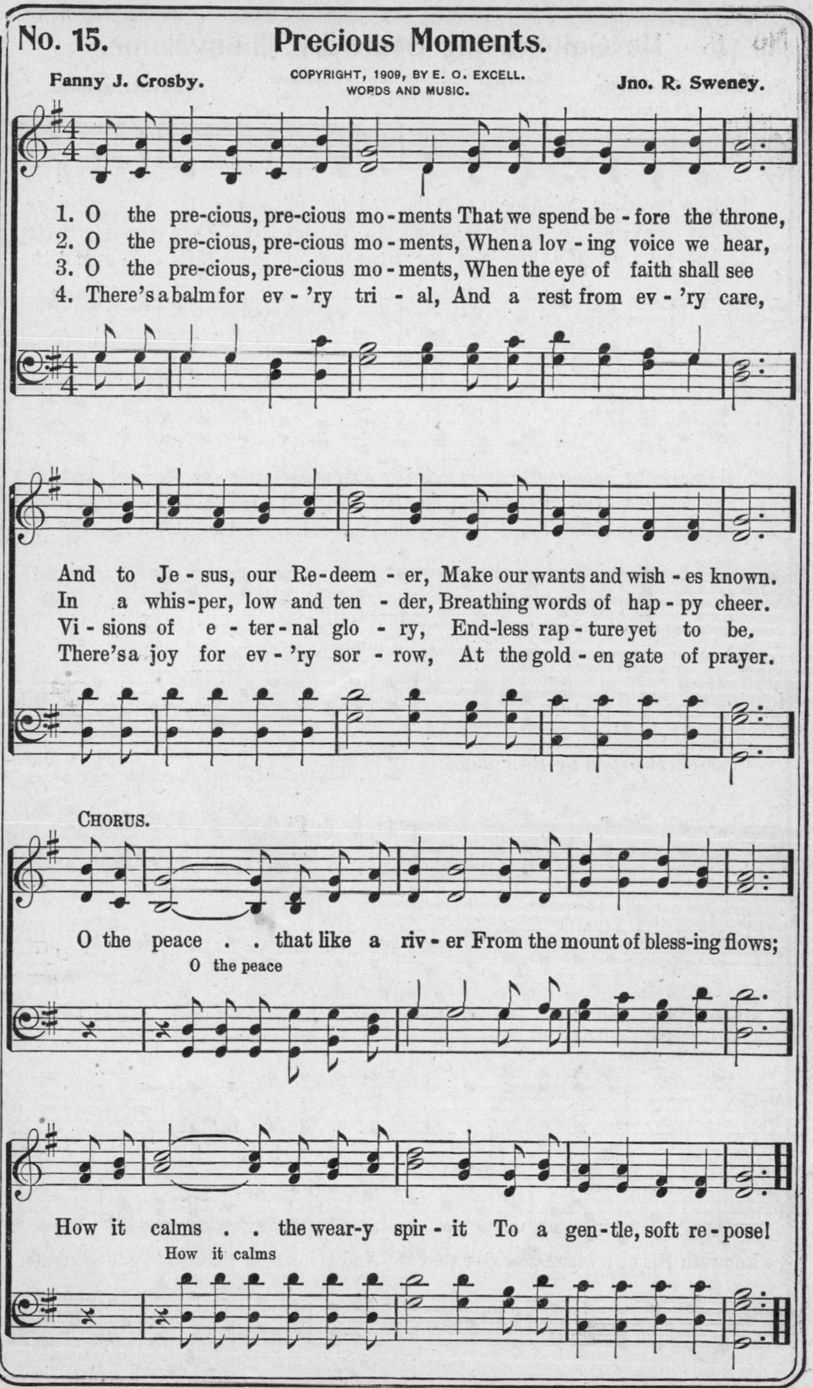
No. 15. Precious Moments.
Fanny J. Crosby.
COPYRIGHT, 1909, BY E. O. EXCELL. WORDS AND MUSIC.
Jno. R. Sweney.
1. O the pre-cious, pre-cious mo-ments That we spend be-fore the throne,
2. O the pre-cious, pre-cious mo-ments, When a lov-ing voice we hear,
3. O the pre-cious, pre-cious mo-ments, When the eye of faith shall see
4. There's a balm for ev-'ry tri-al, And a rest from ev-'ry care,
And to Je-sus, our Re-deem-er, Make our wants and wish-es known.
In a whis-per, low and ten-der, Breathing words of hap-py cheer.
Vi-sions of e-ter-nal glo-ry, End-less rap-ture yet to be.
There's a joy for ev-'ry sor-row, At the gold-en gate of prayer.
CHORUS.
O the peace . . that like a riv-er From the mount of bless-ing flows;
O the peace
How it calms . . the wear-y spir-it To a gen-tle, soft re-pose!
How it calms

No. 16. He Calleth the Stars by Their Name.
Mrs. C. D. Martin.
COPYRIGHT, 1906, BY CHAS. H. GABRIEL.
E. O. EXCELL, OWNER.
Chas. H. Gabriel.
1. How pre-cious the thought that the God of all pow'r Is ev-'ry-where al-ways the same; He know-eth His own where-so-ev-er they be, And He call-eth the stars by their name.
2. The heav-ens de-clare the great glo-ry of God, They spread forth His ex-cel-lent fame; Praise God, I'm His child, and I read in His word That He
3. The gifts of His love and the treas-ures of grace His chil-dren each moment may claim; Some day they shall meet Him and look on His face—He who
CHORUS.
He call - eth the stars . . . . by their name, He call - - eth the stars . . . . . . by their name; He
He call-eth the stars, He calleth the stars by their name, He call-eth the stars, He call-eth the stars by their name;
knoweth His own where-so-ev-er they be, And He calleth the stars by their name.

No. 17. In the Cleft of the Rock.
Lizzie DeArmond.
COPYRIGHT, 1900, BY E. O. EXCELL. WORDS AND MUSIC.
J. S. Fearis.
1. High as the mountain tho' the bil-lows roll, In Je-sus' keep-ing I will trust my soul; He can the rag-ing seas and wind con-trol,
2. O soul, be faith-ful; to the end en-dure, Trust-ing His prom-is-es for-ev-er sure; Kept in the fort-ress of His love se-cure,
3. When thro' the Jor-dan I must take my way, His staff will com-fort me and be my stay; O-ver the riv-er there is end-less day,
In the cleft of the Rock He will hide me.
REFRAIN.
Hide . . . me, safe-ly hide me, Hide . . . me, safe-ly hide me,
Hide me, safe-ly hide, hide . . . . me, safe-ly hide, ... Hide . . . . me, safe-ly
hide me, safe-ly hide, Hide me, safe-ly hide, hide me in the Rock,
Hide . . . me from all dan-ger, In the Rock that was cleft for me.
Hide me from all dan-ger, from all dan-ger,

No. 18. If It Be His Will.
Victor M. Hatfield.
COPYRIGHT, 1908, BY CHAS. H. GABRIEL.
E. O. EXCELL, OWNER.
Chas. H. Gabriel.
1. If it be His will, I shall be sat-is-fied, E-ven tho' my fond-est wish-es be de-nied; I will wait in patience, trust His prom-ise still; I will learn to say, "It is my Mas-ter's will."
2. If it be His will, I'll bid fare-well to ease, Give my time and tal-ent my dear Lord to please, Know-ing all His prom-is-es He will ful-fil: Use me, bless-ed Mas-ter, if it is Thy will.
3. If it be His will, I'll spread the news a-broad, How my sins are par-doned thro' the Lamb of God; How His pre-cious blood a-tones for ev-'ry ill: Lord, I'll speak Thy mes-sage, if it is Thy will.
FINE. CHORUS.
If.......... it be His will,
If it be His will, If it be His will,
I will wait in patience, I will trust His prom-ise still; Tho' my cup of sor-row to the brim He fill,
D.S.—I will sweet-ly say, "It is my Mas-ter's will."
D. S.

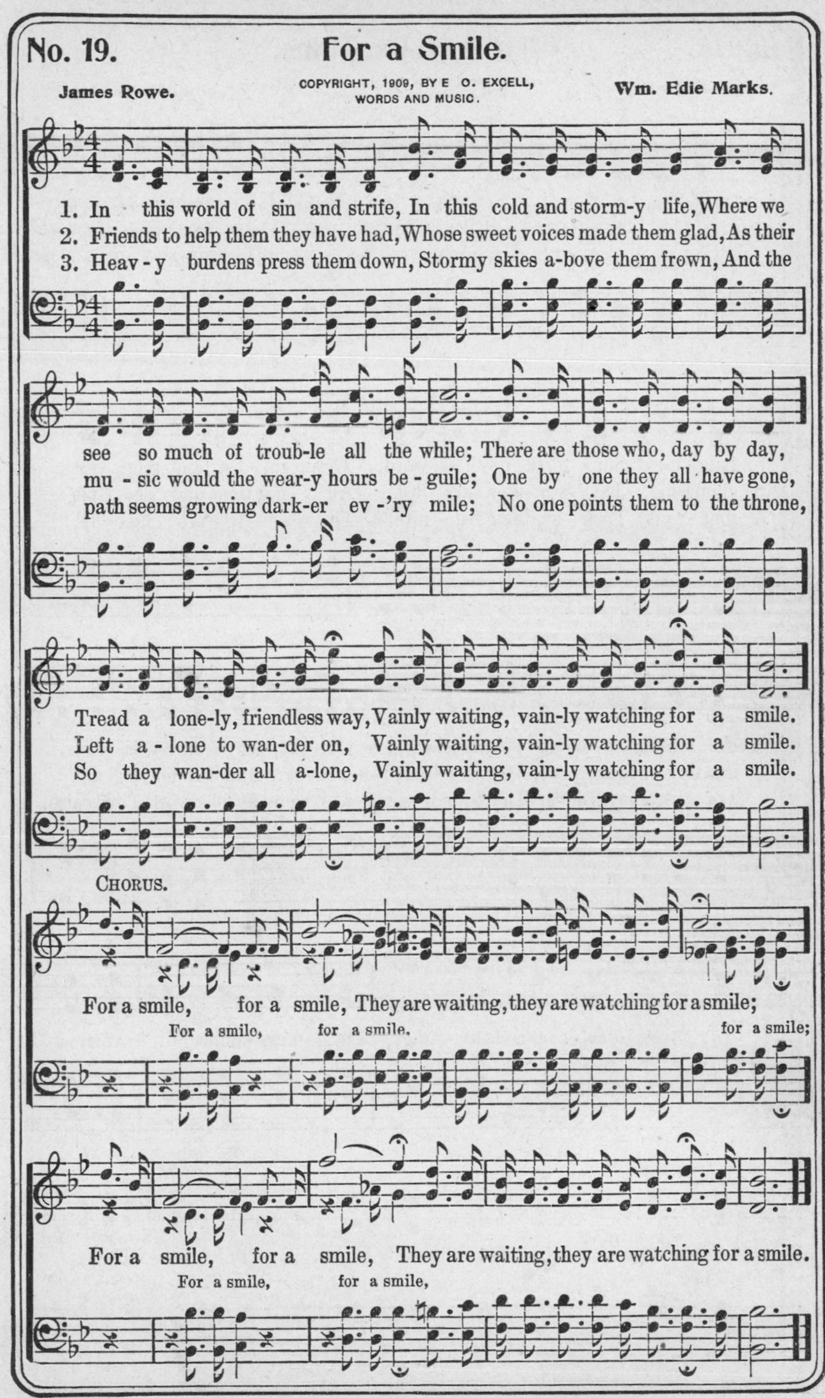
No. 19.
For a Smile.
James Rowe.
COPYRIGHT, 1909, BY E. O. EXCELL, WORDS AND MUSIC.
Wm. Edie Marks.
1. In this world of sin and strife, In this cold and storm-y life, Where we see so much of troub-le all the while; There are those who, day by day, Tread a lone-ly, friendless way, Vainly waiting, vain-ly watching for a smile.
2. Friends to help them they have had, Whose sweet voices made them glad, As their mu - sic would the wear-y hours be - guile; One by one they all have gone, Left a - lone to wan-der on, Vainly waiting, vain-ly watching for a smile.
3. Heav - y burdens press them down, Stormy skies a-bove them frown, And the path seems growing dark-er ev -'ry mile; No one points them to the throne, So they wan-der all a-lone, Vainly waiting, vain-ly watching for a smile.
CHORUS.
For a smile, for a smile, They are waiting, they are watching for a smile;
For a smile, for a smile, for a smile;
For a smile, for a smile, They are waiting, they are watching for a smile.
For a smile, for a smile,

No. 20.
All Glory Be Thine.
Fanny J. Crosby.
COPYRIGHT, 1909, BY E. O. EXCELL.
WORDS AND MUSIC.
Jno. R. Sweney.
1. Thou on-ly art ho-ly, Thou on-ly the Lord; Truth, mer-cy, and judg-ment Shine forth in Thy word. Thou rul-est and reign-est All oth-ers a-bove; Thy throne is e-ter-nal, Thy scep-ter is love.
2. Thou on-ly art ho-ly; In Thee is our trust; Thy laws are un-chang-ing, Thy stat-utes are just. All na-tions and peo-ple Be-fore Thee shall fall, The Fa-ther, Re-deem-er, And Sav-ior of all.
3. Thou on-ly art ho-ly; The an-gels in light With prophets and mar-tyrs Their an-thems u-nite. Thou on-ly art ho-ly, O An-cient of days; The boundless cre-a-tion Is filled with Thy praise.
CHORUS.
Thy reign ev-er-last-ing, Thy king-dom di-vine,
Hence-forth and for-ev-er All glo-ry be Thine.

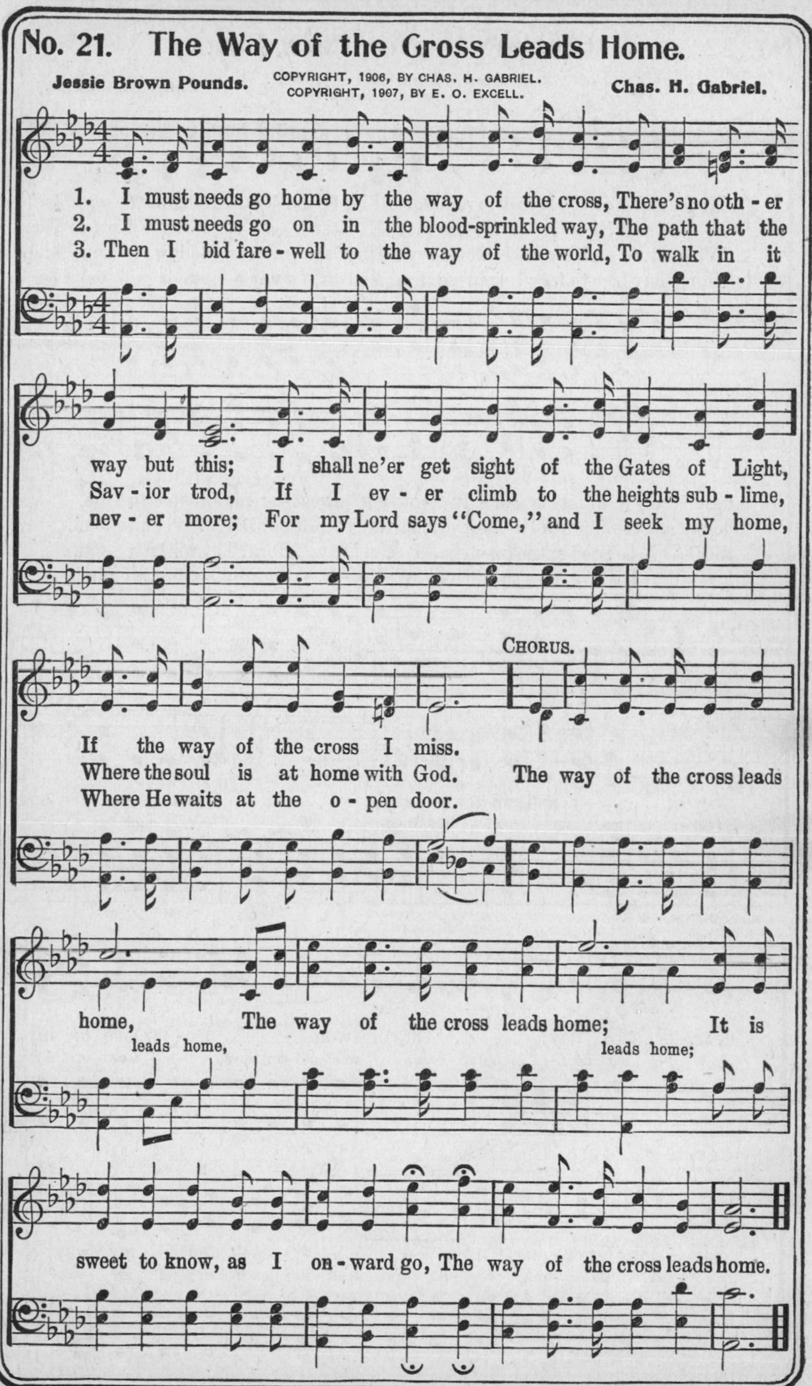
No. 21. The Way of the Cross Leads Home.
Jessie Brown Pounds.
COPYRIGHT, 1906, BY CHAS. H. GABRIEL.
COPYRIGHT, 1907, BY E. O. EXCELL.
Chas. H. Gabriel.
1. I must needs go home by the way of the cross, There's no oth - er way but this; I shall ne'er get sight of the Gates of Light, If the way of the cross I miss.
2. I must needs go on in the blood-sprinkled way, The path that the Sav - ior trod, If I ev - er climb to the heights sub - lime, Where the soul is at home with God.
3. Then I bid fare - well to the way of the world, To walk in it nev - er more; For my Lord says "Come," and I seek my home, Where He waits at the o - pen door.
CHORUS.
The way of the cross leads home, leads home, The way of the cross leads home; leads home; It is sweet to know, as I on - ward go, The way of the cross leads home.

No. 22. Growing Dearer Each Day.
C. H. G.
COPYRIGHT, 1907, BY CHAS. H. GABRIEL.
E. O. EXCELL, OWNER.
Chas. H. Gabriel.
1. How sweet is the love of my Savior! 'Tis bound-less and deep as the sea; And
2. I know He is ev-er be-side me! E - ter - ni-ty on-ly will prove The
3. Wher-ev - er He leads I will fol-low, Thro' sor-row, or shadow, or sun; And
4. Some day face to face I shall see Him, And oh, what a joy it will be To
best of it all, it is dai - ly Grow-ing sweet-er and sweeter to me.
height and the depth of His mercy, And the breadth of His in - fi - nite love.
tho' I be tried in the fur-nace, I can say, "Lord, Thy will be it done."
know that His love, now so precious, Will for-ev - er grow sweeter to me!
CHORUS.
Sweet - er and sweeter to me, ... Dear - er and
Sweet-er to me, grow - ing sweet-er to me, Dear-er each day,
dear-er each day; . . . Oh, won - der-ful love of my
grow - ing dear-er each day; Oh, won-der-ful love, love of my
Sav - ior, Grow-ing dear - - er each step of my way!
Sav - ior, Grow - ing dear-er and dear-er each step of my way!

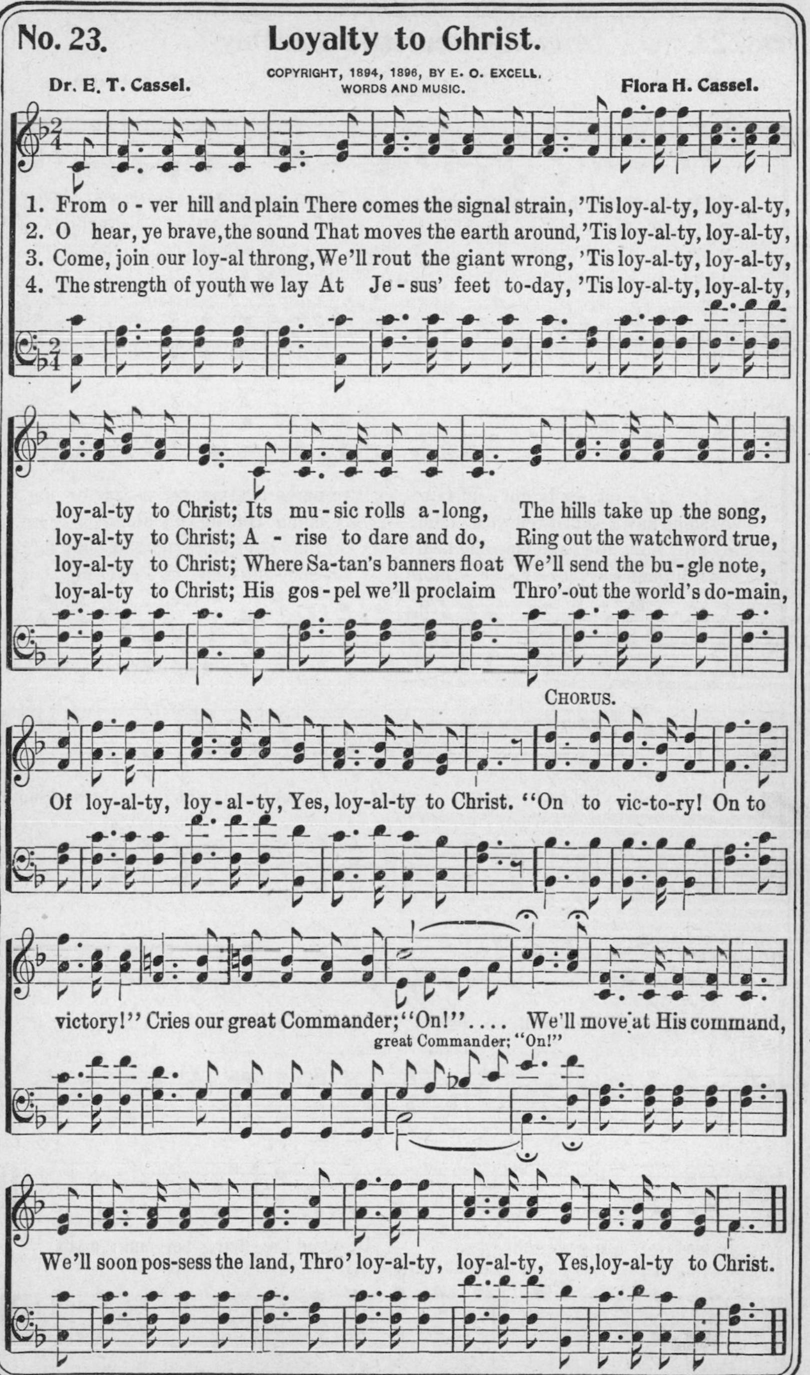
No. 23.
Loyalty to Christ.
COPYRIGHT, 1894, 1896, BY E. O. EXCELL.
WORDS AND MUSIC.
Dr. E. T. Cassel.
Flora H. Cassel.
1. From o - ver hill and plain There comes the signal strain, 'Tis loy-al-ty, loy-al-ty,
2. O hear, ye brave, the sound That moves the earth around, 'Tis loy-al-ty, loy-al-ty,
3. Come, join our loy-al throng, We'll rout the giant wrong, 'Tis loy-al-ty, loy-al-ty,
4. The strength of youth we lay At Je - sus' feet to-day, 'Tis loy-al-ty, loy-al-ty,
loy-al-ty to Christ; Its mu - sic rolls a - long, The hills take up the song,
loy-al-ty to Christ; A - rise to dare and do, Ring out the watchword true,
loy-al-ty to Christ; Where Sa-tan's banners float We'll send the bu - gle note,
loy-al-ty to Christ; His gos - pel we'll proclaim Thro'-out the world's do-main,
CHORUS.
Of loy-al-ty, loy - al - ty, Yes, loy-al-ty to Christ. "On to vic-to-ry! On to
victory!" Cries our great Commander; "On!" .... We'll move at His command,
great Commander; "On!"
We'll soon pos-sess the land, Thro' loy-al-ty, loy-al-ty, Yes, loy-al-ty to Christ.

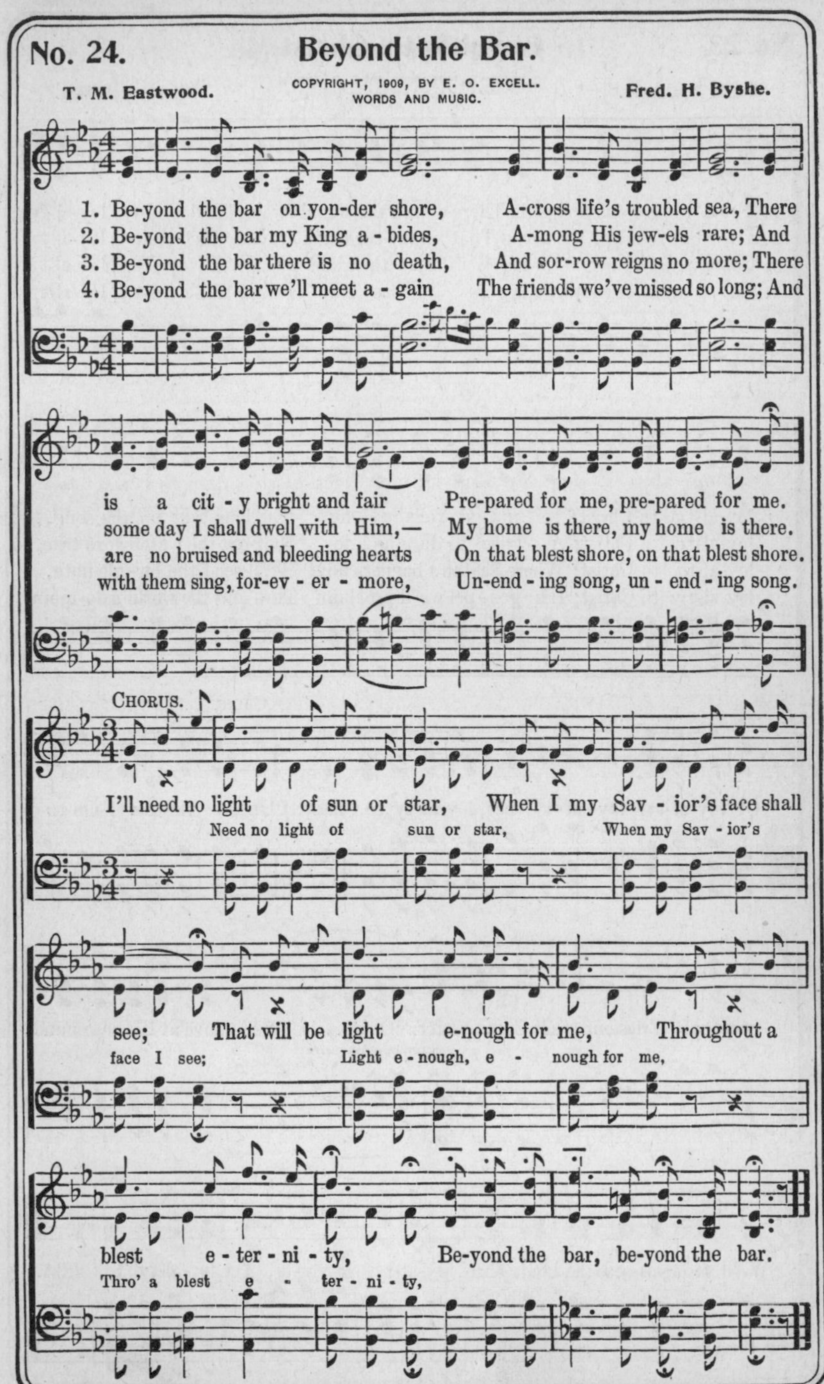
No. 24. Beyond the Bar.
T. M. Eastwood.
COPYRIGHT, 1909, BY E. O. EXCELL. WORDS AND MUSIC.
Fred. H. Byshe.
1. Be-yond the bar on yon-der shore, A-cross life's troubled sea, There
2. Be-yond the bar my King a-bides, A-mong His jew-els rare; And
3. Be-yond the bar there is no death, And sor-row reigns no more; There
4. Be-yond the bar we'll meet a-gain The friends we've missed so long; And
is a cit-y bright and fair Pre-pared for me, pre-pared for me.
some day I shall dwell with Him,— My home is there, my home is there.
are no bruised and bleeding hearts On that blest shore, on that blest shore.
with them sing, for-ev-er-more, Un-end-ing song, un-end-ing song.
CHORUS.
I'll need no light of sun or star, When I my Sav-ior's face shall
Need no light of sun or star, When my Sav-ior's
see; That will be light e-nough for me, Throughout a
face I see; Light e-nough, e-nough for me,
blest e-ter-ni-ty, Be-yond the bar, be-yond the bar.
Thro' a blest e-ter-ni-ty,

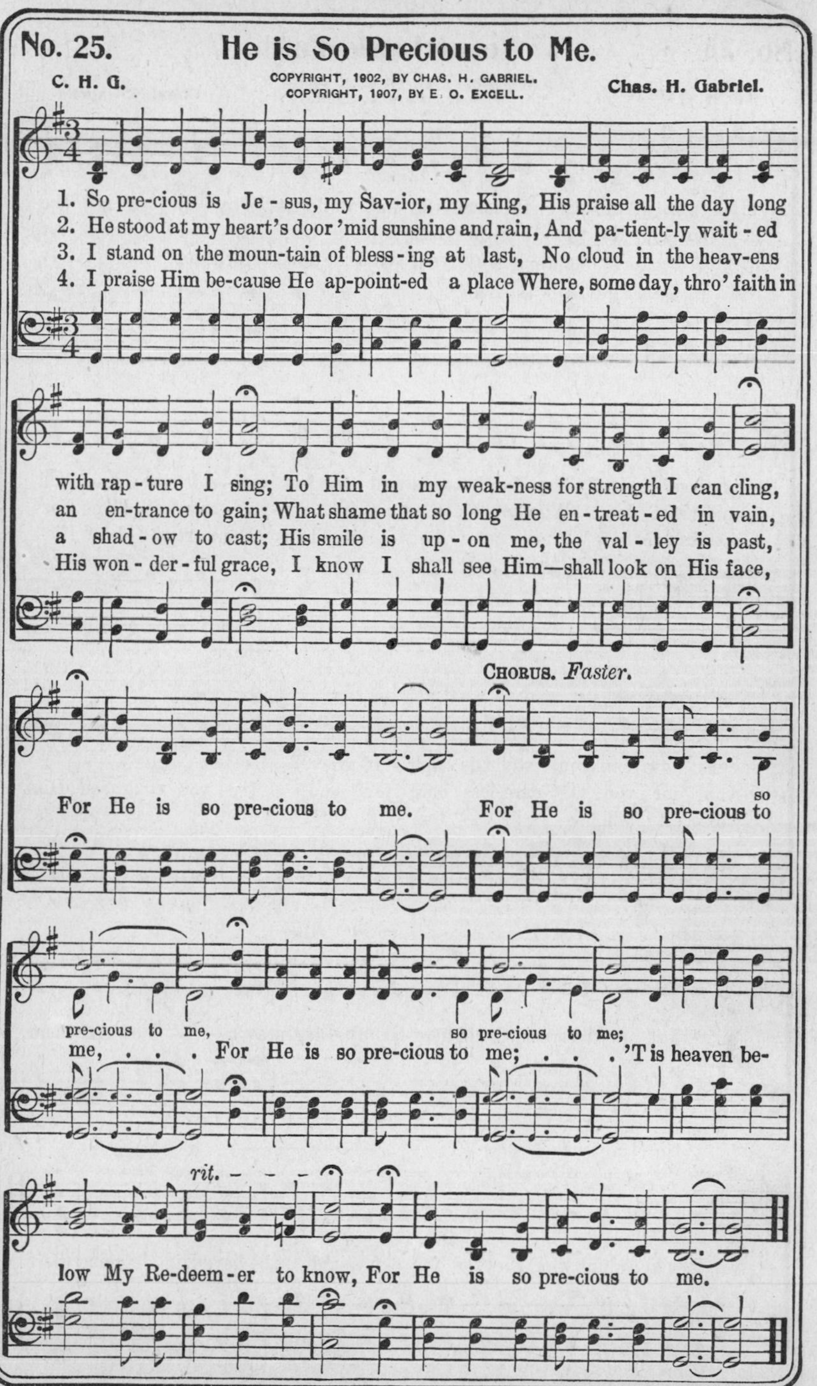
No. 25. He is So Precious to Me.
C. H. G.
COPYRIGHT, 1902, BY CHAS. H. GABRIEL.
COPYRIGHT, 1907, BY E. O. EXCELL.
Chas. H. Gabriel.
1. So pre-cious is Je - sus, my Sav-ior, my King, His praise all the day long
2. He stood at my heart's door 'mid sunshine and rain, And pa-tient-ly wait - ed
3. I stand on the moun-tain of bless - ing at last, No cloud in the heav-ens
4. I praise Him be-cause He ap-point-ed a place Where, some day, thro' faith in
with rap - ture I sing; To Him in my weak-ness for strength I can cling,
an en-trance to gain; What shame that so long He en-treat - ed in vain,
a shad - ow to cast; His smile is up - on me, the val - ley is past,
His won - der - ful grace, I know I shall see Him—shall look on His face,
CHORUS. Faster.
For He is so pre-cious to me. For He is so pre-cious to
so
pre-cious to me,
so pre-cious to me;
me, . . . For He is so pre-cious to me; . . . 'T is heaven be-
rit.
low My Re-deem-er to know, For He is so pre-cious to me.

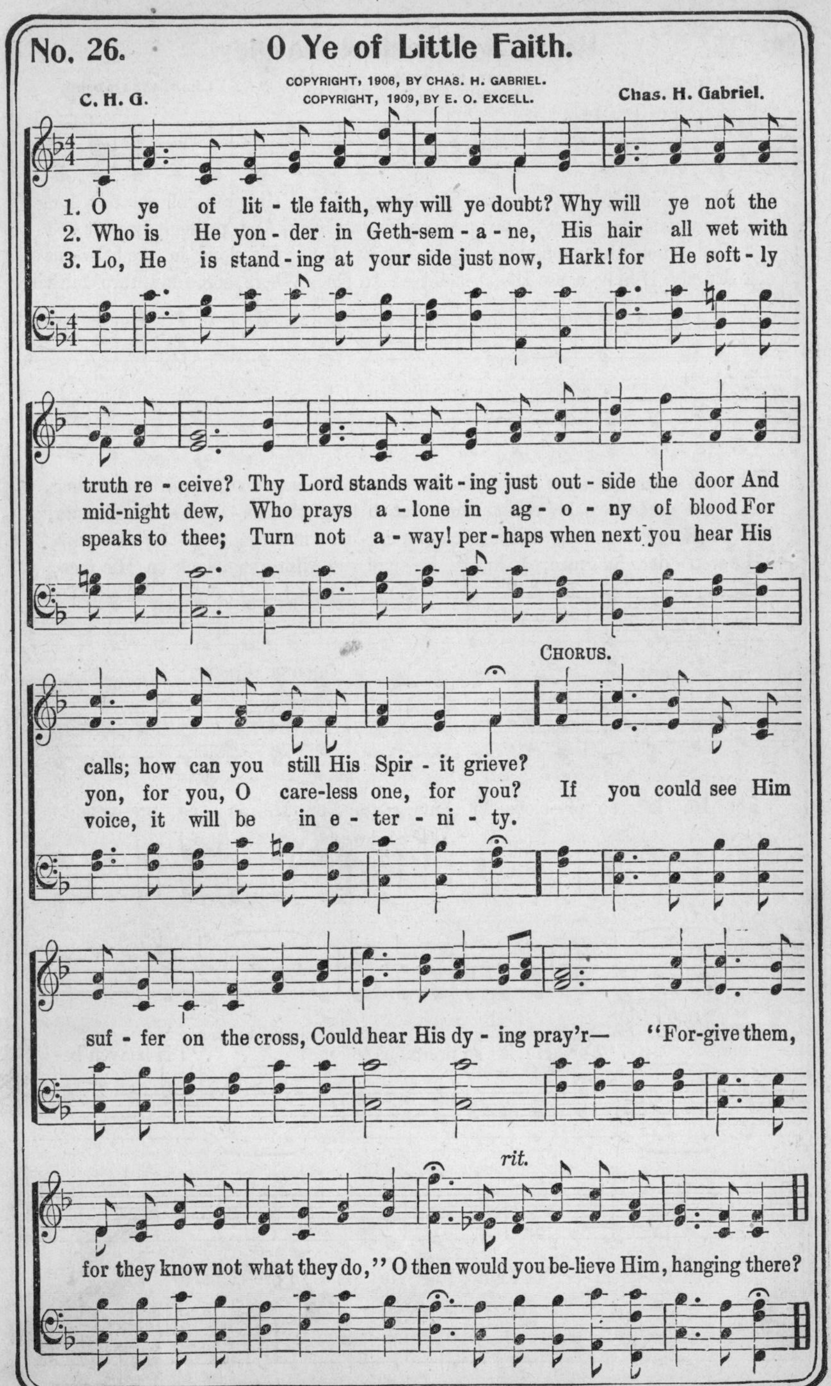
No. 26. O Ye of Little Faith.
COPYRIGHT, 1906, BY CHAS. H. GABRIEL.
COPYRIGHT, 1909, BY E. O. EXCELL.
C. H. G.
Chas. H. Gabriel.
1. O ye of lit - tle faith, why will ye doubt? Why will ye not the truth re - ceive? Thy Lord stands wait - ing just out - side the door And calls; how can you still His Spir - it grieve?
2. Who is He yon - der in Geth-sem - a - ne, His hair all wet with mid-night dew, Who prays a - lone in ag - o - ny of blood For yon, for you, O care-less one, for you?
3. Lo, He is stand - ing at your side just now, Hark! for He soft - ly speaks to thee; Turn not a - way! per - haps when next you hear His voice, it will be in e - ter - ni - ty.
CHORUS.
If you could see Him suf - fer on the cross, Could hear His dy - ing pray'r— "For-give them, for they know not what they do," O then would you be-lieve Him, hanging there?
rit.

No. 27. Where He Leads I'll Follow.
W. A. O.
COPYRIGHT, 1885, BY W. A. OGDEN.
W. A. Ogden.
1. Sweet are the prom-is-es, Kind is the word; Dear-er far than an-y mes-sage man ev-er heard; Pure was the mind of Christ, Sin-less, I see; He the great ex-am-ple is, and pat-tern for me.
2. Sweet is the ten-der love Je-sus hath shown, Sweet-er far than an-y love that mor-tals have known; Kind to the err-ing one, Faith-ful is He; He the great ex-am-ple is, and pat-tern for me.
3. List to His lov-ing words, "Come un-to me!" Wear-y, heav-y-lad-en, there is sweet rest for thee; Trust in His prom-is-es, Faith-ful and sure; Lean up-on the Sav-ior, and thy soul is se-cure.
CHORUS.
Where . . . . He leads I'll fol - - - low,
Where He leads I'll fol-low, Where He leads I'll fol-low,
Fol - - low all the way; Follow Jesus ev-'ry day.
Fol-low all the way, yes, fol-low all the way;

No. 28. The Wonderful Story.
C. H. G.
COPYRIGHT, 1897, BY E. O. EXCELL.
WORDS AND MUSIC.
Chas. H. Gabriel.
1. O sweet is the sto-ry of Je-sus, The won-der-ful Sav-ior of men,
2. He came from the brightest of glo-ry; His blood as a ran-som He gave,
3. His mer-cy flows on like a riv-er; His love is unmeasured and free;
Who suf-fered and died for the sin-ner,—I'll tell it a-gain and a-gain!
To pur-chase e-ter-nal redemption; And, O He is mighty to save!
His grace is for-ev-er suf-fi-cient, It reach-es and pu-ri-fies me.
CHORUS.
O won-der-ful, wonderful sto-ry, The dear-est that
O won-der-ful sto-ry, O won-der-ful sto-ry, The dear-est that ev-
ev-er was told; . . I'll re-peat it in glo-ry, The wonderful
er, that ev-er was told; I'll re-peat it in glo-ry. The
sto-ry, Where I . . . shall His beau-ty be-hold. . .
won-der-ful sto-ry, Where I shall His beau-ty, His beau-ty be-hold.
rit.

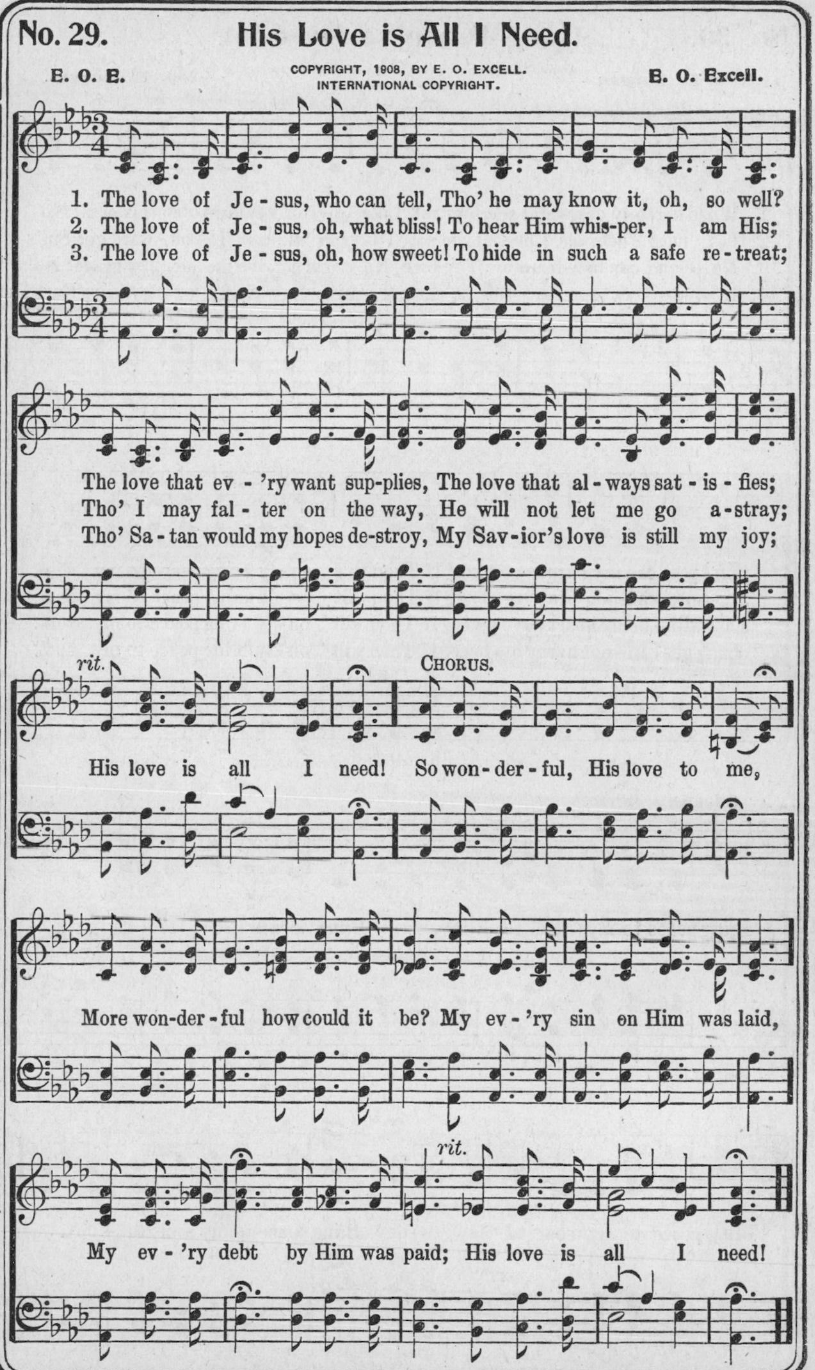
No. 29. His Love is All I Need.
E. O. E.
COPYRIGHT, 1908, BY E. O. EXCELL.
INTERNATIONAL COPYRIGHT.
E. O. Excell.
1. The love of Je - sus, who can tell, Tho' he may know it, oh, so well?
2. The love of Je - sus, oh, what bliss! To hear Him whis-per, I am His;
3. The love of Je - sus, oh, how sweet! To hide in such a safe re - treat;
The love that ev - 'ry want sup-plies, The love that al - ways sat - is - fies;
Tho' I may fal - ter on the way, He will not let me go a - stray;
Tho' Sa - tan would my hopes de-stroy, My Sav - ior's love is still my joy;
rit.
CHORUS.
His love is all I need! So won - der - ful, His love to me,
More won - der - ful how could it be? My ev - 'ry sin on Him was laid,
rit.
My ev - 'ry debt by Him was paid; His love is all I need!

No. 30. Bring Peace to My Soul.
Helen M. Dungan.
WORDS AND MUSIC COPYRIGHT, 1905, BY E. O. EXCELL.
INTERNATIONAL COPYRIGHT SECURED.
J. M. Dungan.
1. When earth-ly cares and sorrows roll Like o-cean's billows o'er my soul, No
2. I need Thee, oh, I need Thee so, To help me as I on-ward go; Sin's
3. No cloud can hide from me Thy face, No storm deprive me of Thy grace, No
4. In joy or sor-row still be near, To drive a-way my ev-'ry fear; Earth's
tem-pest can my barque control, If Thou wilt on-ly bring peace to my soul.
ar-rows can-not lay me low, If Thou wilt on-ly bring peace to my soul.
sin with-in my heart have place, If Thou wilt on-ly bring peace to my soul.
chan-ges can-not harm me here, If Thou wilt on-ly bring peace to my soul.
Chorus.
Bring peace to my soul to-day, . . . Bring peace . . to-day, . . .
to-day, sweet peace to-day,
Bring peace to my soul to-day, to-day, Bring peace to my soul to-day.

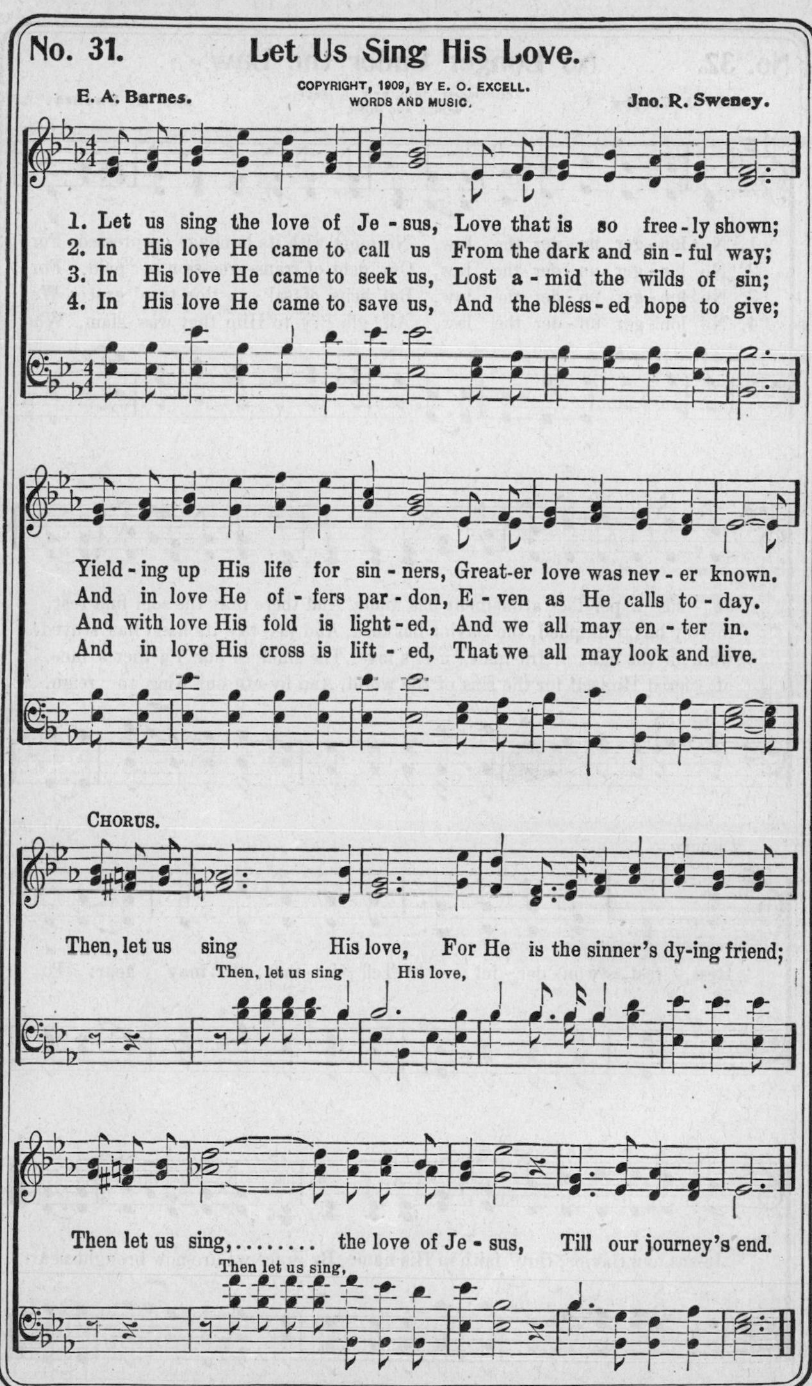
No. 31. Let Us Sing His Love.
COPYRIGHT, 1909, BY E. O. EXCELL. WORDS AND MUSIC.
E. A. Barnes.
Jno. R. Sweney.
1. Let us sing the love of Je - sus, Love that is so free - ly shown;
2. In His love He came to call us From the dark and sin - ful way;
3. In His love He came to seek us, Lost a - mid the wilds of sin;
4. In His love He came to save us, And the bless - ed hope to give;
Yield - ing up His life for sin - ners, Great - er love was nev - er known.
And in love He of - fers par - don, E - ven as He calls to - day.
And with love His fold is light - ed, And we all may en - ter in.
And in love His cross is lift - ed, That we all may look and live.
CHORUS.
Then, let us sing His love, For He is the sinner's dy-ing friend;
Then, let us sing His love,
Then let us sing,........ the love of Je - sus, Till our journey's end.
Then let us sing,

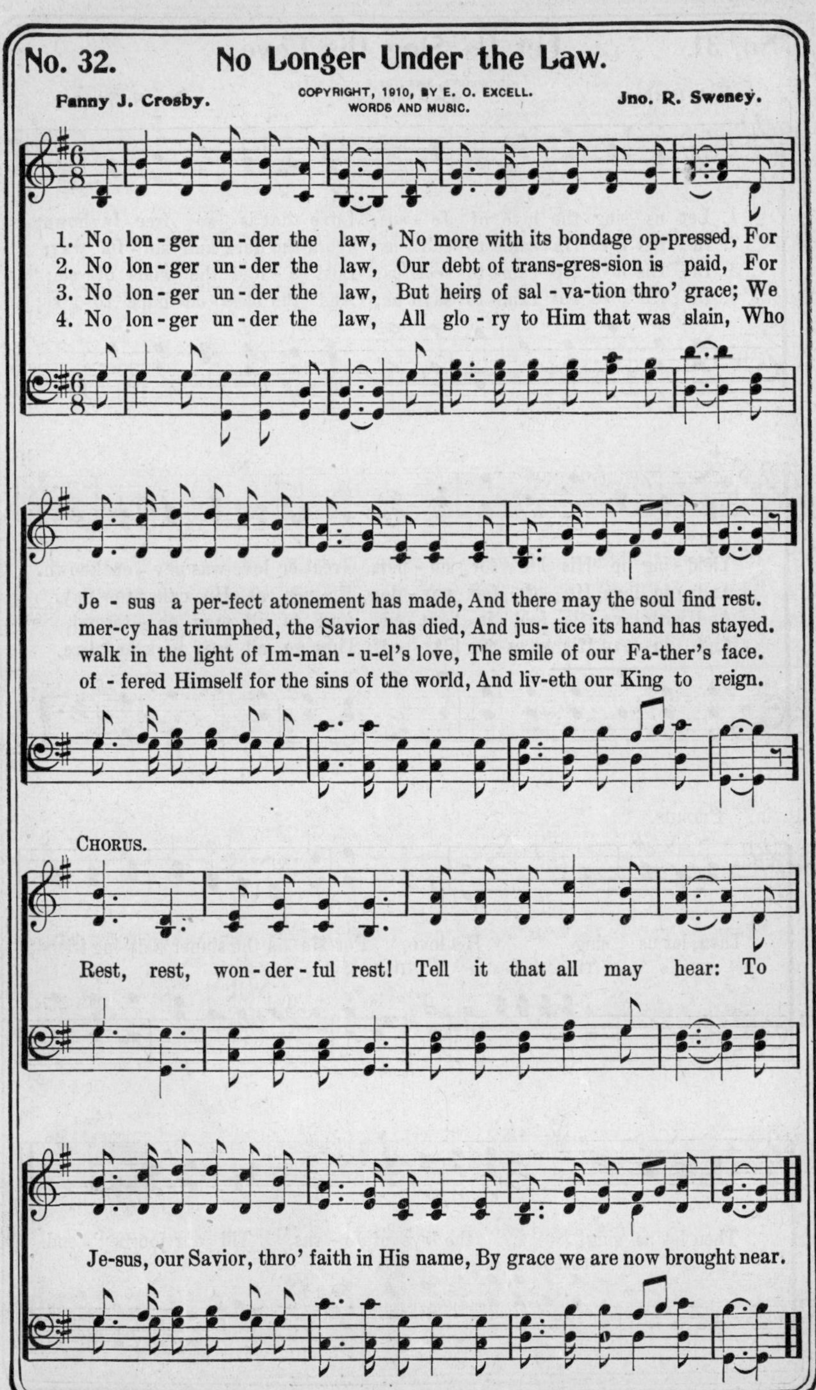
No. 32. No Longer Under the Law.
Fanny J. Crosby.
COPYRIGHT, 1910, BY E. O. EXCELL. WORDS AND MUSIC.
Jno. R. Sweney.
1. No lon-ger un-der the law, No more with its bondage op-pressed, For Je - sus a per-fect atonement has made, And there may the soul find rest.
2. No lon-ger un-der the law, Our debt of trans-gres-sion is paid, For mer-cy has triumphed, the Savior has died, And jus- tice its hand has stayed.
3. No lon-ger un-der the law, But heirs of sal - va-tion thro' grace; We walk in the light of Im-man - u-el's love, The smile of our Fa-ther's face.
4. No lon-ger un-der the law, All glo - ry to Him that was slain, Who of - fered Himself for the sins of the world, And liv-eth our King to reign.
CHORUS.
Rest, rest, won-der-ful rest! Tell it that all may hear: To Je-sus, our Savior, thro' faith in His name, By grace we are now brought near.

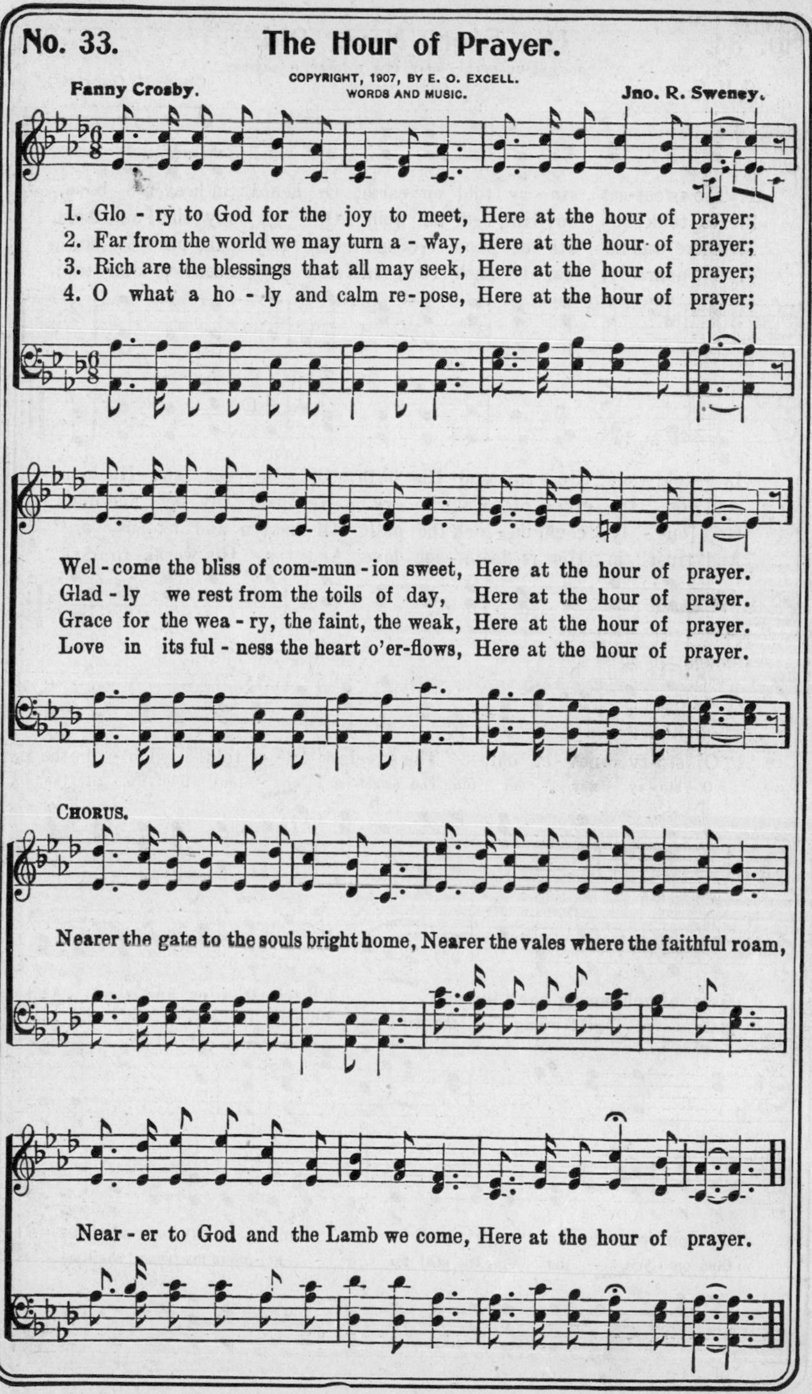
No. 33. The Hour of Prayer.
COPYRIGHT, 1907, BY E. O. EXCELL.
WORDS AND MUSIC.
Fanny Crosby.
Jno. R. Sweney.
1. Glo - ry to God for the joy to meet, Here at the hour of prayer;
2. Far from the world we may turn a - way, Here at the hour of prayer;
3. Rich are the blessings that all may seek, Here at the hour of prayer;
4. O what a ho - ly and calm re - pose, Here at the hour of prayer;
Wel - come the bliss of com - mun - ion sweet, Here at the hour of prayer.
Glad - ly we rest from the toils of day, Here at the hour of prayer.
Grace for the wea - ry, the faint, the weak, Here at the hour of prayer.
Love in its ful - ness the heart o'er-flows, Here at the hour of prayer.
CHORUS.
Nearer the gate to the souls bright home, Nearer the vales where the faithful roam,
Near - er to God and the Lamb we come, Here at the hour of prayer.

No. 34. The Story Never Old.
WORDS AND MUSIC COPYRIGHT, 1906, BY CHAS. H. GABRIEL.
E. O. EXCELL, OWNER.
C. H. G.
Chas. H. Gabriel.
1. The sweet-est sto - ry told on earth, Or heard in heav'n a - bove,
2. He took up - on Him-self the guilt Of all my sins and thine,
3. "There was no oth - er good e-nough To pay the price of sin;
4. "O dear - ly, dear - ly hath He loved And we must love Him too,
Is told of Je - sus and His birth, Of Je - sus and His love.
And on the cross of Cal - va - ry He paid thy debt and mine.
He on - ly could un - lock the gate Of heav'n and let us in."
And trust in His re-deem - ing love, And try His works to do."
CHORUS.
O sto-ry nev-er old, The sweetest ev - er told! Un-til the
O sto - ry nev - er old, The sweet-est ev - er told! Un - til the
gates of gold swing back for me;...... I'll tell it o'er and o'er, And
gates of gold swing back for me; I'll tell it o'er and o'er, And
then on yon-der shore It still for - ev - er-more my song shall be.
then on yon - der shore, It still for - ev - er - more my song shall be.

No. 35. Till the Boat Comes By.
Fanny J. Crosby.
COPYRIGHT, 1900, BY LIZZIE E. SWENEY.
E. O. EXCELL, OWNER.
Jno. R. Sweney.
1. In the house of ma - ny man-sions, With its por-tals bright and fair,
2. I have seen it in the dis-tance As it bent its snow - y sail,
3. In the house of ma - ny man-sions Dwells my Sav - ior and my King;
4. Oh, that boat will soon be com - ing, It will bear me home, I know,
I am lay - ing up my treas-ures, And my heart has long been there.
To the mu - sic of the wa - ters And the whis-per of the gale.
I shall see Him in His beau - ty And His praise my tongue shall sing.
To the house of ma - ny man-sions, And the friends of long a - go.
CHORUS.
At...... the riv - er that...... di-vides me From my
At the flow - ing riv - er, riv - er that di - vides me From my
Fa - ther's house.... on high,.... I........ am wait-ing,
Fa-ther's house, from my Fa - ther's home on high, I am wait - ing, wait - ing,
I....... am watching Till.... the boat comes by..........
I am watch-ing, watch - ing Till the boat, till the boat comes by.

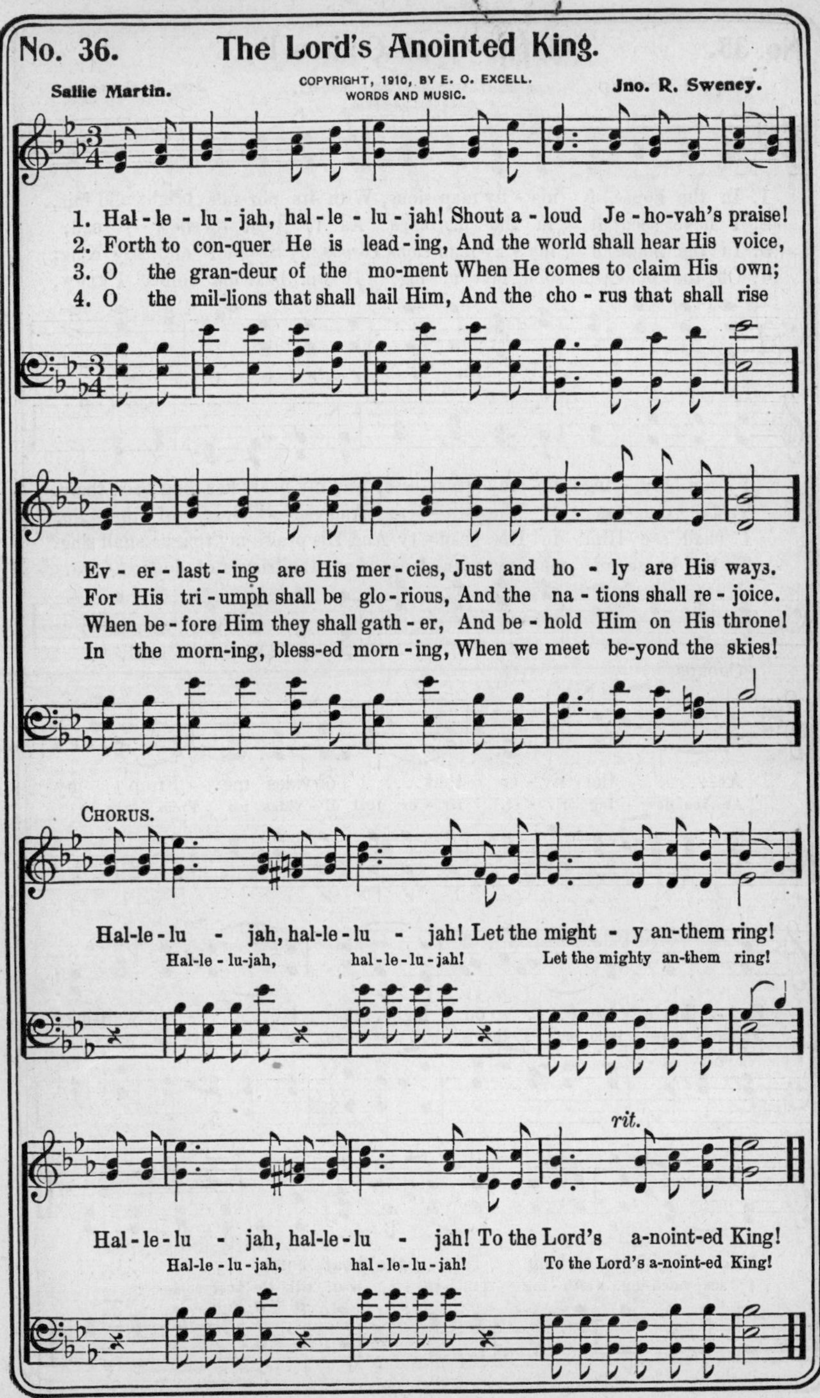
No. 36. The Lord's Anointed King.
Sallie Martin.
COPYRIGHT, 1910, BY E. O. EXCELL.
WORDS AND MUSIC.
Jno. R. Sweney.
1. Hal-le-lu-jah, hal-le-lu-jah! Shout a-loud Je-ho-vah's praise!
2. Forth to con-quer He is lead-ing, And the world shall hear His voice,
3. O the gran-deur of the mo-ment When He comes to claim His own;
4. O the mil-lions that shall hail Him, And the cho-rus that shall rise
Ev-er-last-ing are His mer-cies, Just and ho-ly are His ways.
For His tri-umph shall be glo-rious, And the na-tions shall re-joice.
When be-fore Him they shall gath-er, And be-hold Him on His throne!
In the morn-ing, bless-ed morn-ing, When we meet be-yond the skies!
CHORUS.
Hal-le-lu-jah, hal-le-lu-jah! Let the might-y an-them ring!
Hal-le-lu-jah, hal-le-lu-jah! Let the mighty an-them ring!
rit.
Hal-le-lu-jah, hal-le-lu-jah! To the Lord's a-noint-ed King!
Hal-le-lu-jah, hal-le-lu-jah! To the Lord's a-noint-ed King!

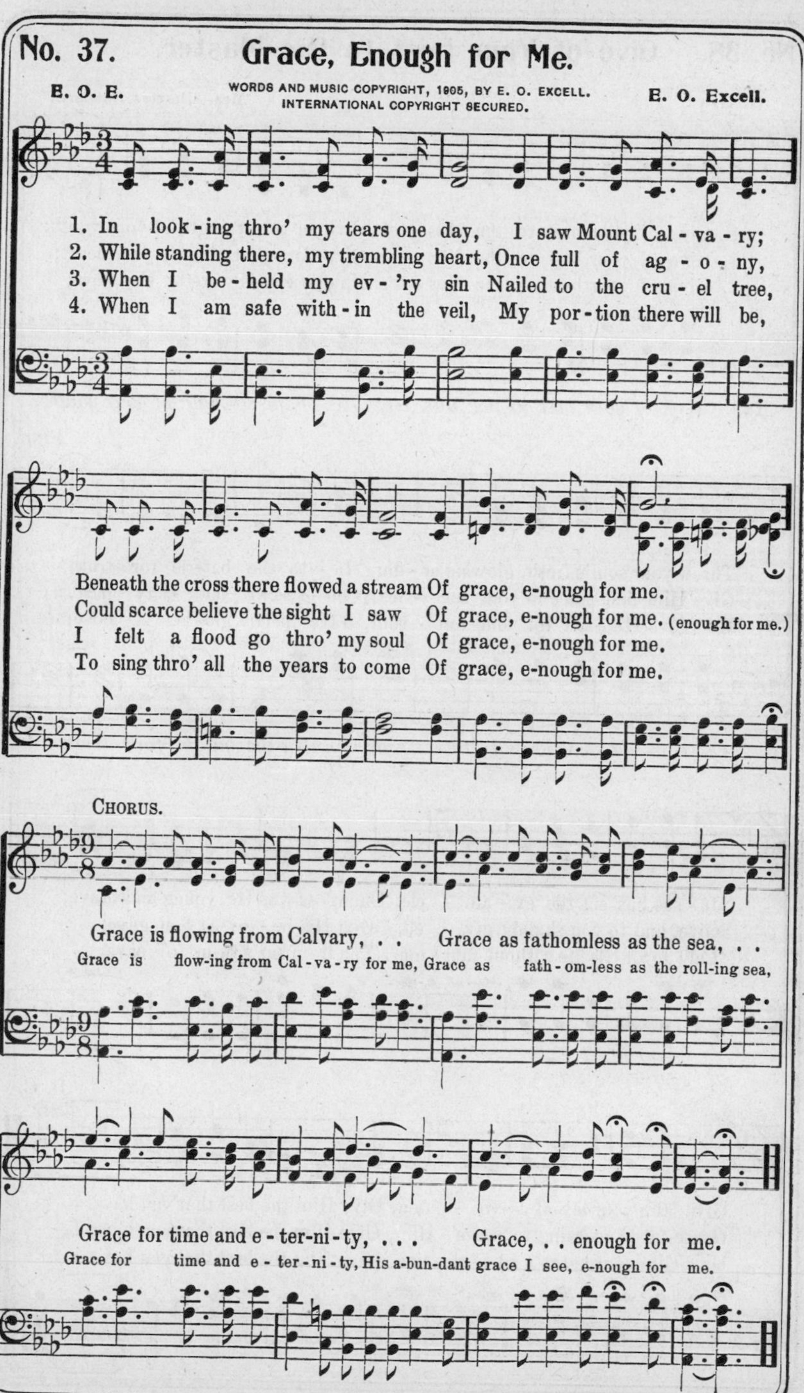
No. 37. Grace, Enough for Me.
E. O. E.
WORDS AND MUSIC COPYRIGHT, 1905, BY E. O. EXCELL.
INTERNATIONAL COPYRIGHT SECURED.
E. O. Excell.
1. In looking thro' my tears one day, I saw Mount Cal - va - ry;
2. While standing there, my trembling heart, Once full of ag - o - ny,
3. When I be - held my ev - 'ry sin Nailed to the cru - el tree,
4. When I am safe with - in the veil, My por - tion there will be,
Beneath the cross there flowed a stream Of grace, e-nough for me.
Could scarce believe the sight I saw Of grace, e-nough for me. (enough for me.)
I felt a flood go thro' my soul Of grace, e-nough for me.
To sing thro' all the years to come Of grace, e-nough for me.
CHORUS.
Grace is flowing from Calvary, . . Grace as fathomless as the sea, . .
Grace is flow-ing from Cal - va - ry for me, Grace as fath - om-less as the roll-ing sea,
Grace for time and e - ter-ni - ty, . . . Grace, . . enough for me.
Grace for time and e - ter - ni - ty, His a-bun-dant grace I see, e-nough for me.

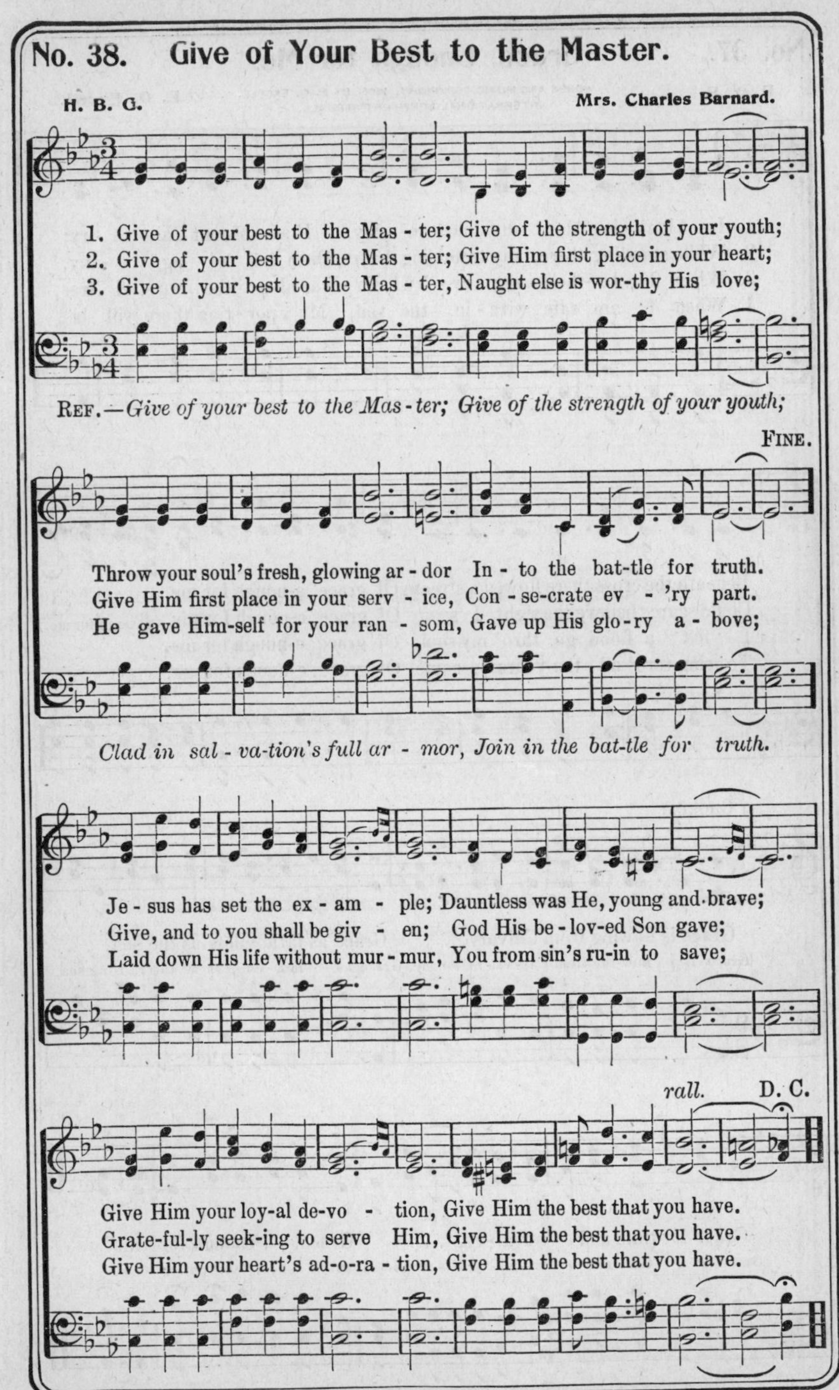
No. 38. Give of Your Best to the Master.
H. B. G.
Mrs. Charles Barnard.
1. Give of your best to the Mas - ter; Give of the strength of your youth;
2. Give of your best to the Mas - ter; Give Him first place in your heart;
3. Give of your best to the Mas - ter, Naught else is wor-thy His love;
REF.—Give of your best to the Mas - ter; Give of the strength of your youth;
FINE.
Throw your soul's fresh, glowing ar - dor In - to the bat-tle for truth.
Give Him first place in your serv - ice, Con - se-crate ev - 'ry part.
He gave Him-self for your ran - som, Gave up His glo-ry a - bove;
Clad in sal - va-tion's full ar - mor, Join in the bat-tle for truth.
Je - sus has set the ex - am - ple; Dauntless was He, young and brave;
Give, and to you shall be giv - en; God His be - lov-ed Son gave;
Laid down His life without mur - mur, You from sin's ru-in to save;
rall.
D. C.
Give Him your loy-al de-vo - tion, Give Him the best that you have.
Grate-ful-ly seek-ing to serve Him, Give Him the best that you have.
Give Him your heart's ad-o-ra - tion, Give Him the best that you have.

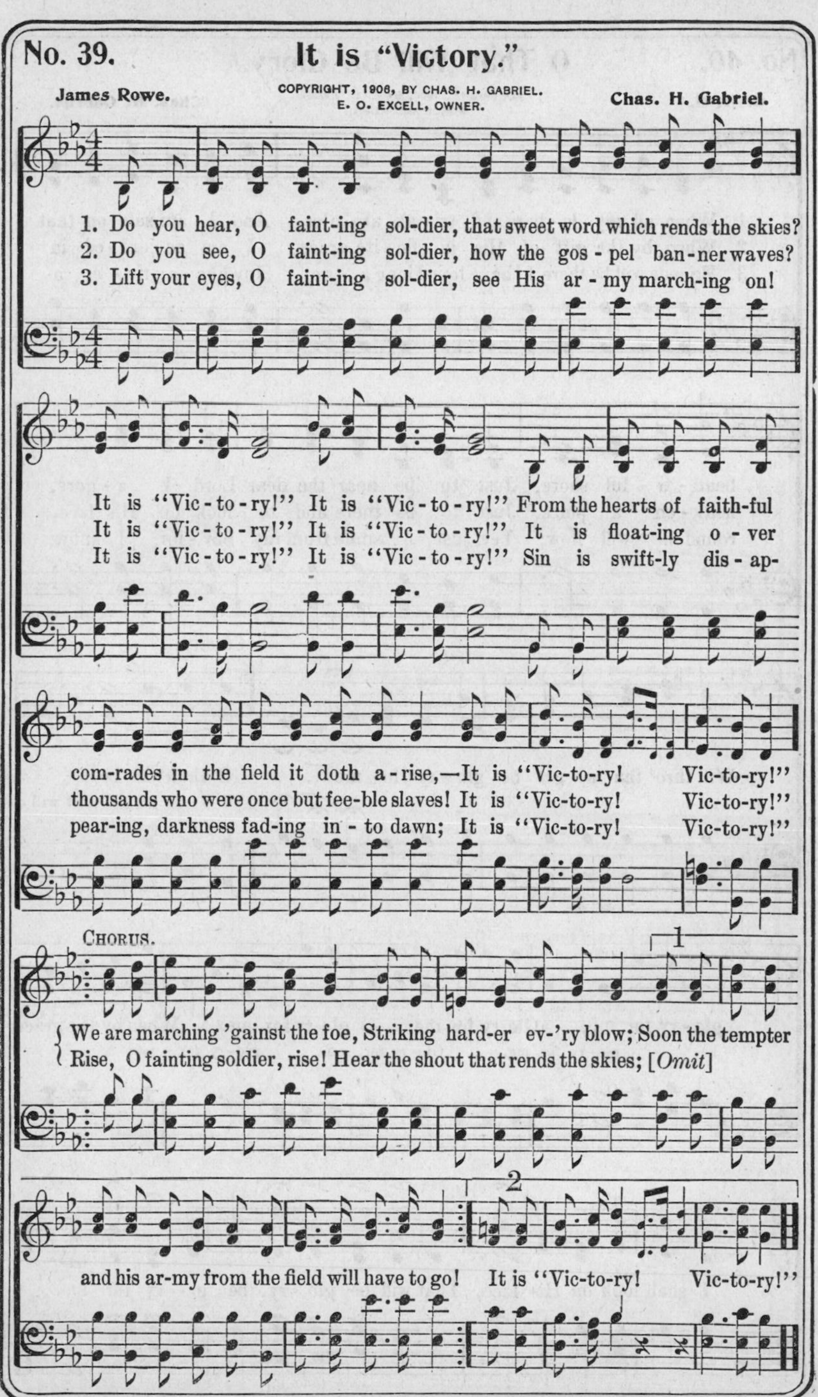
No. 39. It is "Victory."
James Rowe.
COPYRIGHT, 1906, BY CHAS. H. GABRIEL. E. O. EXCELL, OWNER.
Chas. H. Gabriel.
1. Do you hear, O faint-ing sol-dier, that sweet word which rends the skies?
2. Do you see, O faint-ing sol-dier, how the gos-pel ban-ner waves?
3. Lift your eyes, O faint-ing sol-dier, see His ar-my march-ing on!
It is "Vic-to-ry!" It is "Vic-to-ry!" From the hearts of faith-ful
It is "Vic-to-ry!" It is "Vic-to-ry!" It is float-ing o-ver
It is "Vic-to-ry!" It is "Vic-to-ry!" Sin is swift-ly dis-ap-
com-rades in the field it doth a-rise,—It is "Vic-to-ry! Vic-to-ry!"
thousands who were once but fee-ble slaves! It is "Vic-to-ry! Vic-to-ry!"
pear-ing, darkness fad-ing in-to dawn; It is "Vic-to-ry! Vic-to-ry!"
CHORUS.
We are marching 'gainst the foe, Striking hard-er ev-'ry blow; Soon the tempter
Rise, O fainting soldier, rise! Hear the shout that rends the skies; [Omit]
and his ar-my from the field will have to go! It is "Vic-to-ry! Vic-to-ry!"
1
2

No. 40. O That Will Be Glory.
C. H. G.
COPYRIGHT, 1900, BY E. O. EXCELL. WORDS AND MUSIC.
Chas. H. Gabriel.
1. When all my la-bors and tri-als are o'er, And I am safe on that beau-ti-ful shore, Just to be near the dear Lord I a-dore, Will thro' the a-ges be glo-ry for me . .
2. When, by the gift of His in-fin-ite grace, I am ac-cord-ed in heav-en a place, Just to be there and to look on His face,
3. Friends will be there I have loved long a-go; Joy like a riv-er a-round me will flow; Yet, just a smile from my Sav-ior, I know,
Rit.
CHORUS.
O that will be glo-ry for me, Glo-ry for me, glo-ry for me; When by His grace I shall look on His face, That will be glo-ry, be glo-ry for me.
O . . . . that will be glo-ry for me, Glo-ry for me, glo-ry for me; . . . .
rit.

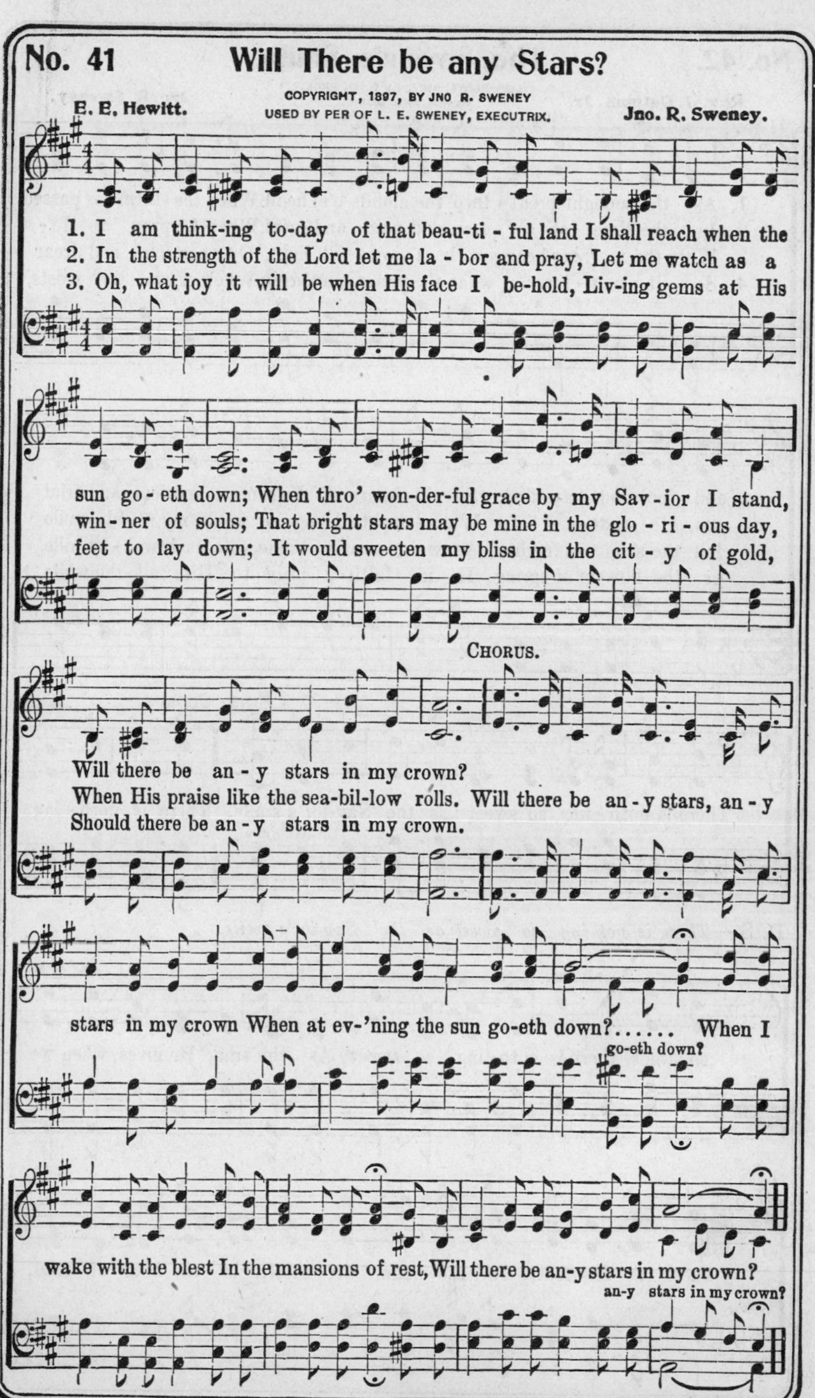
No. 41 Will There be any Stars?
COPYRIGHT, 1897, BY JNO R. SWENEY
USED BY PER OF L. E. SWENEY, EXECUTRIX.
E. E. Hewitt.
Jno. R. Sweney.
1. I am think-ing to-day of that beau-ti - ful land I shall reach when the
2. In the strength of the Lord let me la - bor and pray, Let me watch as a
3. Oh, what joy it will be when His face I be-hold, Liv-ing gems at His
sun go - eth down; When thro' won-der-ful grace by my Sav - ior I stand,
win - ner of souls; That bright stars may be mine in the glo - ri - ous day,
feet to lay down; It would sweeten my bliss in the cit - y of gold,
CHORUS.
Will there be an - y stars in my crown?
When His praise like the sea-bil-low rolls. Will there be an - y stars, an - y
Should there be an - y stars in my crown.
stars in my crown When at ev-'ning the sun go-eth down?...... When I
go-eth down?
wake with the blest In the mansions of rest, Will there be an-y stars in my crown?
an-y stars in my crown?

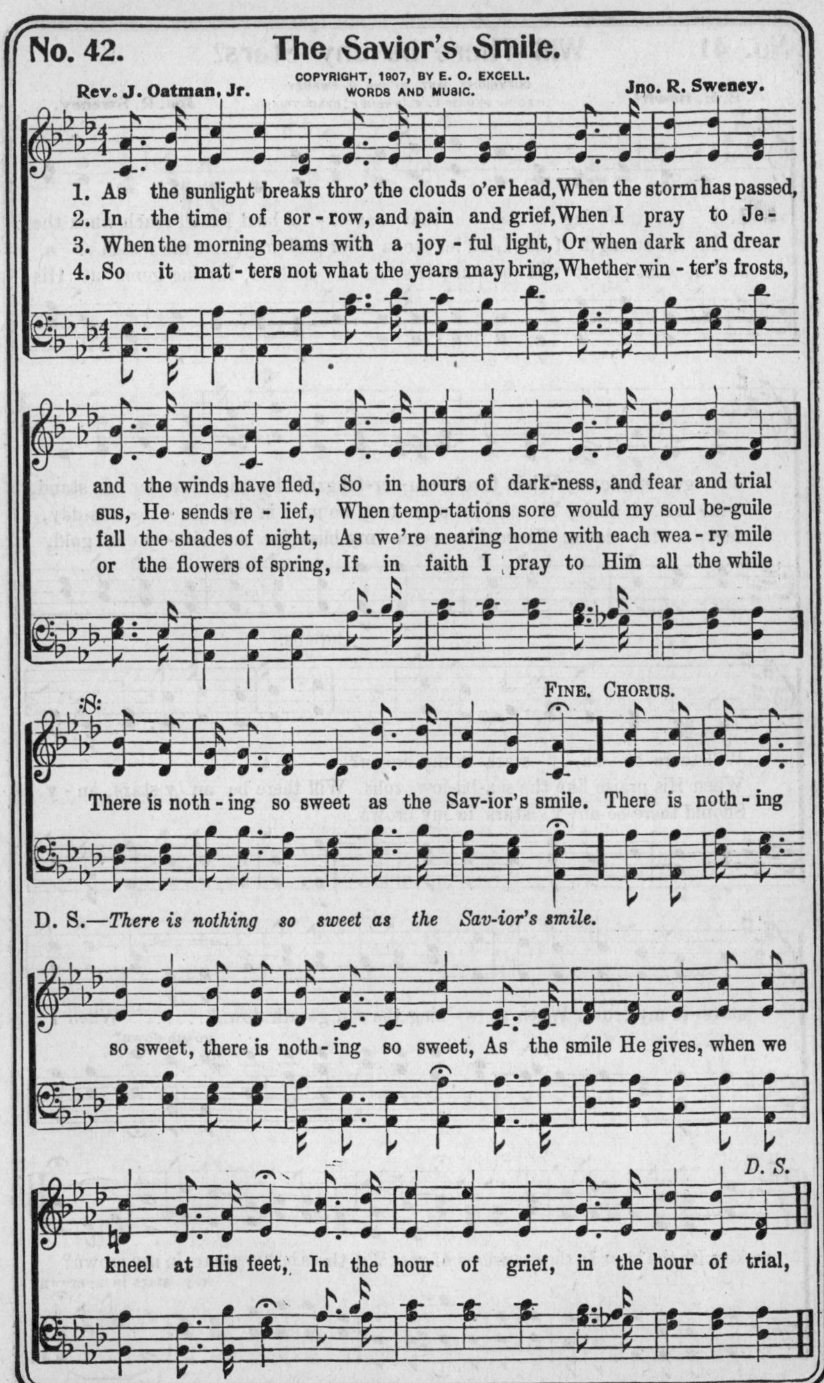
No. 42. The Savior's Smile.
COPYRIGHT, 1907, BY E. O. EXCELL. WORDS AND MUSIC.
Rev. J. Oatman, Jr.
Jno. R. Sweney.
1. As the sunlight breaks thro' the clouds o'er head, When the storm has passed,
2. In the time of sor - row, and pain and grief, When I pray to Je-
3. When the morning beams with a joy - ful light, Or when dark and drear
4. So it mat - ters not what the years may bring, Whether win - ter's frosts,
and the winds have fled, So in hours of dark-ness, and fear and trial
sus, He sends re - lief, When temp-tations sore would my soul be-guile
fall the shades of night, As we're nearing home with each wea - ry mile
or the flowers of spring, If in faith I pray to Him all the while
FINE. CHORUS.
There is noth - ing so sweet as the Sav-ior's smile. There is noth - ing
D. S.—There is nothing so sweet as the Sav-ior's smile.
so sweet, there is noth - ing so sweet, As the smile He gives, when we
D. S.
kneel at His feet, In the hour of grief, in the hour of trial,

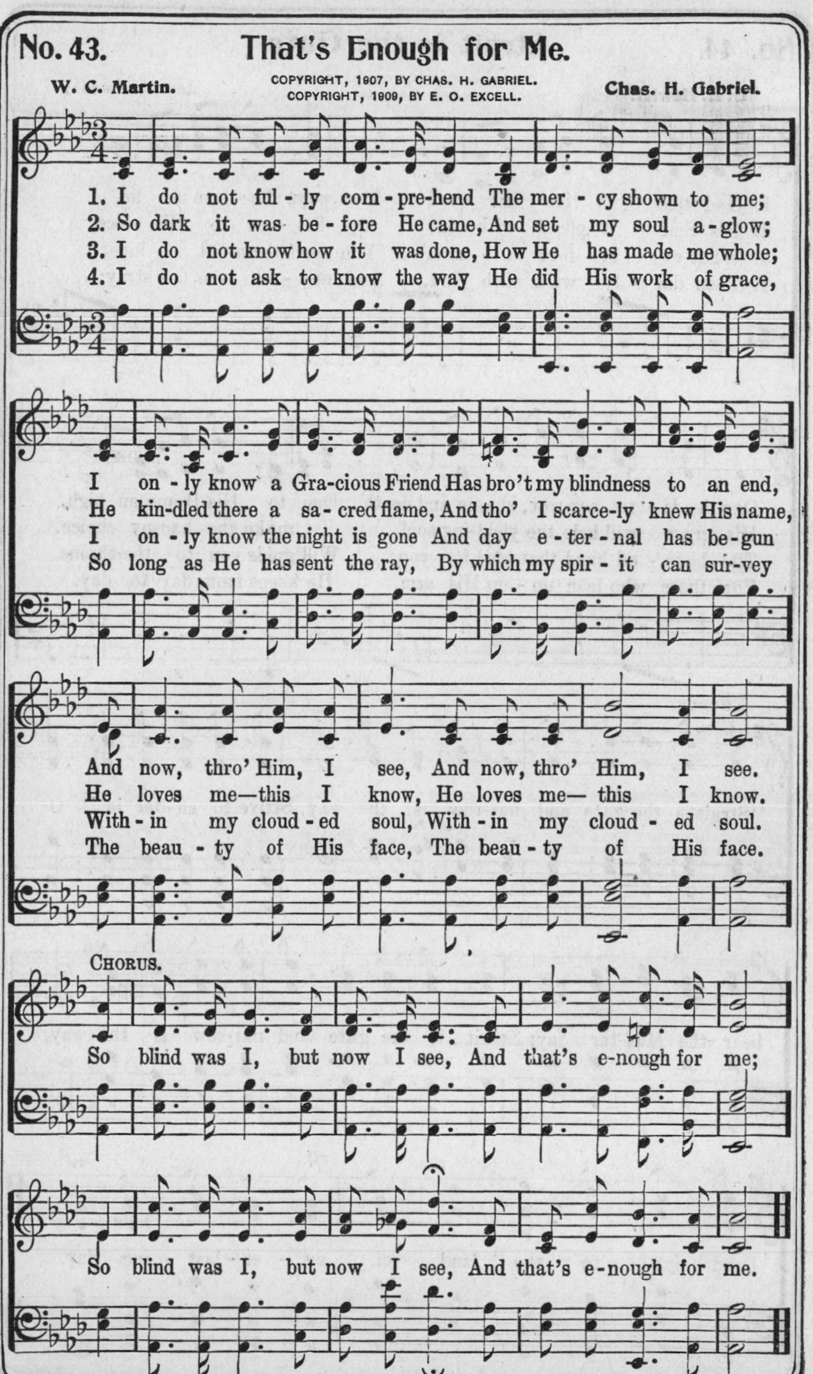
No. 43.
That's Enough for Me.
W. C. Martin.
COPYRIGHT, 1907, BY CHAS. H. GABRIEL.
COPYRIGHT, 1909, BY E. O. EXCELL.
Chas. H. Gabriel.
1. I do not ful - ly com - pre-hend The mer - cy shown to me;
2. So dark it was be - fore He came, And set my soul a - glow;
3. I do not know how it was done, How He has made me whole;
4. I do not ask to know the way He did His work of grace,
I on - ly know a Gra-cious Friend Has bro't my blindness to an end,
He kin-dled there a sa - cred flame, And tho' I scarce-ly knew His name,
I on - ly know the night is gone And day e - ter - nal has be-gun
So long as He has sent the ray, By which my spir - it can sur-vey
And now, thro' Him, I see, And now, thro' Him, I see.
He loves me—this I know, He loves me— this I know.
With - in my cloud - ed soul, With - in my cloud - ed soul.
The beau - ty of His face, The beau - ty of His face.
CHORUS.
So blind was I, but now I see, And that's e-nough for me;
So blind was I, but now I see, And that's e-nough for me.

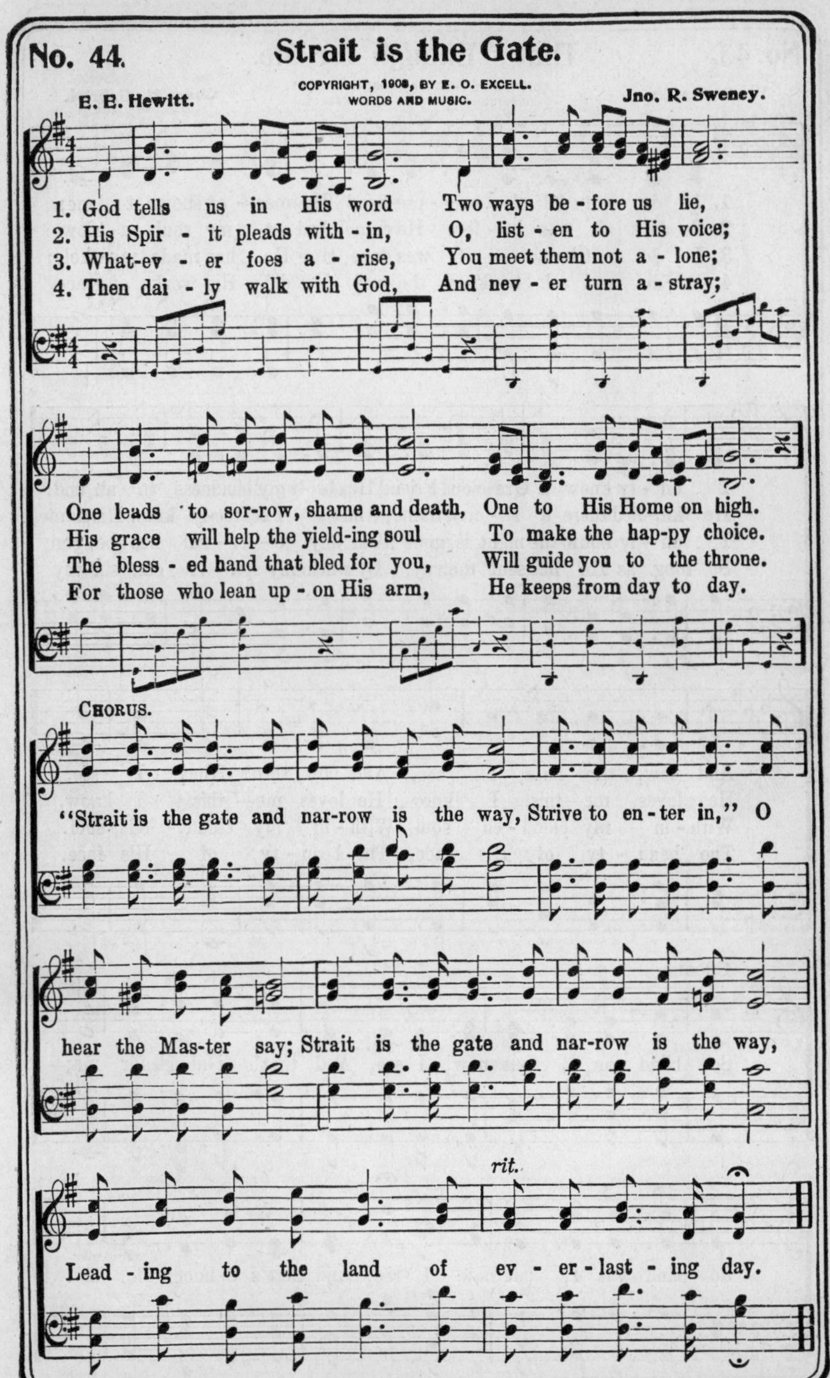
No. 44.
Strait is the Gate.
COPYRIGHT, 1908, BY E. O. EXCELL.
WORDS AND MUSIC.
E. E. Hewitt.
Jno. R. Sweney.
1. God tells us in His word Two ways be - fore us lie,
2. His Spir - it pleads with - in, O, list - en to His voice;
3. What-ev - er foes a - rise, You meet them not a - lone;
4. Then dai - ly walk with God, And nev - er turn a - stray;
One leads to sor-row, shame and death, One to His Home on high.
His grace will help the yield-ing soul To make the hap-py choice.
The bless - ed hand that bled for you, Will guide you to the throne.
For those who lean up - on His arm, He keeps from day to day.
CHORUS.
"Strait is the gate and nar-row is the way, Strive to en-ter in," O
hear the Mas-ter say; Strait is the gate and nar-row is the way,
rit.
Lead - ing to the land of ev - er - last - ing day.

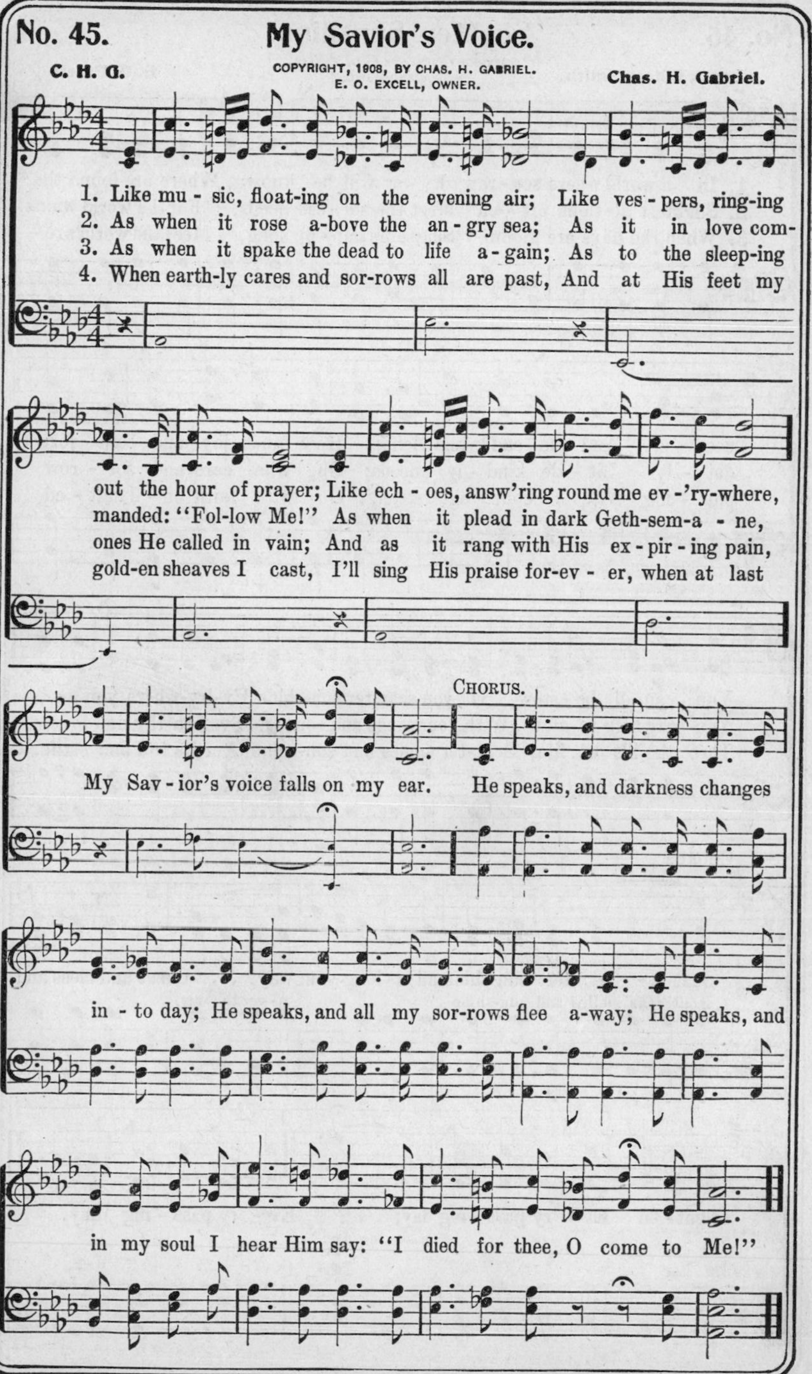
No. 45.
My Savior's Voice.
C. H. G.
COPYRIGHT, 1908, BY CHAS. H. GABRIEL.
E. O. EXCELL, OWNER.
Chas. H. Gabriel.
1. Like mu - sic, float-ing on the evening air; Like ves - pers, ring-ing
2. As when it rose a-bove the an - gry sea; As it in love com-
3. As when it spake the dead to life a - gain; As to the sleep-ing
4. When earth-ly cares and sor-rows all are past, And at His feet my
out the hour of prayer; Like ech - oes, answ'ring round me ev -'ry-where,
manded: "Fol-low Me!" As when it plead in dark Geth-sem-a - ne,
ones He called in vain; And as it rang with His ex - pir - ing pain,
gold-en sheaves I cast, I'll sing His praise for-ev - er, when at last
Chorus.
My Sav - ior's voice falls on my ear. He speaks, and darkness changes
in - to day; He speaks, and all my sor-rows flee a-way; He speaks, and
in my soul I hear Him say: "I died for thee, O come to Me!"

No. 46. Scatter Sunshine.
COPYRIGHT, 1892, BY E. O. EXCELL. WORDS AND MUSIC.
Lanta Wilson Smith.
E. O. Excell.
1. In a world where sor-row Ev-er will be known, Where are found the need-y, And the sad and lone; How much joy and com-fort You can all be-stow, If you scat-ter sun-shine Ev-'ry-where you go.
2. Slightest ac-tions oft-en Meet the sor-est needs, For the world wants dai-ly Lit-tle kind-ly deeds; Oh, what care and sor-row You may help re-move, With your songs and courage, Sym-pa-thy and love.
3. When the days are gloom-y Sing some hap-py song, Meet the world's re-pin-ing With a cour-age strong; Go with faith un-daunt-ed Thro' the ills of life; Scat-ter smiles and sun-snine O'er its toil and strife.
CHORUS.
Scat - - ter sun-shine all a-long your way, . . Cheer and bless and bright-en Ev-'ry pass-ing day; . . . Ev-'ry pass-ing day.
Scatter the smiles and sun-shine o-ver the way,
pass-ing day;

No. 47. Marching Orders.
Eleanor W. Long.
COPYRIGHT, 1908, BY CHAS. H. GABRIEL.
E. O. EXCELL, OWNER.
Chas. H. Gabriel.
1. There's a war to wage with sin, Foes with-out and foes with-in, Gird your ar-mor on! Gird your ar-mor on! We've a Captain tried and true, And He says to me, to you, It is time to dare and do—Gird your ar - mor on!
2. Tho' to - day the warfare cease, And the world seem hushed in peace, Keep your ar-mor on! Keep your ar-mor on! Not far off the camp-fires shine; Soon there'll be for thee and thine Fighting all a-long the line—Keep your ar - mor on!
3. When our Captain gives command, At "At-ten-tion!" we will stand, With our ar-mor on! With our ar-mor on! We are sol-diers of His grace; We shall see Him face to face, And He'll find us in our place With our ar - mor on!
ar - mor on! Gird your ar - mor on!
Chorus.
We will march, march, march, By night at well as day, We are step-ping ev - er firm and stead - y! Yes, we'll
march, march, march Where He may lead the way—When the or - der comes to [Omit. . . . .] march, we are read - y!

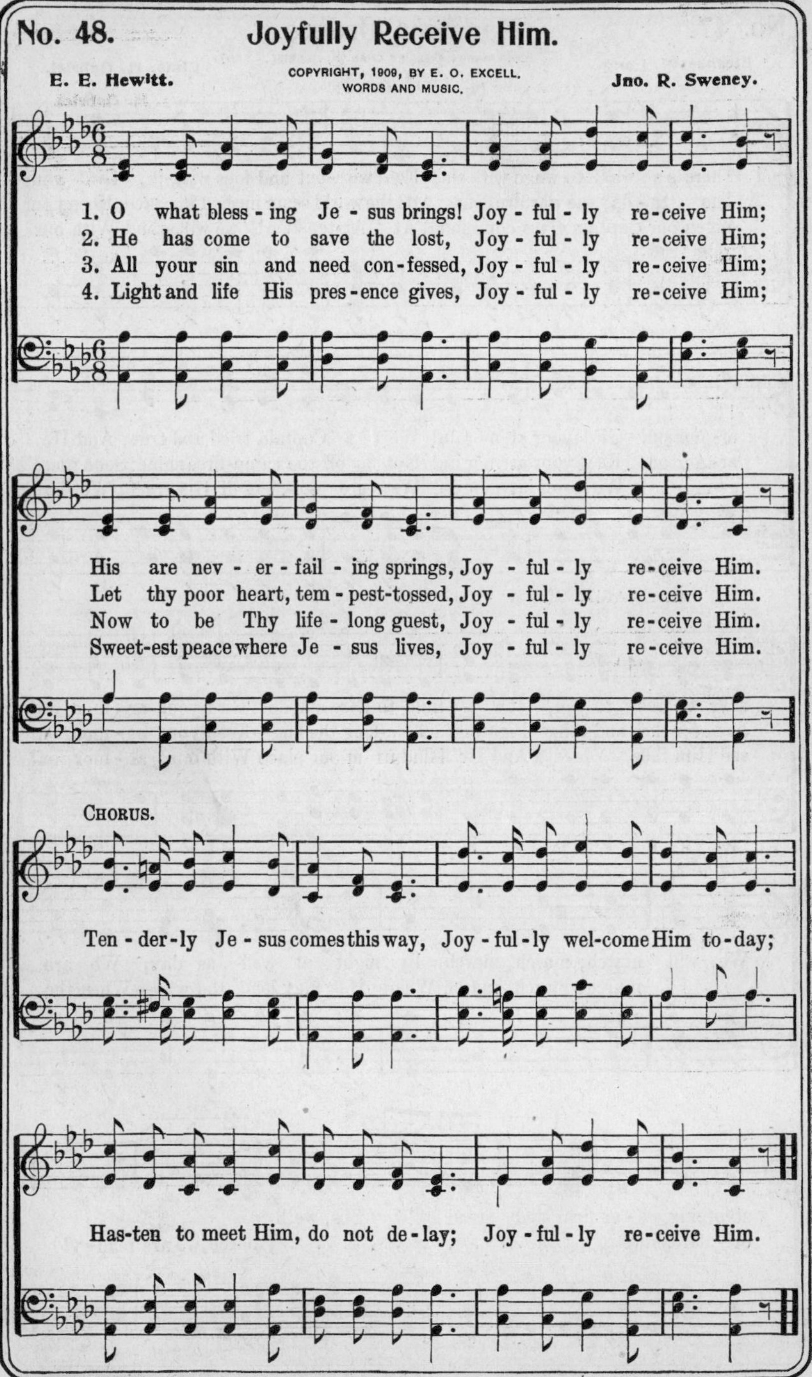
No. 48. Joyfully Receive Him.
E. E. Hewitt.
COPYRIGHT, 1909, BY E. O. EXCELL.
WORDS AND MUSIC.
Jno. R. Sweney.
1. O what bless - ing Je - sus brings! Joy - ful - ly re - ceive Him;
2. He has come to save the lost, Joy - ful - ly re - ceive Him;
3. All your sin and need con - fessed, Joy - ful - ly re - ceive Him;
4. Light and life His pres - ence gives, Joy - ful - ly re - ceive Him;
His are nev - er - fail - ing springs, Joy - ful - ly re - ceive Him.
Let thy poor heart, tem - pest - tossed, Joy - ful - ly re - ceive Him.
Now to be Thy life - long guest, Joy - ful - ly re - ceive Him.
Sweet - est peace where Je - sus lives, Joy - ful - ly re - ceive Him.
CHORUS.
Ten - der - ly Je - sus comes this way, Joy - ful - ly wel - come Him to - day;
Has - ten to meet Him, do not de - lay; Joy - ful - ly re - ceive Him.

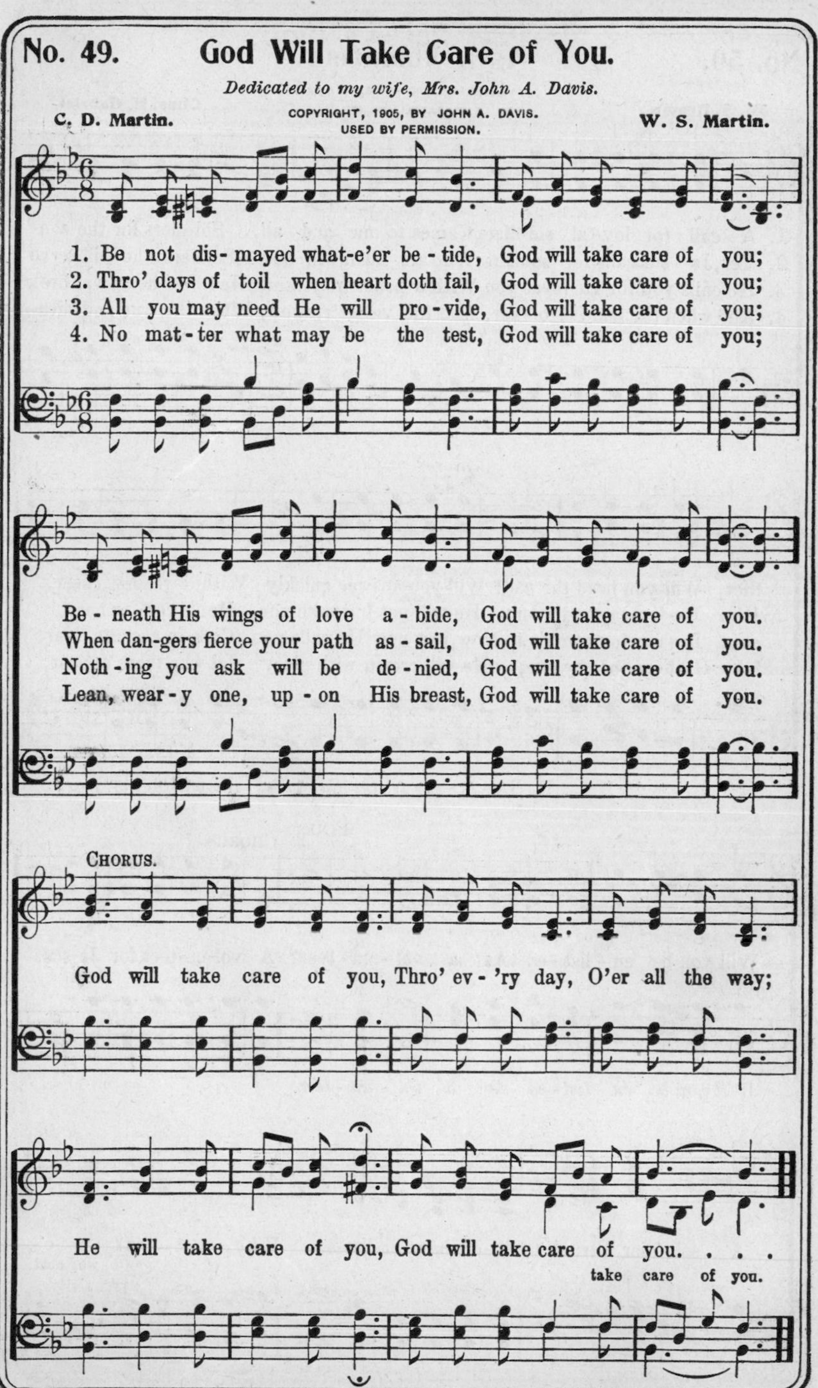
No. 49. God Will Take Care of You.
Dedicated to my wife, Mrs. John A. Davis.
C. D. Martin.
COPYRIGHT, 1905, BY JOHN A. DAVIS. USED BY PERMISSION.
W. S. Martin.
1. Be not dis-mayed what-e'er be-tide, God will take care of you;
2. Thro' days of toil when heart doth fail, God will take care of you;
3. All you may need He will pro-vide, God will take care of you;
4. No mat-ter what may be the test, God will take care of you;
Be-neath His wings of love a-bide, God will take care of you.
When dan-gers fierce your path as-sail, God will take care of you.
Noth-ing you ask will be de-nied, God will take care of you.
Lean, wear-y one, up-on His breast, God will take care of you.
CHORUS.
God will take care of you, Thro' ev-'ry day, O'er all the way;
He will take care of you, God will take care of you. . . .
take care of you.

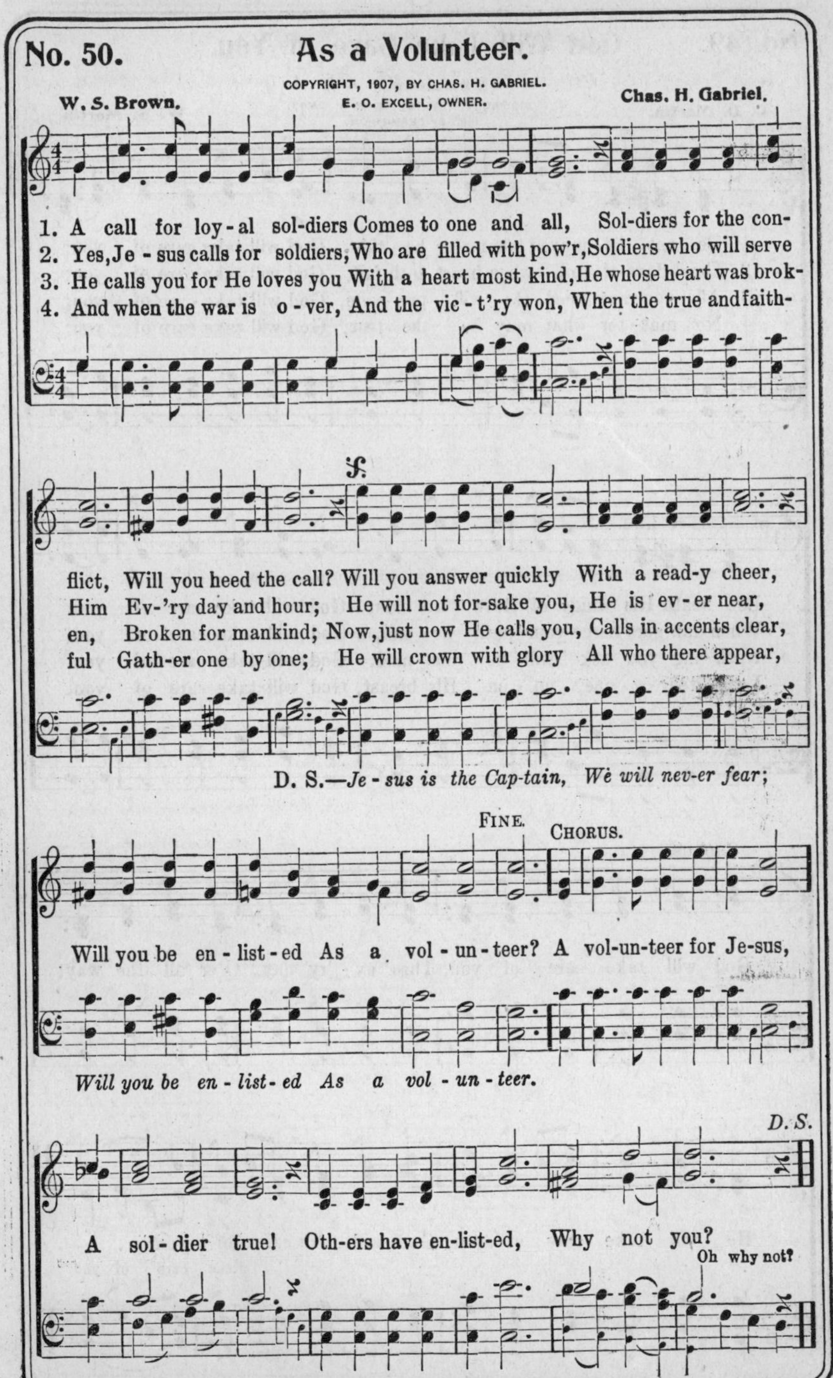
No. 50.
As a Volunteer.
COPYRIGHT, 1907, BY CHAS. H. GABRIEL.
E. O. EXCELL, OWNER.
W. S. Brown.
Chas. H. Gabriel.
1. A call for loy-al sol-diers Comes to one and all, Sol-diers for the con-
2. Yes, Je-sus calls for soldiers, Who are filled with pow'r, Soldiers who will serve
3. He calls you for He loves you With a heart most kind, He whose heart was brok-
4. And when the war is o-ver, And the vic-t'ry won, When the true and faith-
flict, Will you heed the call? Will you answer quickly With a read-y cheer,
Him Ev-'ry day and hour; He will not for-sake you, He is ev-er near,
en, Broken for mankind; Now, just now He calls you, Calls in accents clear,
ful Gath-er one by one; He will crown with glory All who there appear,
D. S.—Je-sus is the Cap-tain, We will nev-er fear;
FINE.
CHORUS.
Will you be en-list-ed As a vol-un-teer? A vol-un-teer for Je-sus,
Will you be en-list-ed As a vol-un-teer.
D. S.
A sol-dier true! Oth-ers have en-list-ed, Why not you?
Oh why not?

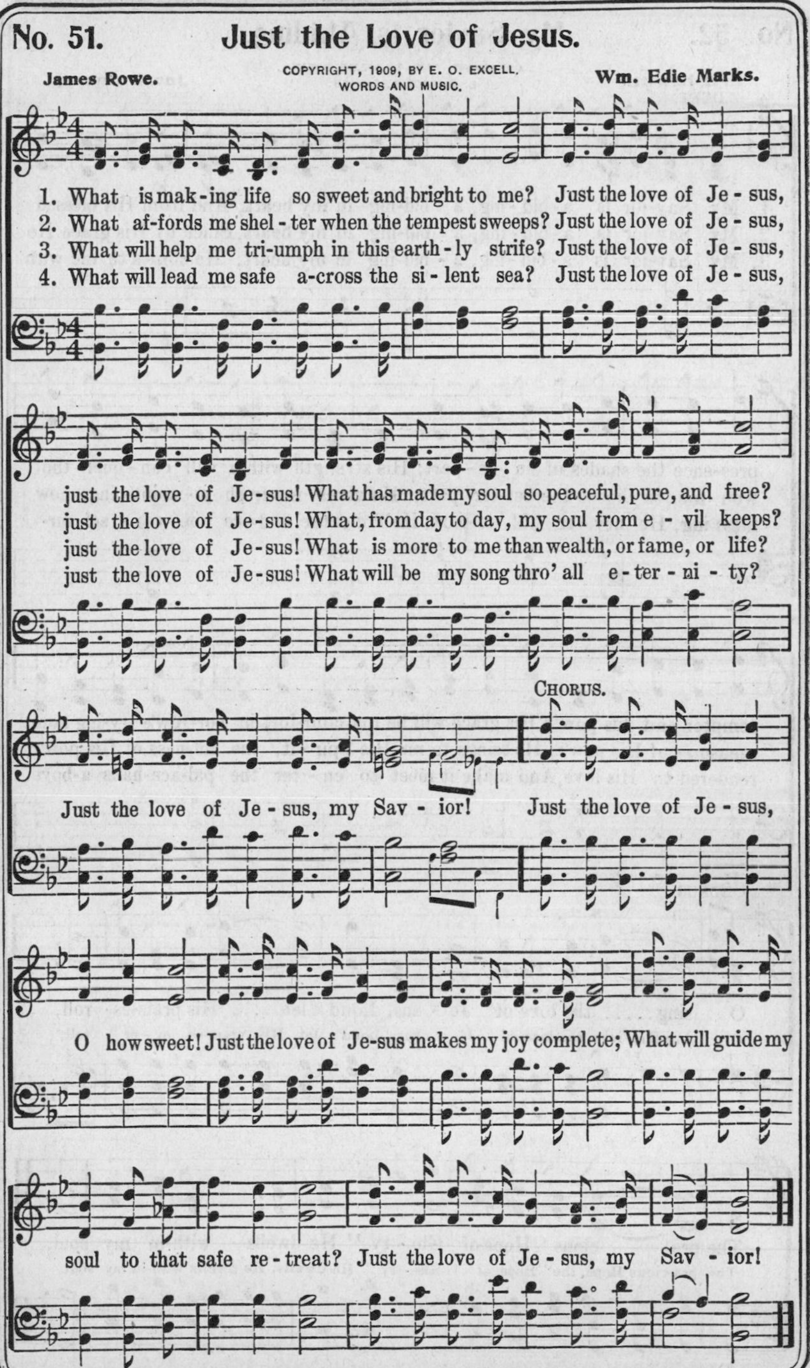
No. 51. Just the Love of Jesus.
James Rowe.
COPYRIGHT, 1909, BY E. O. EXCELL. WORDS AND MUSIC.
Wm. Edie Marks.
1. What is mak-ing life so sweet and bright to me? Just the love of Je - sus,
2. What af-fords me shel - ter when the tempest sweeps? Just the love of Je - sus,
3. What will help me tri-umph in this earth - ly strife? Just the love of Je - sus,
4. What will lead me safe a-cross the si - lent sea? Just the love of Je - sus,
just the love of Je - sus! What has made my soul so peaceful, pure, and free?
just the love of Je - sus! What, from day to day, my soul from e - vil keeps?
just the love of Je - sus! What is more to me than wealth, or fame, or life?
just the love of Je - sus! What will be my song thro' all e - ter - ni - ty?
CHORUS.
Just the love of Je - sus, my Sav - ior! Just the love of Je - sus,
O how sweet! Just the love of Je-sus makes my joy complete; What will guide my
soul to that safe re - treat? Just the love of Je - sus, my Sav - ior!

No. 52. My Savior is Abiding.
COPYRIGHT, 1900, BY LIZZIE SWENEY.
E. O. EXCELL, OWNER.
E. E. Hewitt.
Jno. R. Sweney.
DUET.
1. My Sav-ior is a-bid-ing, a-bid-ing in my heart, And from His blessed
2. My Sav-ior is a-bid-ing, a-bid-ing in my heart, Since by His grace He
3. My Sav-ior is a-bid-ing, a-bid-ing in my heart, He comes to me with
pres-ence the shades of sin de-part; His strength within will con-quer the
won me, to choose the bet-ter part; He gives me fresh a-noint-ing, new
bless-ing, He nev-er will de-part; He'll cleanse and use the ves-sel sur-
tempter and his pow'r, His grace will be my com-fort in sor-row's try-ing hour.
measures of His pow'r, He brings to me His Spir-it, the ful-ness of His pow'r.
rendered to His love, And make it meet to en-ter the pal-ace-halls a-bove.
CHORUS.
O sing..... the love of Je-sus, Loud let..... His prais-es roll,
O sing His love, the love of Je-sus, Loud let His prais-es ev-er roll,
The pre-cious "Hope of Glo-ry," He dwells with-in my soul.
The pre-cious Hope, the "Hope of Glo-ry," He dwells, He dwells with-in my soul.

No. 53.
Drifting Away.
To the Evangelist, Wm. A. Sunday.
E. A. Barnes.
COPYRIGHT, 1910, BY E. O. EXCELL.
WORDS AND MUSIC.
E. O. Excell.
1. From God and His pre-cepts So ho - ly and bright; From paths that are pleasant
2. From words that were spoken When Je-sus was here; From all His kind teachings,
3. From grace that is wait-ing New prospects to give; From love that will help them
Be-cause they are right; From truths in the Bi-ble That all should o - bey—'T is
So sim - ple, so dear; From hope in His fa-vor, That soul-cheer-ing ray—'T is
A new life to live; From heaven's bright portals At life's fi - nal day—'T is
Refrain.
sad that so man - y are drift-ing a - way! Drift-ing a - way,
drift-ing a - way, 'T is sad that so man - y are drift-ing a - way!

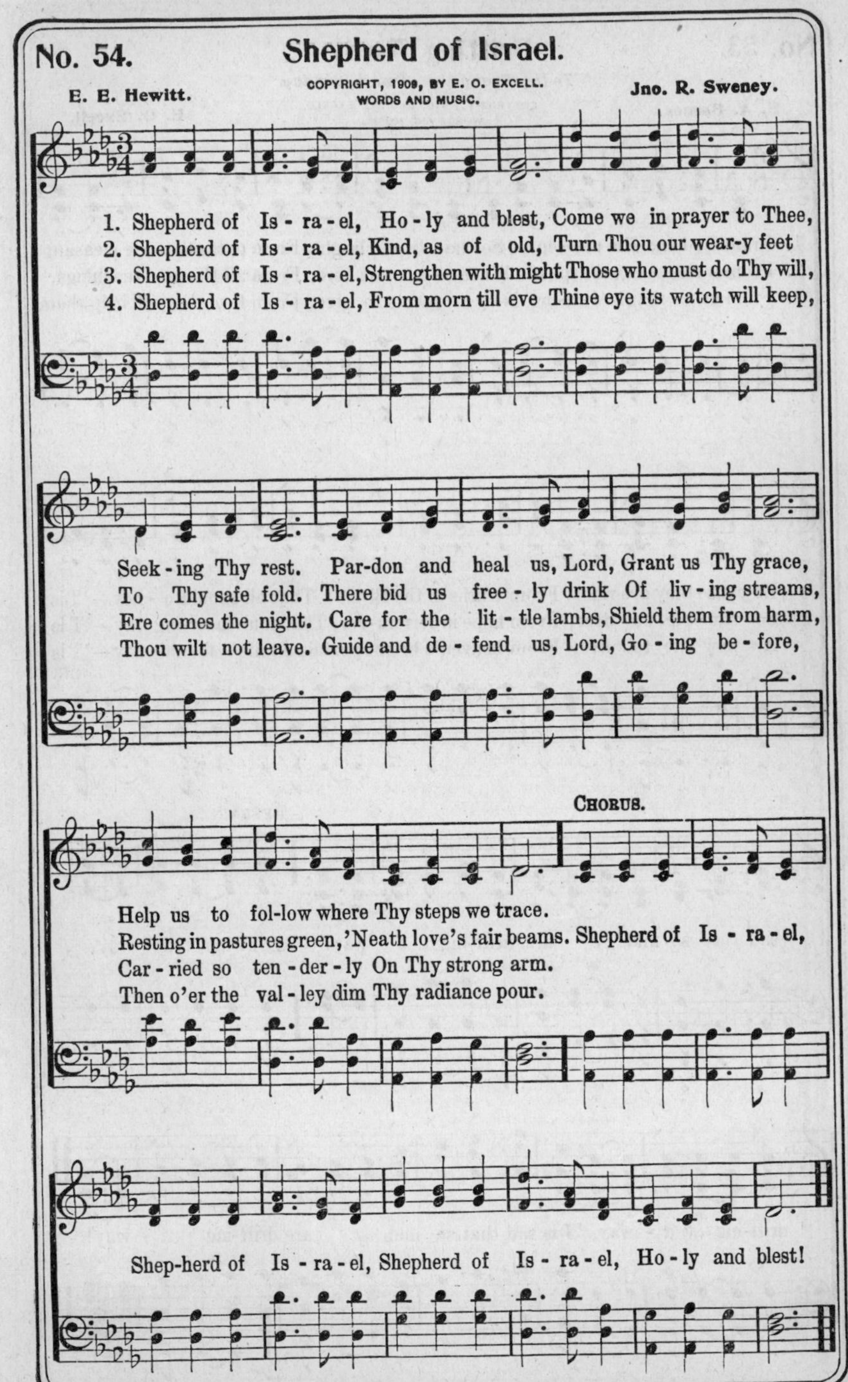
No. 54.
Shepherd of Israel.
E. E. Hewitt.
COPYRIGHT, 1909, BY E. O. EXCELL.
WORDS AND MUSIC.
Jno. R. Sweney.
1. Shepherd of Is - ra - el, Ho - ly and blest, Come we in prayer to Thee,
2. Shepherd of Is - ra - el, Kind, as of old, Turn Thou our wear-y feet
3. Shepherd of Is - ra - el, Strengthen with might Those who must do Thy will,
4. Shepherd of Is - ra - el, From morn till eve Thine eye its watch will keep,
Seek - ing Thy rest. Par-don and heal us, Lord, Grant us Thy grace,
To Thy safe fold. There bid us free - ly drink Of liv - ing streams,
Ere comes the night. Care for the lit - tle lambs, Shield them from harm,
Thou wilt not leave. Guide and de - fend us, Lord, Go - ing be - fore,
CHORUS.
Help us to fol-low where Thy steps we trace.
Resting in pastures green, 'Neath love's fair beams. Shepherd of Is - ra - el,
Car - ried so ten - der - ly On Thy strong arm.
Then o'er the val - ley dim Thy radiance pour.
Shep-herd of Is - ra - el, Shepherd of Is - ra - el, Ho - ly and blest!

No. 55. Let Him In.
Rev. J. B. Atchinson. COPYRIGHT, 1909, BY E. O. EXCELL. RENEWAL. E. O. Excell.
1. There's a Strang-er at the door, Let Him in;
2. O - pen now to Him your heart, Let Him in;
3. Hear you now His lov - ing voice? Let Him in;
4. Now ad - mit the heav'n-ly Guest Let Him in;
Let the Sav-ior in, Let the Sav-ior in;
He has been there oft be - fore, Let Him in;
If you wait He will de - part, Let Him in;
Now, oh, now make Him your choice, Let Him in;
He will make for you a feast, Let Him in;
Let the Sav - ior in, Let the Sav - ior in;
Let Him in, ere He is gone, Let Him in, the Ho - ly One,
Let Him in, He is your friend, He your soul will sure de - fend,
He is stand-ing at your door, Joy to you He will re - store,
He will speak your sins for - giv'n, And when earth ties all are riv'n,
Je - sus Christ, the Fa-ther's Son, Let Him in.
He will keep you to the end, Let Him in.
And His name you will a - dore, Let Him in.
He will take you home to heav'n, Let Him in.
Let the Sav - ior in, Let the Sav - ior in.

No. 56. I Am Happy in Him.
E. O. E.
COPYRIGHT, 1902, BY E. O. EXCELL.
WORDS AND MUSIC.
E. O. Excell.
1. My soul is so hap-py in Je - sus, For He is so precious to me;
2. He sought me so long ere I knew Him, When wand'ring afar from the fold;
3. His love and His mer-cy surround me, His grace like a riv-er doth flow;
4. They say I shall some day be like Him, My cross and my burden lay down;
His voice it is music to hear it, His face it is heaven to see.
Safe home in His arms He hath bro't me, To where there are pleasures untold.
His Spir - it, to guide and to comfort, Is with me wher-ev-er I go.
Till then I will ev-er be faith-ful, In gath - er-ing gems for His crown.
CHORUS.
I am hap-py in Him, . . I am hap-py in Him; . .
I . . . . am hap-py in Him, I . . . . am hap-py in Him;
My soul with de-light He fills day and night, For I am hap-py in Him.

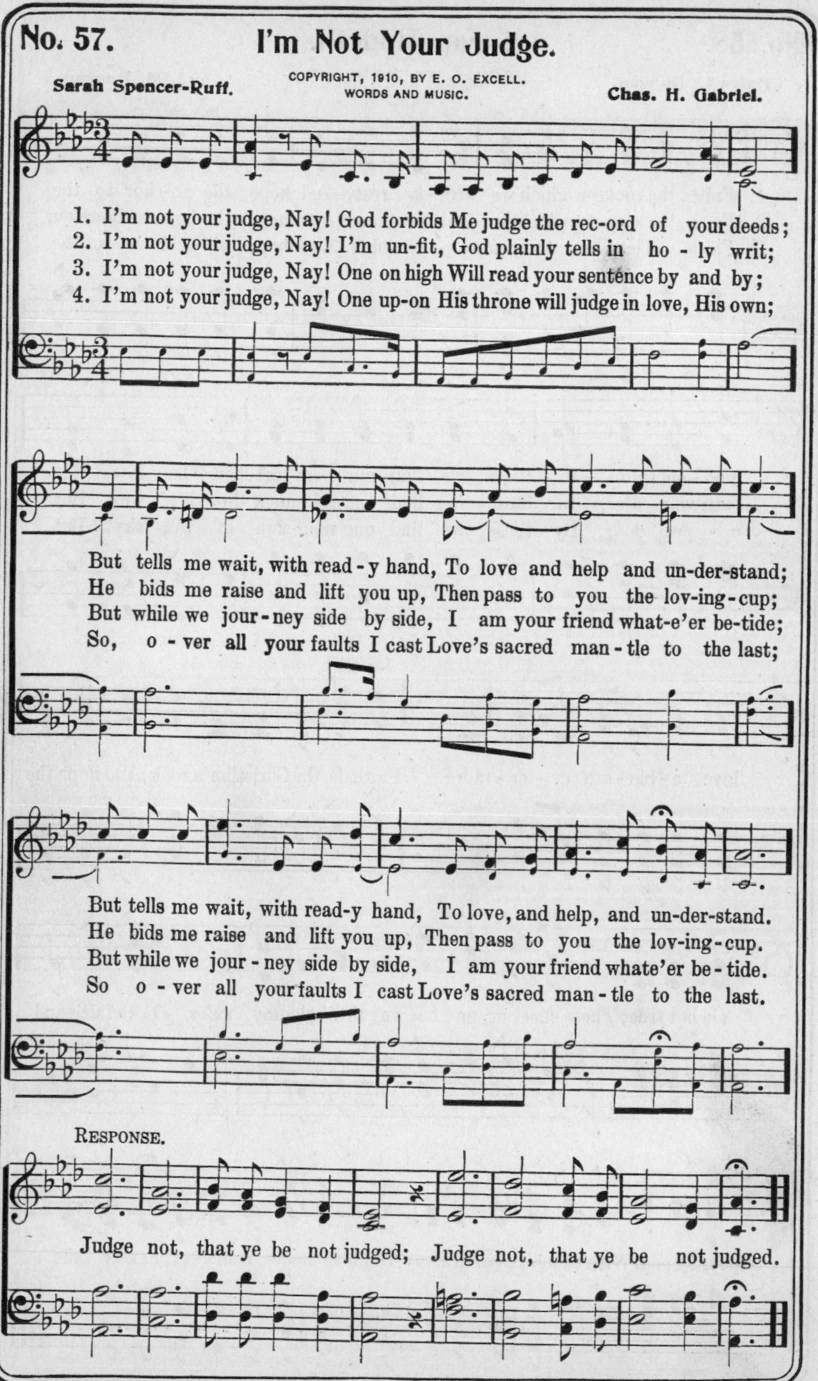
No. 57.
I'm Not Your Judge.
COPYRIGHT, 1910, BY E. O. EXCELL.
WORDS AND MUSIC.
Sarah Spencer-Ruff.
Chas. H. Gabriel.
1. I'm not your judge, Nay! God forbids Me judge the rec-ord of your deeds;
2. I'm not your judge, Nay! I'm un-fit, God plainly tells in ho-ly writ;
3. I'm not your judge, Nay! One on high Will read your sentence by and by;
4. I'm not your judge, Nay! One up-on His throne will judge in love, His own;
But tells me wait, with read-y hand, To love and help and un-der-stand;
He bids me raise and lift you up, Then pass to you the lov-ing-cup;
But while we jour-ney side by side, I am your friend what-e'er be-tide;
So, o-ver all your faults I cast Love's sacred man-tle to the last;
But tells me wait, with read-y hand, To love, and help, and un-der-stand.
He bids me raise and lift you up, Then pass to you the lov-ing-cup.
But while we jour-ney side by side, I am your friend whate'er be-tide.
So o-ver all your faults I cast Love's sacred man-tle to the last.
Response.
Judge not, that ye be not judged; Judge not, that ye be not judged.

No. 58.
Love Abideth.
Helen L. Dungan.
COPYRIGHT, 1910, BY E. O. EXCELL.
WORDS AND MUSIC.
J. M. Dungan.
1. Faith, the rock on which we firm - ly rest, And hope, the an-chor to the
2. Faith, the star to which we look for peace, And hope, the light it shows our
3. Faith will lead us to our home on high, And hope will guide us to the
gold - en shore,—In these we find our com-fort here be low, But
path-way o'er,—In these we find our guid-ance thro' life's way, But
o - pen door; By these we find our man-sion in the sky, But
love a - bid - eth ev - er - more.
CHORUS.
Faith is the Christian's rock, And hope the
anchor true; These cheer us on our way thro' gloomy vales. Both faith and
hope may pass With things of earth away, But love abides; it nev - er, nev - er fails.

No. 59.
Thy Kingdom Come!
Rev. C. McKibbin.
COPYRIGHT, 1909, BY CHAS. H. GABRIEL.
HENRY DATE, OWNER.
Chas. H. Gabriel.
1. Thy kingdom come! and shall not each one sing it, On land and sea, where'er His ban-ner goes? Thy kingdom come! shall we not strive to bring it, The grace that saves the world from hu-man woes?
2. Thy kingdom come! O haste to tell the message, The world is dy-ing for the word of God; Send out the light, that Christ may see the fruitage, The world re-deemed that His own feet have trod.
3. Thy kingdom come! He waits to bless the nations, 'T is ours to bring them quickly to His feet; Make this the time to tram-ple sin's foundations, And lead the err-ing to the mer-cy-seat.
CHORUS.
Thy kingdom come! the glo-rious tri-umph has-ten, When peoples all shall crown Him King of kings; Saints shall re-joice, and angels stop to lis-ten, While earth His ev-er-last-ing glo-ry sings.
shall crown Him King of kings;

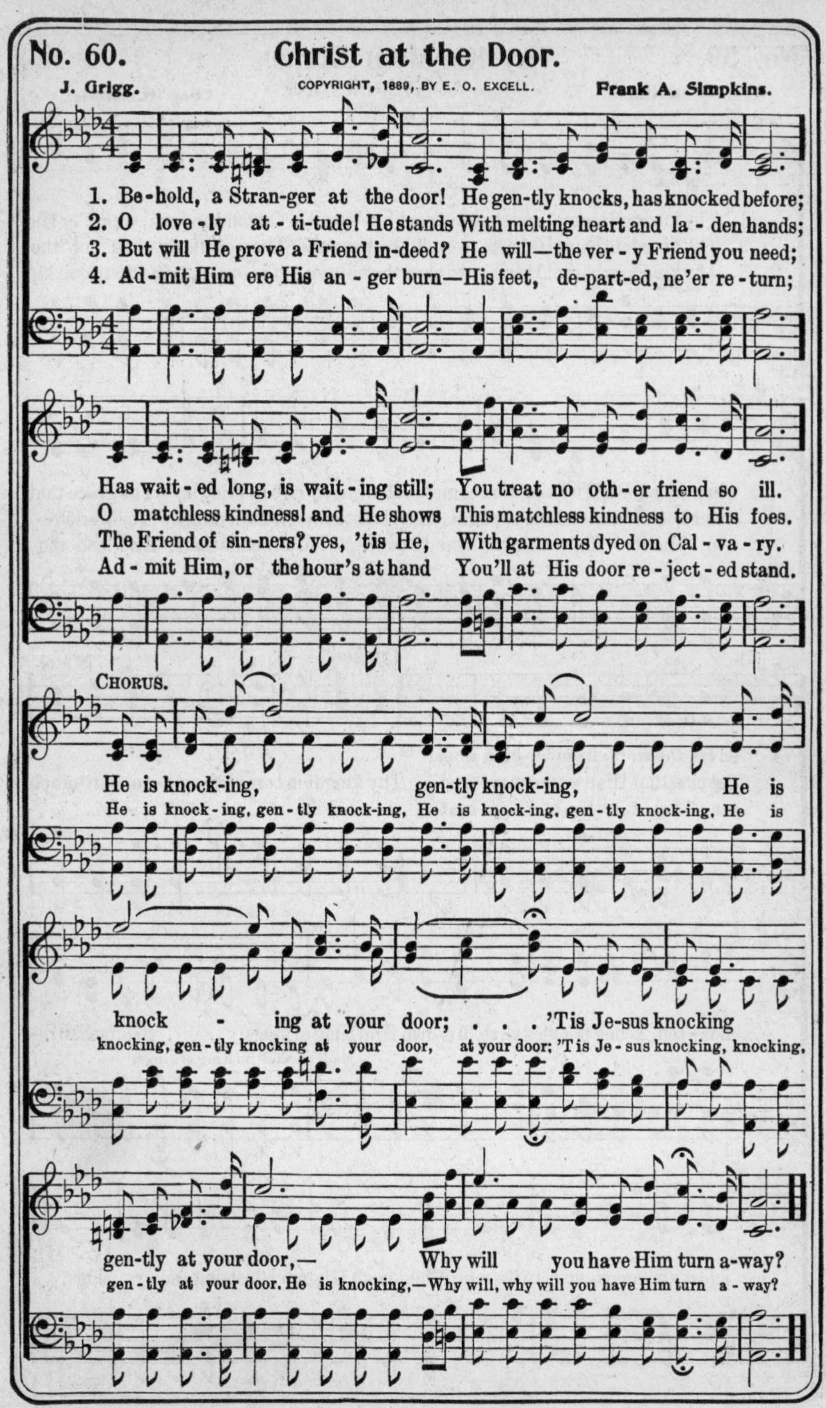
No. 60.
Christ at the Door.
J. Grigg.
COPYRIGHT, 1889, BY E. O. EXCELL.
Frank A. Simpkins.
1. Be-hold, a Stran-ger at the door! He gen-tly knocks, has knocked before;
2. O love-ly at-ti-tude! He stands With melting heart and la-den hands;
3. But will He prove a Friend in-deed? He will—the ver-y Friend you need;
4. Ad-mit Him ere His an-ger burn—His feet, de-part-ed, ne'er re-turn;
Has wait-ed long, is wait-ing still; You treat no oth-er friend so ill.
O matchless kindness! and He shows This matchless kindness to His foes.
The Friend of sin-ners? yes, 'tis He, With garments dyed on Cal-va-ry.
Ad-mit Him, or the hour's at hand You'll at His door re-ject-ed stand.
CHORUS.
He is knock-ing, gen-tly knock-ing, He is
He is knock-ing, gen-tly knock-ing, He is knock-ing, gen-tly knock-ing, He is
knock - ing at your door; . . . 'Tis Je-sus knocking
knocking, gen-tly knocking at your door, at your door; 'T is Je-sus knocking, knocking,
gen-tly at your door,— Why will you have Him turn a-way?
gen-tly at your door. He is knocking,—Why will, why will you have Him turn a-way?

No. 61. It Can Never Be Told.
Mrs. Frank A. Breck.
COPYRIGHT, 1910, BY E. O. EXCELL. WORDS AND MUSIC.
Chas. H. Gabriel.
1. How great is the kind-ness of Je-sus our King, Who came from His glo-ry, sal-va-tion to bring! Who tells us, on Him all our sins may be rolled,—
2. He heal-eth the sick, and the lame, and the blind; He lead-eth His flock like a shepherd most kind; He bringeth the lost one a-gain to His fold,—
3. He grieves for the err-ing when-ev-er they fall; He par-dons trans-gres-sions, forgetting them all; He bless-es the young, and He comforts the old,—
4. For us He hath build-ed, where com-eth no night, A beau-ti-ful home in a cit-y of light; His face He has promised that we shall be-hold,—
His great lov-ing-kindness can nev-er be told.
CHORUS.
It can nev - - - er be told, ... It can nev - - - er be told, ... His great lov-ing-kind-ness can nev-er be told.
It can nev-er be told, No, nev-er be told, It can nev-er be told, No, nev-er be told,

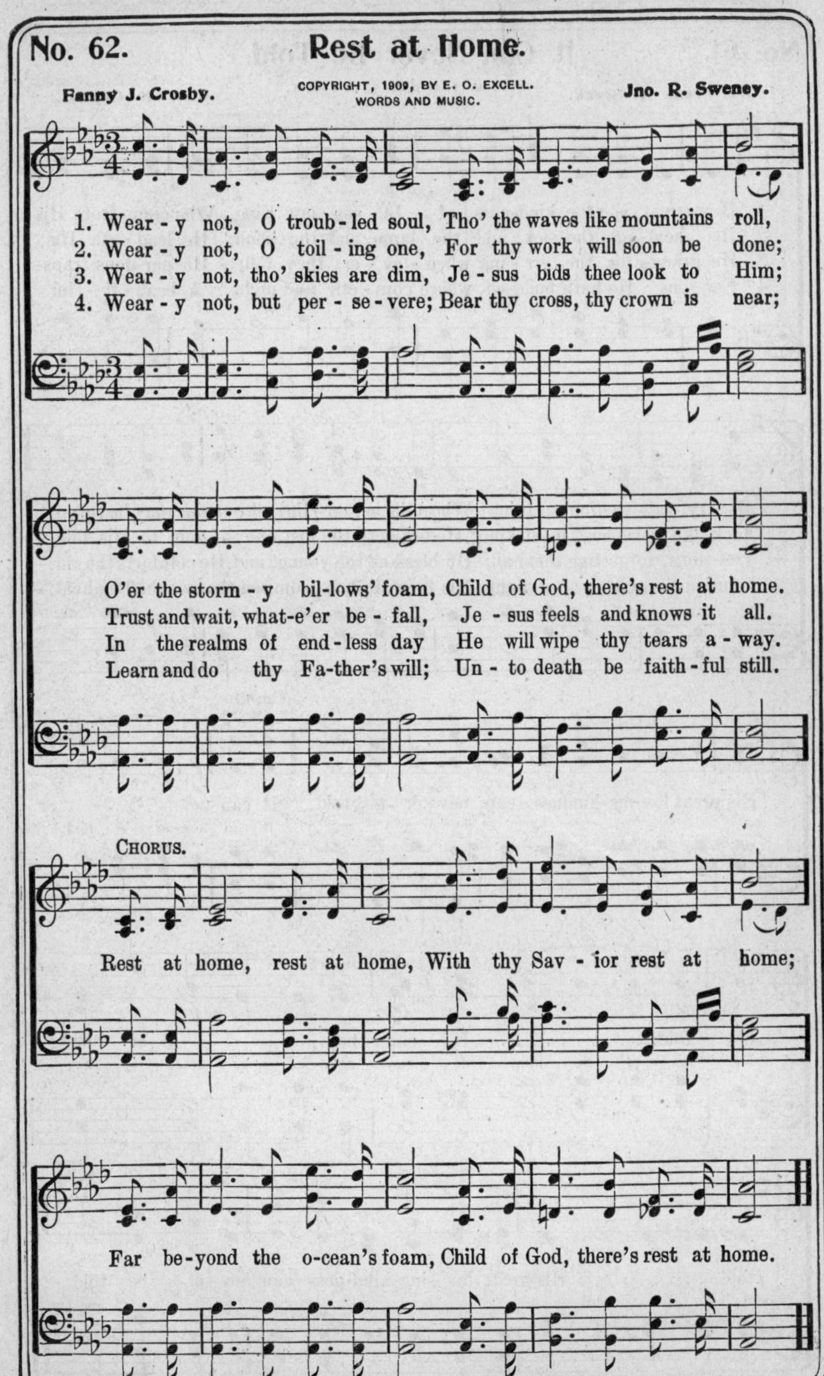

No. 62.
Rest at Home.
Fanny J. Crosby.
COPYRIGHT, 1909, BY E. O. EXCELL.
WORDS AND MUSIC.
Jno. R. Sweney.
1. Wear - y not, O troub - led soul, Tho' the waves like mountains roll,
2. Wear - y not, O toil - ing one, For thy work will soon be done;
3. Wear - y not, tho' skies are dim, Je - sus bids thee look to Him;
4. Wear - y not, but per - se - vere; Bear thy cross, thy crown is near;
O'er the storm - y bil - lows' foam, Child of God, there's rest at home.
Trust and wait, what - e'er be - fall, Je - sus feels and knows it all.
In the realms of end - less day He will wipe thy tears a - way.
Learn and do thy Fa - ther's will; Un - to death be faith - ful still.
CHORUS.
Rest at home, rest at home, With thy Sav - ior rest at home;
Far be - yond the o - cean's foam, Child of God, there's rest at home.

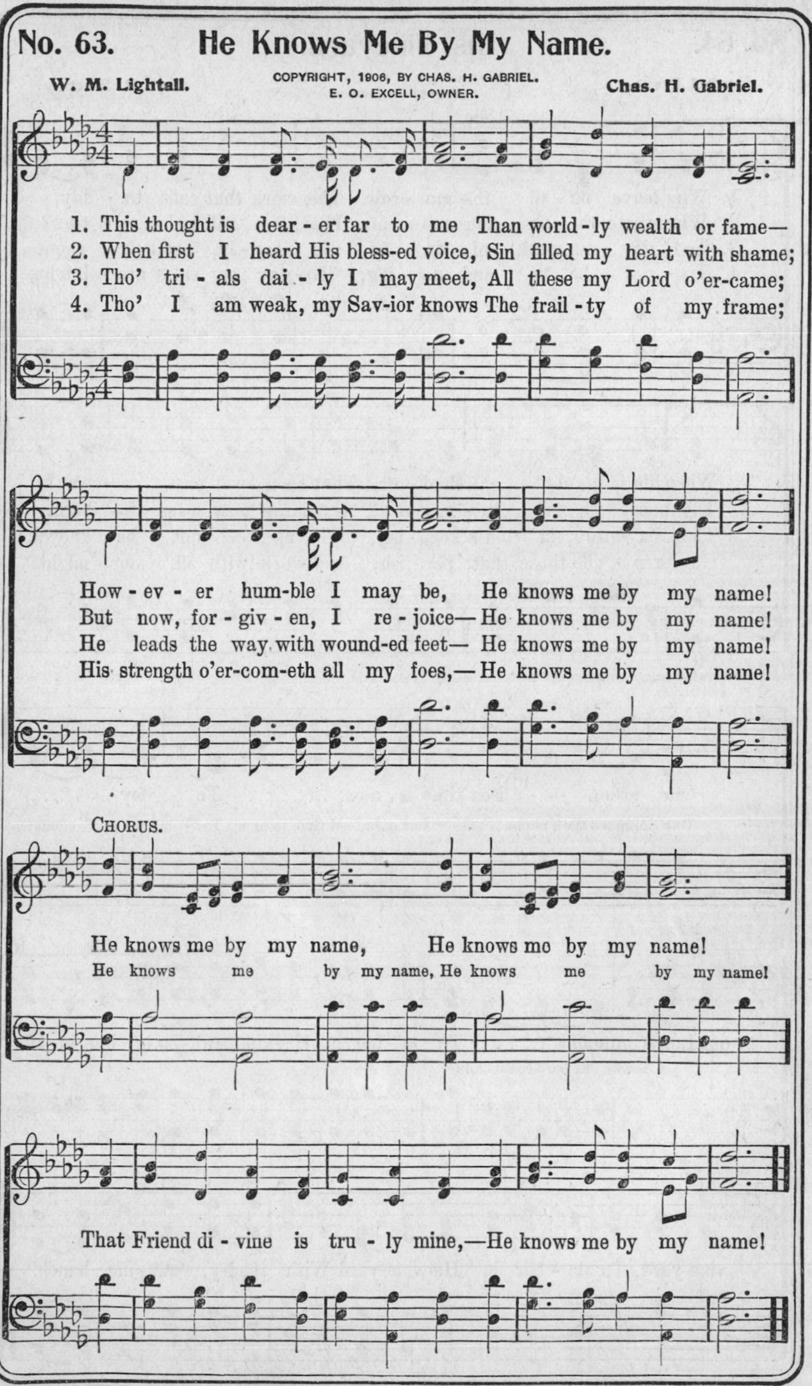
No. 63. He Knows Me By My Name.
W. M. Lightall.
COPYRIGHT, 1906, BY CHAS. H. GABRIEL.
E. O. EXCELL, OWNER.
Chas. H. Gabriel.
1. This thought is dear - er far to me Than world - ly wealth or fame—
2. When first I heard His bless-ed voice, Sin filled my heart with shame;
3. Tho' tri - als dai - ly I may meet, All these my Lord o'er-came;
4. Tho' I am weak, my Sav-ior knows The frail - ty of my frame;
How - ev - er hum-ble I may be, He knows me by my name!
But now, for - giv - en, I re - joice—He knows me by my name!
He leads the way with wound-ed feet— He knows me by my name!
His strength o'er-com-eth all my foes,—He knows me by my name!
CHORUS.
He knows me by my name, He knows me by my name!
He knows me by my name, He knows me by my name!
That Friend di - vine is tru - ly mine,—He knows me by my name!

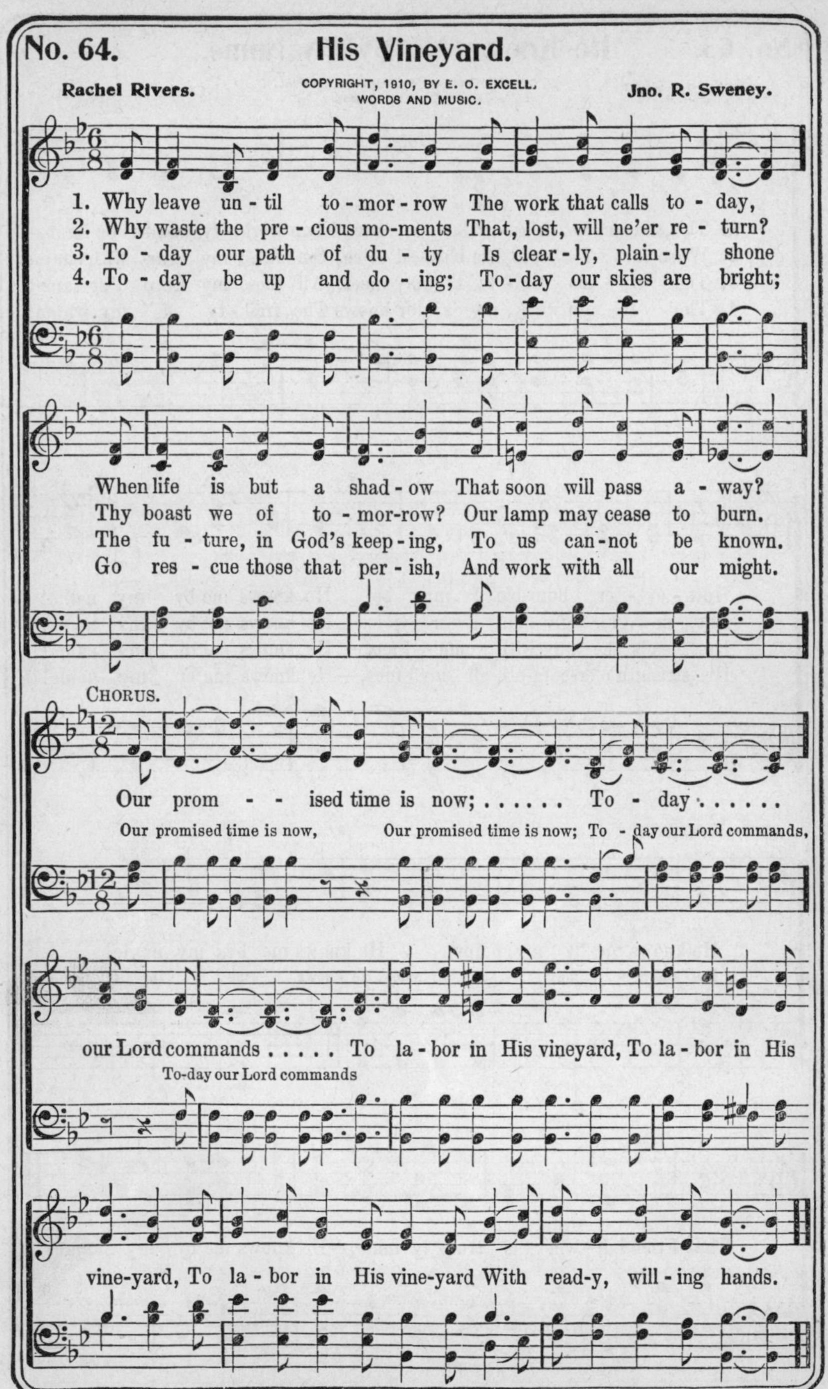
No. 64.
His Vineyard.
Rachel Rivers.
COPYRIGHT, 1910, BY E. O. EXCELL.
WORDS AND MUSIC.
Jno. R. Sweney.
1. Why leave un - til to - mor - row The work that calls to - day,
2. Why waste the pre - cious mo-ments That, lost, will ne'er re - turn?
3. To - day our path of du - ty Is clear - ly, plain - ly shone
4. To - day be up and do - ing; To - day our skies are bright;
When life is but a shad - ow That soon will pass a - way?
Thy boast we of to - mor-row? Our lamp may cease to burn.
The fu - ture, in God's keep - ing, To us can - not be known.
Go res - cue those that per - ish, And work with all our might.
CHORUS.
Our prom - - ised time is now; . . . . . . To - day . . . . . .
Our promised time is now, Our promised time is now; To - day our Lord commands,
our Lord commands . . . . . To la - bor in His vineyard, To la - bor in His
To-day our Lord commands
vine-yard, To la - bor in His vine-yard With read - y, will - ing hands.

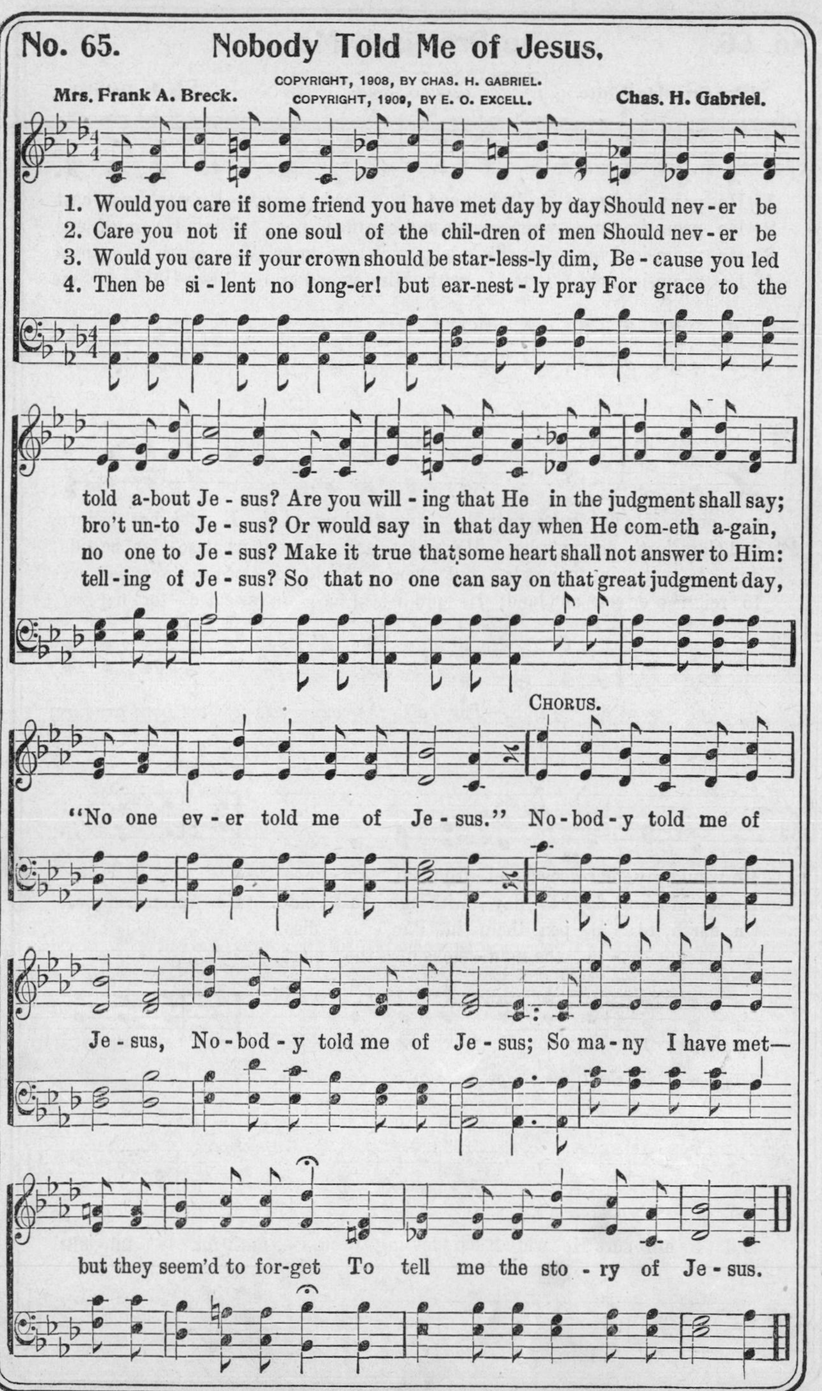
No. 65. Nobody Told Me of Jesus.
COPYRIGHT, 1908, BY CHAS. H. GABRIEL.
COPYRIGHT, 1909, BY E. O. EXCELL.
Mrs. Frank A. Breck.
Chas. H. Gabriel.
1. Would you care if some friend you have met day by day Should nev - er be
2. Care you not if one soul of the chil-dren of men Should nev - er be
3. Would you care if your crown should be star-less-ly dim, Be - cause you led
4. Then be si - lent no long-er! but ear-nest - ly pray For grace to the
told a-bout Je - sus? Are you will - ing that He in the judgment shall say;
bro't un-to Je - sus? Or would say in that day when He com-eth a-gain,
no one to Je - sus? Make it true that some heart shall not answer to Him:
tell-ing of Je - sus? So that no one can say on that great judgment day,
CHORUS.
"No one ev - er told me of Je - sus." No-bod-y told me of
Je - sus, No-bod - y told me of Je - sus; So ma-ny I have met—
but they seem'd to for-get To tell me the sto - ry of Je - sus.

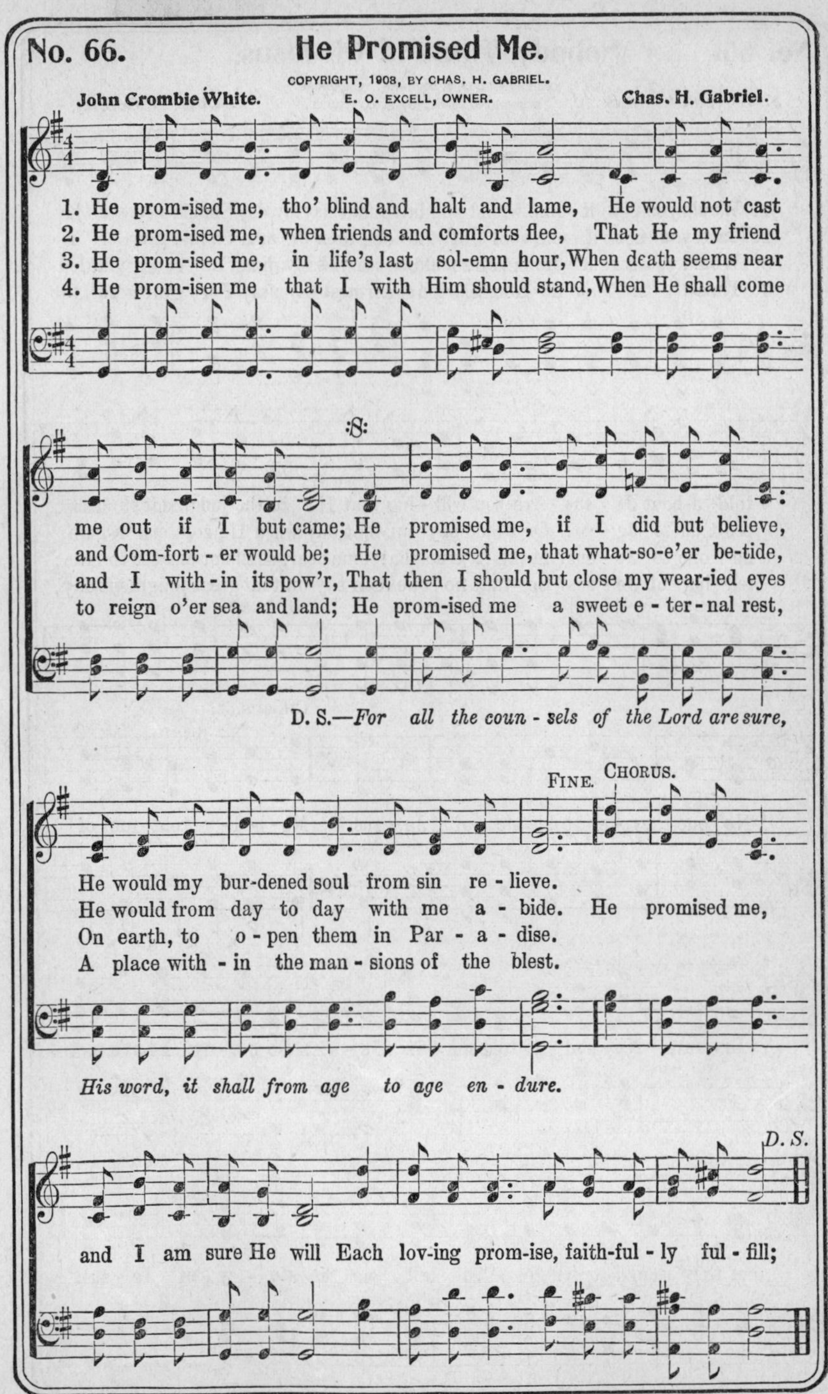
No. 66.
He Promised Me.
COPYRIGHT, 1908, BY CHAS. H. GABRIEL.
E. O. EXCELL, OWNER.
John Crombie White.
Chas. H. Gabriel.
1. He prom-ised me, tho' blind and halt and lame, He would not cast
2. He prom-ised me, when friends and comforts flee, That He my friend
3. He prom-ised me, in life's last sol-emn hour, When death seems near
4. He prom-isen me that I with Him should stand, When He shall come
me out if I but came; He promised me, if I did but believe,
and Com-fort - er would be; He promised me, that what-so-e'er be-tide,
and I with - in its pow'r, That then I should but close my wear-ied eyes
to reign o'er sea and land; He prom-ised me a sweet e - ter - nal rest,
D. S.—For all the coun - sels of the Lord are sure,
FINE.
CHORUS.
He would my bur-dened soul from sin re - lieve.
He would from day to day with me a - bide. He promised me,
On earth, to o - pen them in Par - a - dise.
A place with - in the man - sions of the blest.
His word, it shall from age to age en - dure.
D. S.
and I am sure He will Each lov-ing prom-ise, faith-ful - ly ful - fill;

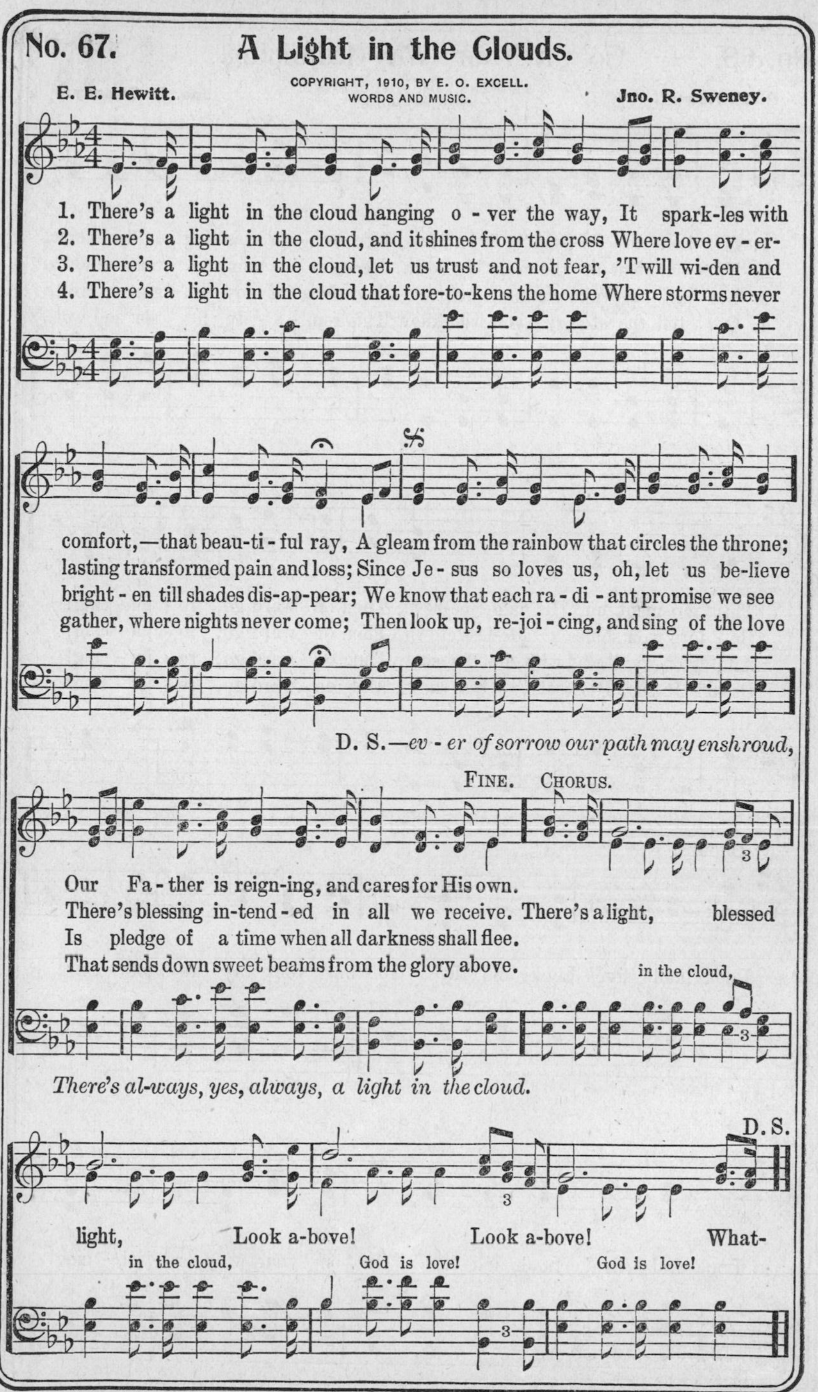
No. 67. A Light in the Clouds.
E. E. Hewitt.
COPYRIGHT, 1910, BY E. O. EXCELL. WORDS AND MUSIC.
Jno. R. Sweney.
1. There's a light in the cloud hanging o - ver the way, It spark-les with
2. There's a light in the cloud, and it shines from the cross Where love ev - er-
3. There's a light in the cloud, let us trust and not fear, 'T will wi-den and
4. There's a light in the cloud that fore-to-kens the home Where storms never
comfort,—that beau-ti - ful ray, A gleam from the rainbow that circles the throne;
lasting transformed pain and loss; Since Je - sus so loves us, oh, let us be-lieve
bright - en till shades dis-ap-pear; We know that each ra - di - ant promise we see
gather, where nights never come; Then look up, re-joi - cing, and sing of the love
D. S.—ev - er of sorrow our path may enshroud,
FINE. CHORUS.
Our Fa - ther is reign-ing, and cares for His own.
There's blessing in-tend - ed in all we receive. There's a light, blessed
Is pledge of a time when all darkness shall flee.
That sends down sweet beams from the glory above.
in the cloud,
There's al-ways, yes, always, a light in the cloud.
D. S.
light, Look a-bove! Look a-bove! What-
in the cloud, God is love! God is love!

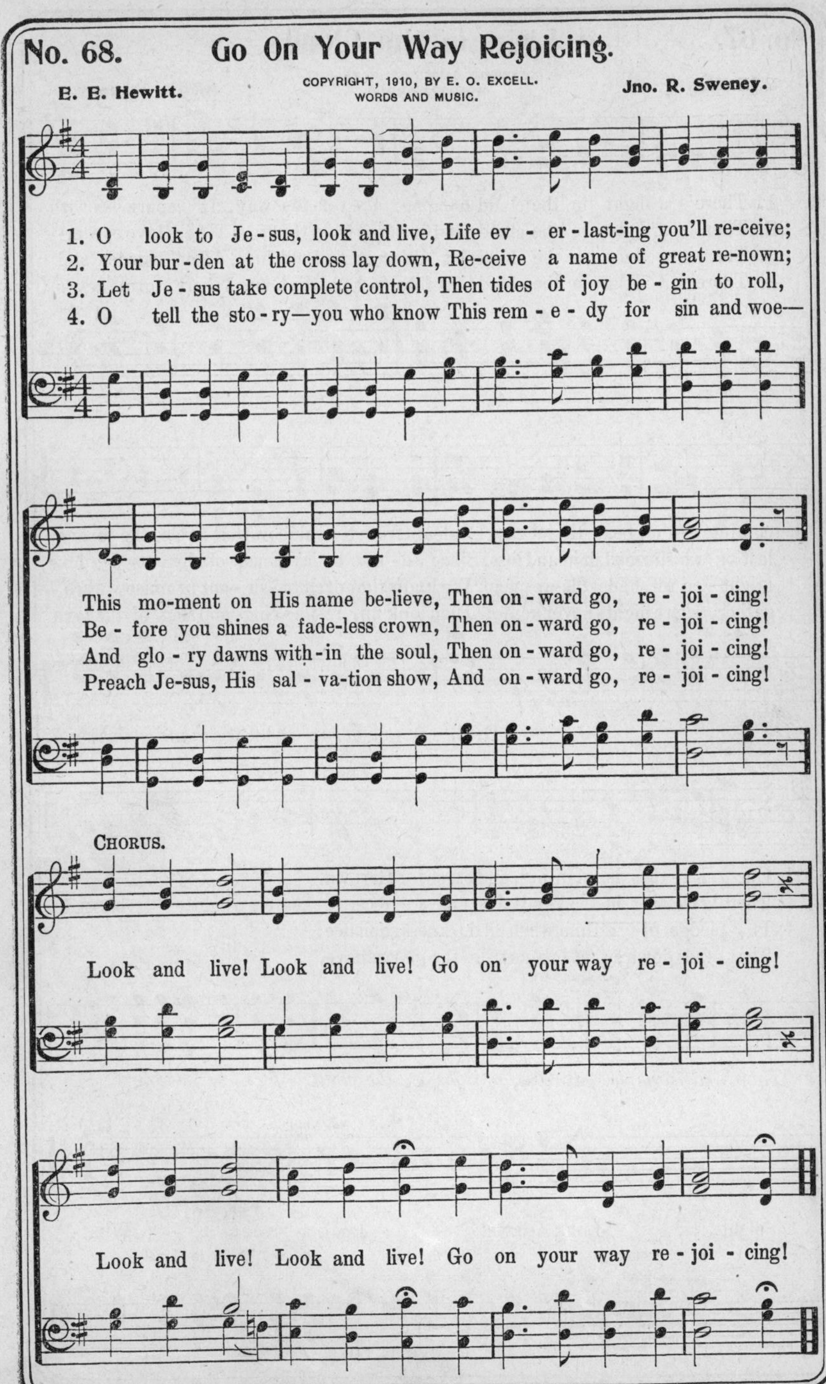
No. 68. Go On Your Way Rejoicing.
E. E. Hewitt.
COPYRIGHT, 1910, BY E. O. EXCELL.
WORDS AND MUSIC.
Jno. R. Sweney.
1. O look to Je-sus, look and live, Life ev-er-last-ing you'll re-ceive;
2. Your bur-den at the cross lay down, Re-ceive a name of great re-nown;
3. Let Je-sus take complete control, Then tides of joy be-gin to roll,
4. O tell the sto-ry—you who know This rem-e-dy for sin and woe—
This mo-ment on His name be-lieve, Then on-ward go, re-joi-cing!
Be-fore you shines a fade-less crown, Then on-ward go, re-joi-cing!
And glo-ry dawns with-in the soul, Then on-ward go, re-joi-cing!
Preach Je-sus, His sal-va-tion show, And on-ward go, re-joi-cing!
CHORUS.
Look and live! Look and live! Go on your way re-joi-cing!
Look and live! Look and live! Go on your way re-joi-cing!

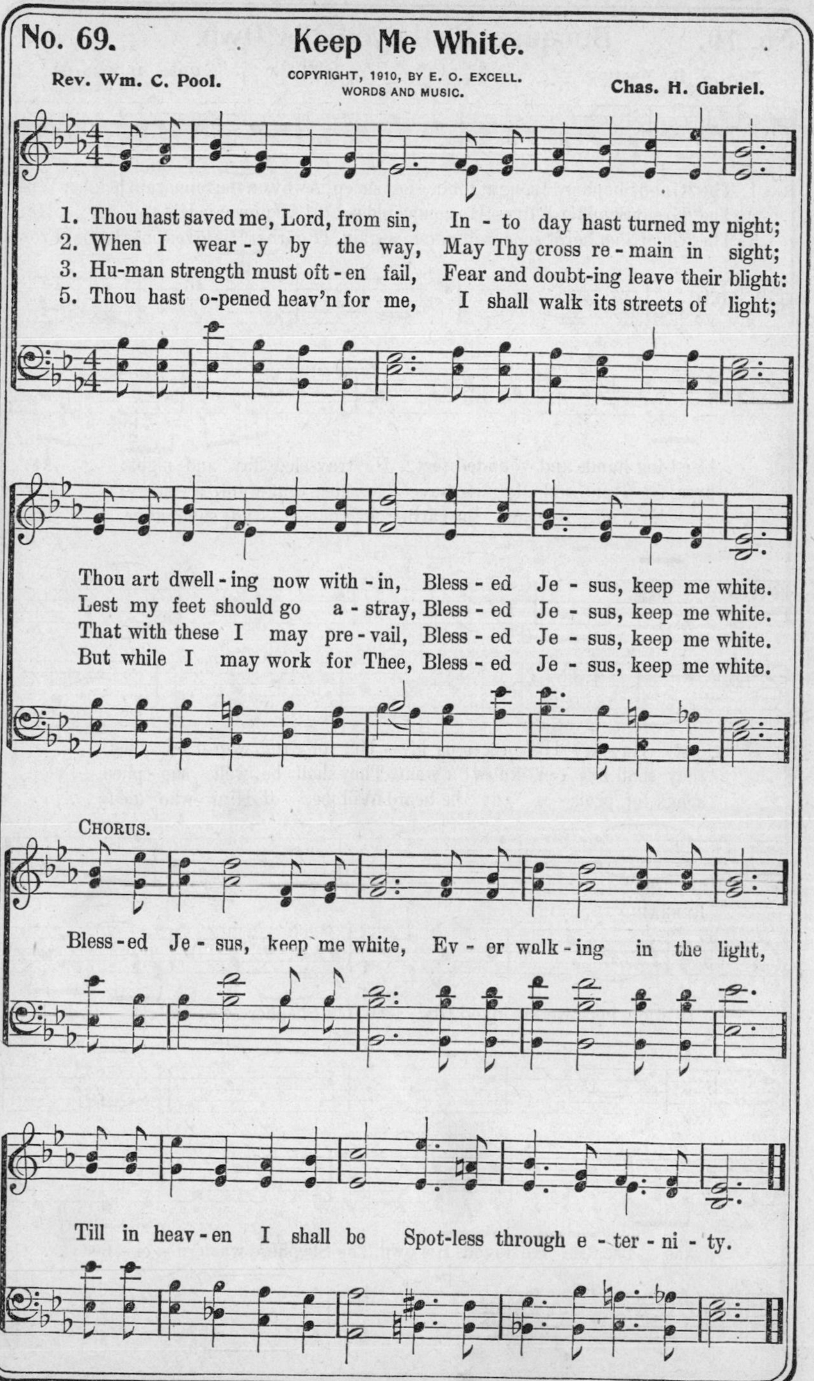
No. 69. Keep Me White.
Rev. Wm. C. Pool.
COPYRIGHT, 1910, BY E. O. EXCELL. WORDS AND MUSIC.
Chas. H. Gabriel.
1. Thou hast saved me, Lord, from sin, In - to day hast turned my night;
2. When I wear - y by the way, May Thy cross re - main in sight;
3. Hu-man strength must oft - en fail, Fear and doubt-ing leave their blight:
5. Thou hast o-pened heav'n for me, I shall walk its streets of light;
Thou art dwell - ing now with - in, Bless - ed Je - sus, keep me white.
Lest my feet should go a - stray, Bless - ed Je - sus, keep me white.
That with these I may pre - vail, Bless - ed Je - sus, keep me white.
But while I may work for Thee, Bless - ed Je - sus, keep me white.
CHORUS.
Bless - ed Je - sus, keep me white, Ev - er walk - ing in the light,
Till in heav - en I shall be Spot-less through e - ter - ni - ty.

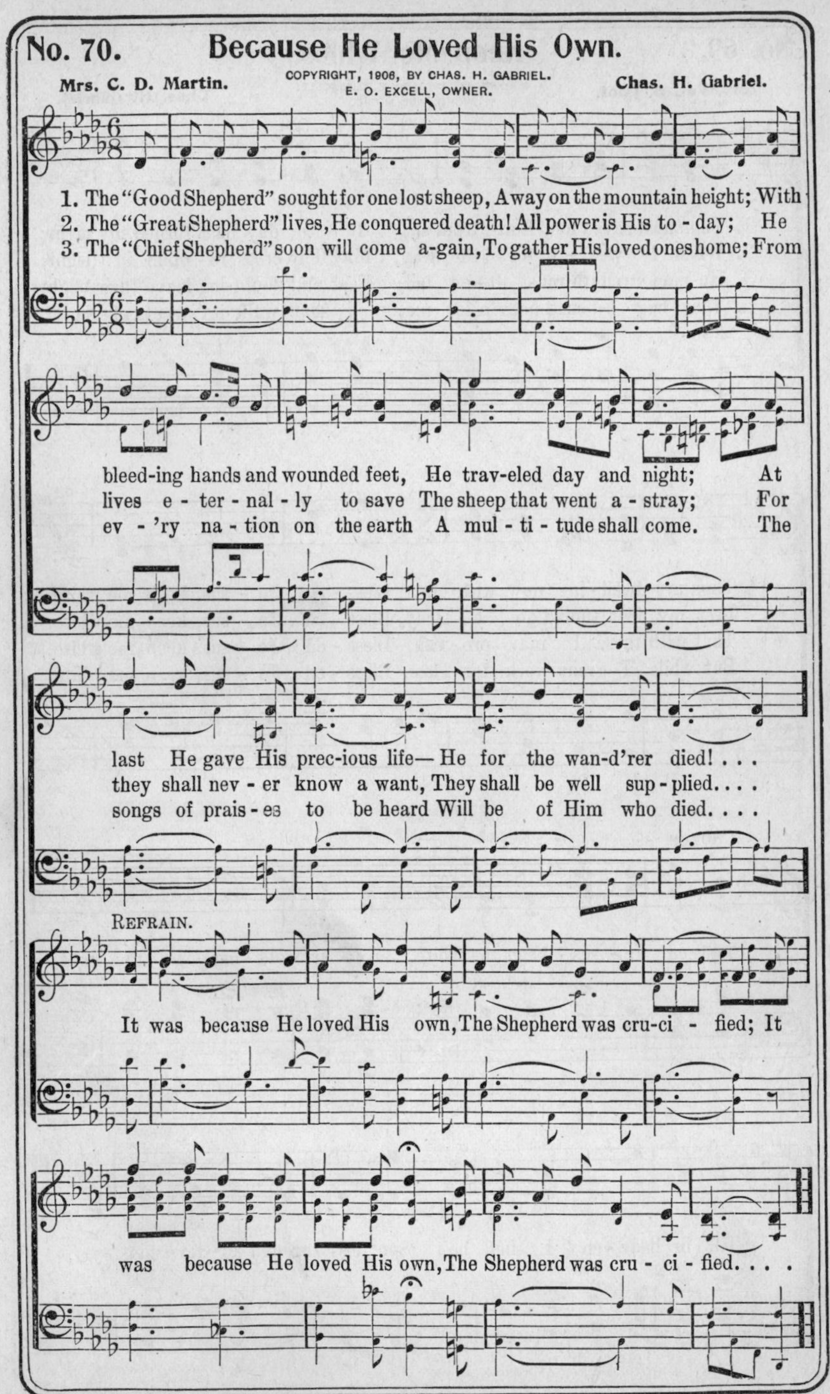

No. 70. Because He Loved His Own.
COPYRIGHT, 1906, BY CHAS. H. GABRIEL.
E. O. EXCELL, OWNER.
Mrs. C. D. Martin.
Chas. H. Gabriel.
1. The "Good Shepherd" sought for one lost sheep, Away on the mountain height; With
2. The "Great Shepherd" lives, He conquered death! All power is His to - day; He
3. The "Chief Shepherd" soon will come a-gain, To gather His loved ones home; From
bleed-ing hands and wounded feet, He trav-eled day and night; At
lives e - ter - nal - ly to save The sheep that went a - stray; For
ev - 'ry na - tion on the earth A mul - ti - tude shall come. The
last He gave His prec-ious life— He for the wan-d'rer died! . . .
they shall nev - er know a want, They shall be well sup-plied. . . .
songs of prais - es to be heard Will be of Him who died. . . .
REFRAIN.
It was because He loved His own, The Shepherd was cru-ci - fied; It
was because He loved His own, The Shepherd was cru - ci - fied. . . .

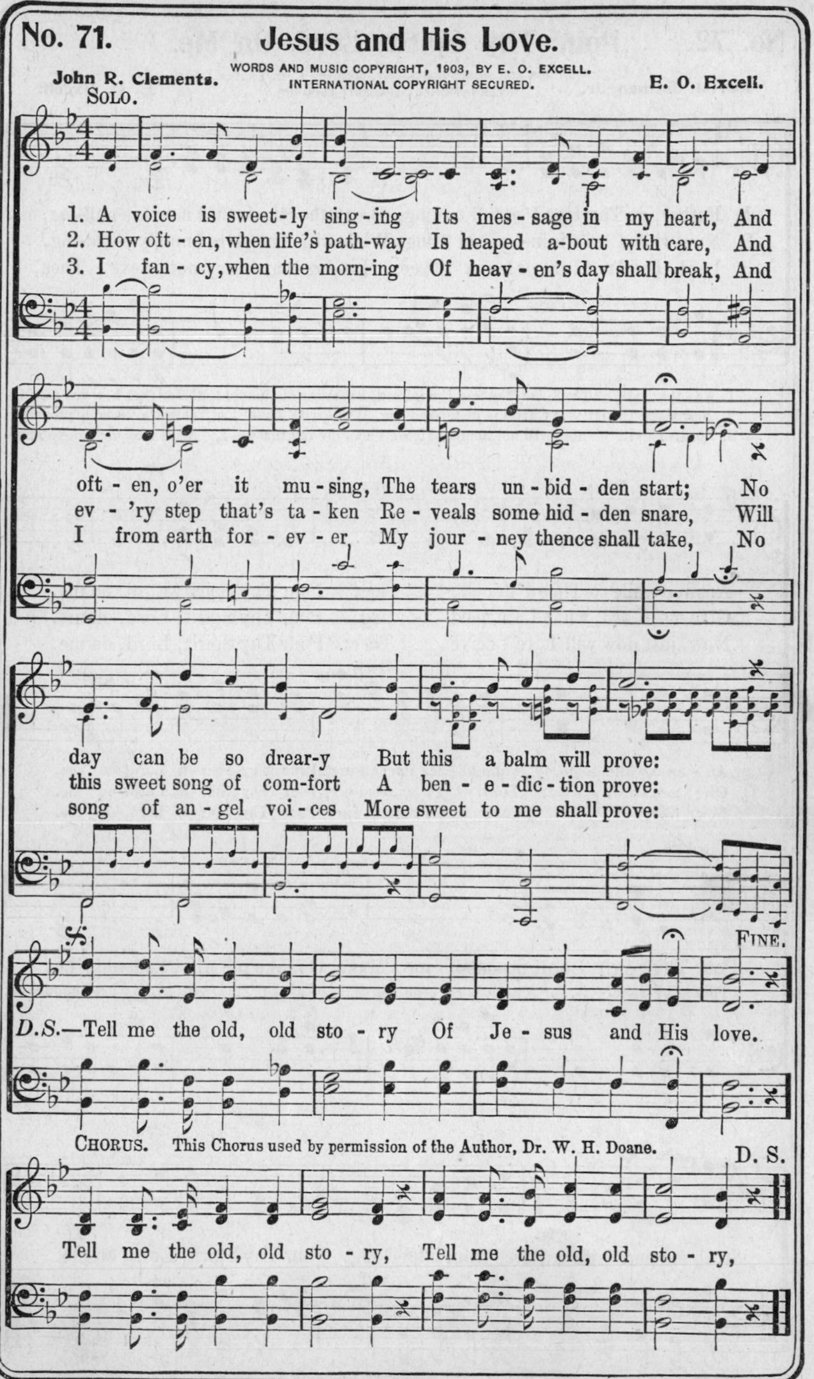
No. 71. Jesus and His Love.
WORDS AND MUSIC COPYRIGHT, 1903, BY E. O. EXCELL.
INTERNATIONAL COPYRIGHT SECURED.
John R. Clements.
E. O. Excell.
SOLO.
1. A voice is sweet-ly sing-ing Its mes-sage in my heart, And oft-en, o'er it mu-sing, The tears un-bid-den start; No day can be so drear-y But this a balm will prove:
2. How oft-en, when life's path-way Is heaped a-bout with care, And ev-'ry step that's ta-ken Re-veals some hid-den snare, Will this sweet song of com-fort A ben-e-dic-tion prove:
3. I fan-cy, when the morn-ing Of heav-en's day shall break, And I from earth for-ev-er My jour-ney thence shall take, No song of an-gel voi-ces More sweet to me shall prove:
FINE.
D.S.—Tell me the old, old sto-ry Of Je-sus and His love.
CHORUS. This Chorus used by permission of the Author, Dr. W. H. Doane.
D. S.
Tell me the old, old sto-ry, Tell me the old, old sto-ry,

No. 72. Pour Thy Spirit, Lord, On Me.
WORDS AND MUSIC COPYRIGHT, 1903, BY E. O. EXCELL.
INTERNATIONAL COPYRIGHT SECURED.
Rev. J. Oatman, Jr.
E. O. Excell.
1. Father, at Thy feet I'm fall - ing, Break the chains that now are gall-ing,
2. Now while Christ is in-ter-ced - ing, While with Thee I'm humbly plead-ing,
3. Lord, I will not turn or leave Thee, Liv-ing that I may not grieve Thee,
1. Fa - ther, at Thy, at Thy feet I'm falling, Break the chains that, chains that now are galling,
2. Now while Christ is, Christ is in-ter-ced-ing, While with Thee I'm, Thee I'm humbly pleading,
3. Lord, I will not, will not turn and leave Thee, Liv-ing that I, that I may not grieve Thee,
Answer while to Thee I'm call - ing; Pour Thy Spirit, Lord, on me.
Give me, Lord, what I am need - ing; Pour Thy Spirit, Lord, on me.
Now, just now will I re - ceive Thee; Pour Thy Spirit, Lord, on me.
An - swer while to, while to Thee I'm call-ing; Pour Thy Spir - it, Lord, on me.
Give me, Lord, what, Lord, what I am need-ing; Pour Thy Spir - it, Lord, on me.
Now, just now will, now will I receive Thee; Pour Thy Spir - it, Lord, on me.
CHORUS.
Pour Thy Spirit, Lord, up-on me, Make, O make me what I should be;
Pour Thy Spir - it, pour it, Lord, upon me, Make, O make me, make me what I should be;
Keep me pure with-in, free from inbred sin, Pour Thy Spirit, Lord, on me.

No. 73. Gently, O My Savior, Lead Me.

Dr. M. Victor Staley. COPYRIGHT, 1902, BY CHAS. H. GABRIEL. E. O. EXCELL, OWNER. Chas. H. Gabriel.

No. 74. Open the Door for the Children.
Mary E. Kidder.
COPYRIGHT, 1885, BY E. O. EXCELL.
E. O. Excell.
1. O-pen the door for the chil-dren, Ten-der-ly gath-er them in,—
2. O-pen the door for the chil-dren, See, they are com-ing in throngs!
3. O-pen the door for the chil-dren, Take the dear lambs by the hand;
In from the high-ways and hedg-es, In from the plac-es of sin;
Bid them sit down to the ban-quet, Teach them your beau-ti-ful songs;
Point them to truth and to good-ness, Lead them to Ca-naan's fair land.
Some are so young and so help-less, Some are so hun-gry and cold;
Pray for the Fa-ther to bless them, Pray you that grace may be giv'n;
Some are so young and so help-less, Some are so hun-gry and cold;
FINE.
D. S.–O-pen the door for the chil-dren, Gath-er them in-to the fold.
O-pen the door for the chil-dren, Theirs is the king-dom of heav'n.
O-pen the door for the chil-dren, Gath-er them in-to the fold.
CHORUS.
D. S.
O - pen the door, . . Gath - er them in, . . .
O-pen the door, o-pen the door, Gath-er them in, gath-er them in,

No. 75. O to Do Something!
Ida Tremain.
COPYRIGHT, 1909, BY E. O. EXCELL. WORDS AND MUSIC.
Jno. R. Sweney.
1. O to do something, some-thing! Something, my Sav-ior, for Thee;
2. O to do something, some-thing! A word—or a light—or a song,—
3. O to do something, some-thing! Where others Thy likeness may see;
FINE.
D.S.–To show forth the won-drous pow-er Of the love that could save even me.
To speak—or to shine for the Mas-ter, Or sing,—to win lost ones from wrong.
That self may be lost in serv-ice, And our lives on-ly glo-ri-fy Thee.
Some-thing to do in Thy vine-yard, Tho' sim-ple the service may be;
The cup of cold wa-ter to of-fer To those who in wear-i-ness stray,—
Read-y to work or to suf-fer, Which-ev-er Thy love shall command;
Something—Thy grace can find use for, To win oth-er wand'rers to Thee.
Thy "sure word of promise" to whisper To those whom temptations dis-may.
Se-cure, whether shadow or sunshine—They are all from Thy lov-ing hand.
CHORUS.
D. S.
O . . . . to do some-thing! Something, my Sav-ior, for Thee;
O to do some-thing.

No. 76. Leaning On the Everlasting Arms.
COPYRIGHT BY A. J. SHOWALTER.
USED BY PER.
Rev. E. A. Hoffman.
A. J. Showalter.
1. What a fel-low-ship, what a joy di-vine, Lean-ing on the ev-er-last-ing arms; What a bless-ed-ness, what a peace is mine, Lean-ing on the ev-er-last-ing arms.
2. Oh, how sweet to walk in this pil-grim way, Lean-ing on the ev-er-last-ing arms; Oh, how bright the path grows from day to day,
3. What have I to dread, what have I to fear, Lean-ing on the ev-er-last-ing arms; I have bless-ed peace with my Lord so near,
REFRAIN.
Lean - ing, lean - - ing, Safe and se-cure from all a-larms;
Lean-ing on Je-sus, lean-ing on Je-sus,
Lean - ing, lean - ing, Lean-ing on the ev-er-last-ing arms.
Lean-ing on Je-sus, lean-ing on Je-sus,

No. 77. He Never Will Turn Me Away.
Mrs. Frank A. Breck.
COPYRIGHT, 1906, BY CHAS. H. GABRIEL. E. O. EXCELL, OWNER.
Chas. H. Gabriel.
1. I am glad that I know Je - sus loves me so well, And will - ing - ly hears when I pray, That He free-ly for-gives, and tho' oft I re - bel,
2. I am glad that He ev - er is pa-tient and kind, And com-forts my heart day by day; And that, when I am tempted, I al-ways shall find
3. When I come to my Sav - ior and tell Him my sin, And prom - ise His word to o - bey, Then He gives this as-sur-ance—I have it with - in—
He nev-er will turn me a - way.
CHORUS.
He nev - - er will turn me a - way, He nev - - er will turn me a - way; To him that o'er-com-eth He giv-eth a crown, And He nev-er will turn me a - way.
He nev - er, no, nev - er will
nev - er, no, nev-er

No. 78. I Love to Hear the Story.

Jennie Ree. Arr.

Chas. H. Gabriel.

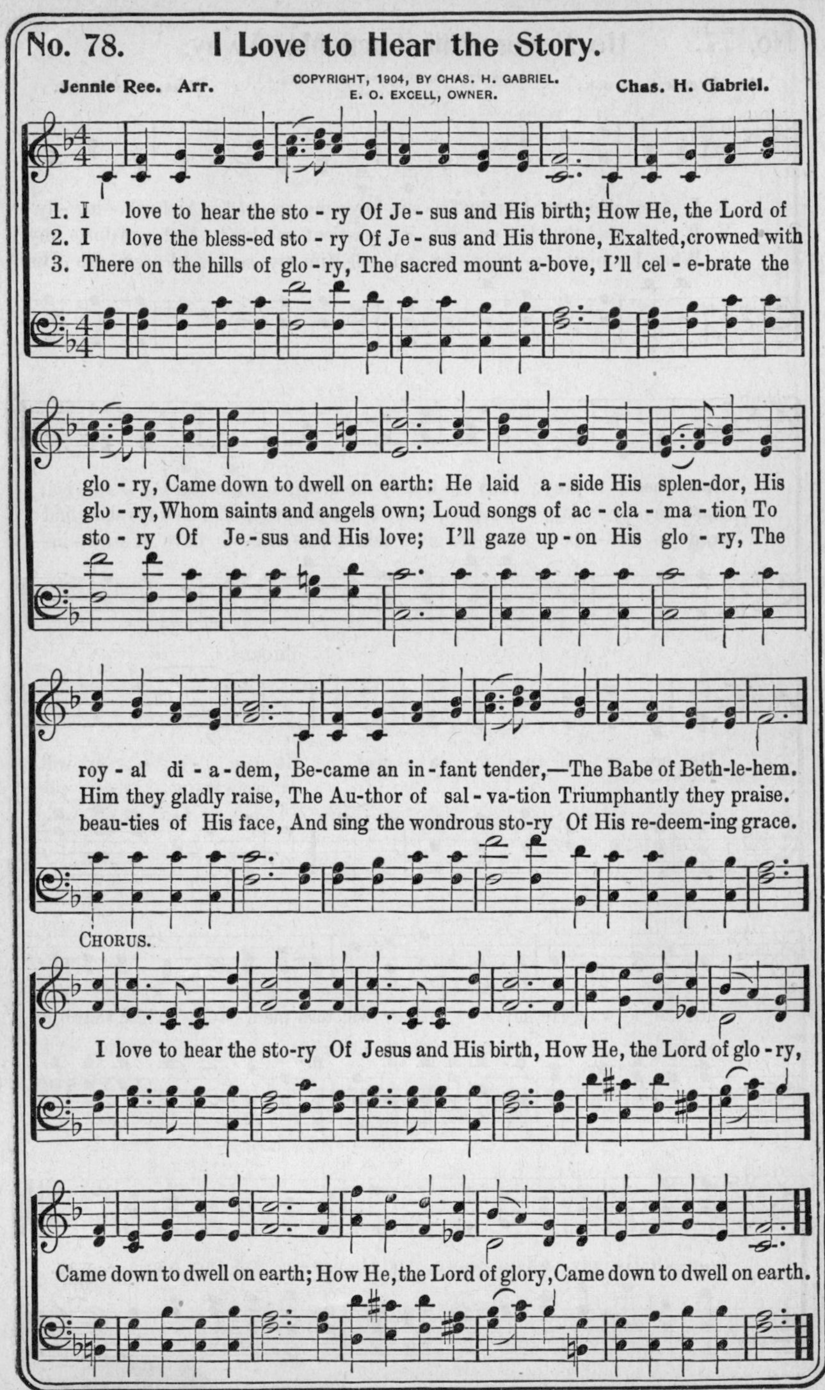

No. 79. Singing on My Way.
E. E. Hewitt.
COPYRIGHT, 1908, BY E. O. EXCELL.
WORDS AND MUSIC.
Jno. R. Sweney.
1. When-ev - er ills op-press me, When storms of sor - row roll, There's
2. O what a pre-cious Sav - ior! O what a Friend is mine! How
3. His wondrous love and mer - cy Re - stored me to His fold; Thro'
One whose words can give me Sweet peace within my soul; Down at the
gen - tle is His lead - ing, His coun-sel, how di - vine! His Spir - it
faith in His sal - va - tion I shall His face be - hold; For strength for
feet of Je - sus My bur-dens I will lay, And, trusting in my Sav - ior,
dwells within me, For help to Him I pray, And, trusting in my Sav - ior,
ev - 'ry tri - al I look to Him each day, And, trusting in my Sav - ior,
CHORUS.
Go sing-ing on my way. Sing-ing (singing) ev - 'ry day, Sing-ing (singing)
on my way, And, trusting in my Sav-ior, Go sing-ing on my way.

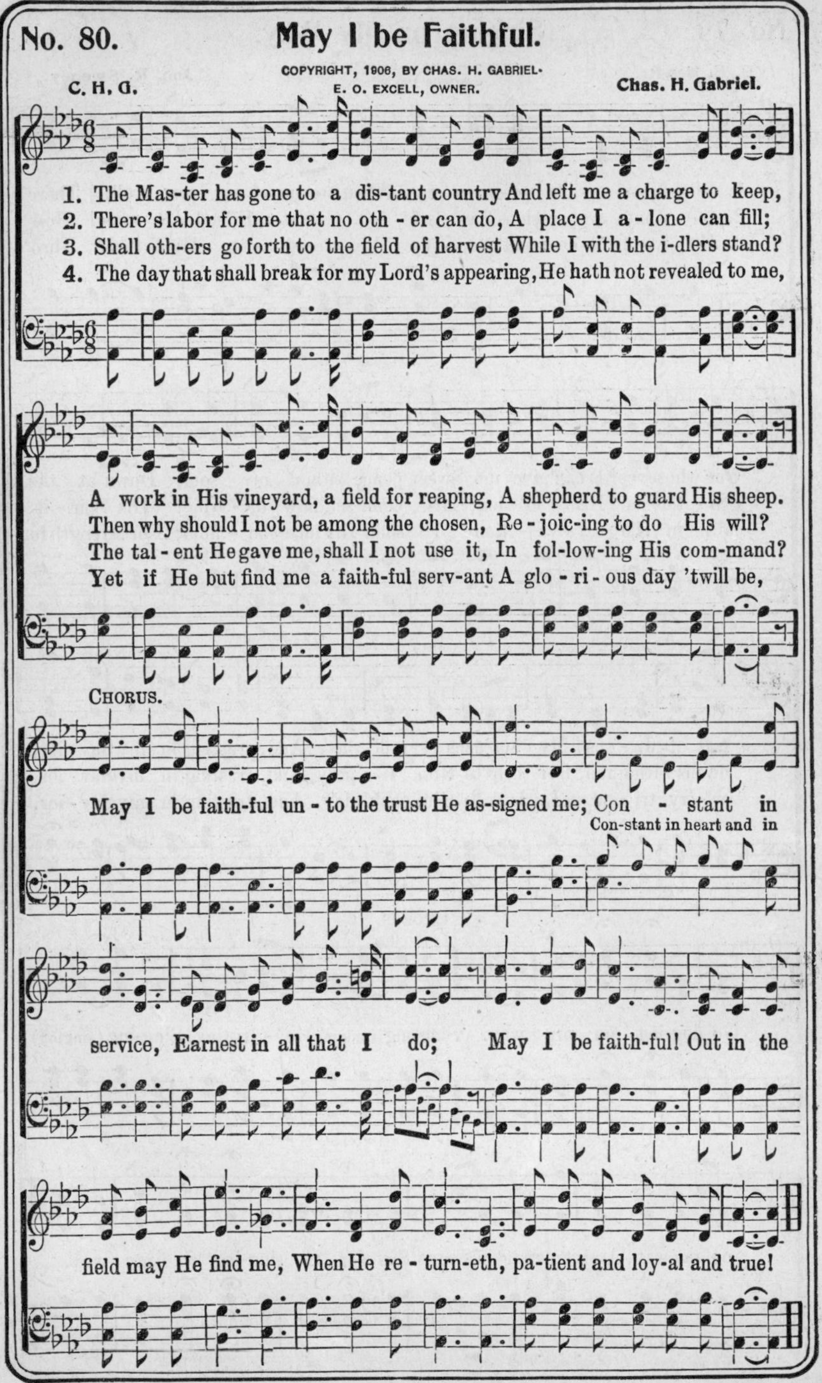
No. 80.
May I be Faithful.
COPYRIGHT, 1906, BY CHAS. H. GABRIEL.
E. O. EXCELL, OWNER.
C. H. G.
Chas. H. Gabriel.
1. The Mas-ter has gone to a dis-tant country And left me a charge to keep,
2. There's labor for me that no oth - er can do, A place I a - lone can fill;
3. Shall oth-ers go forth to the field of harvest While I with the i-dlers stand?
4. The day that shall break for my Lord's appearing, He hath not revealed to me,
A work in His vineyard, a field for reaping, A shepherd to guard His sheep.
Then why should I not be among the chosen, Re - joic-ing to do His will?
The tal - ent He gave me, shall I not use it, In fol-low-ing His com-mand?
Yet if He but find me a faith-ful serv-ant A glo - ri - ous day 'twill be,
CHORUS.
May I be faith-ful un - to the trust He as-signed me; Con - stant in
Con-stant in heart and in
service, Earnest in all that I do; May I be faith-ful! Out in the
field may He find me, When He re - turn-eth, pa-tient and loy-al and true!

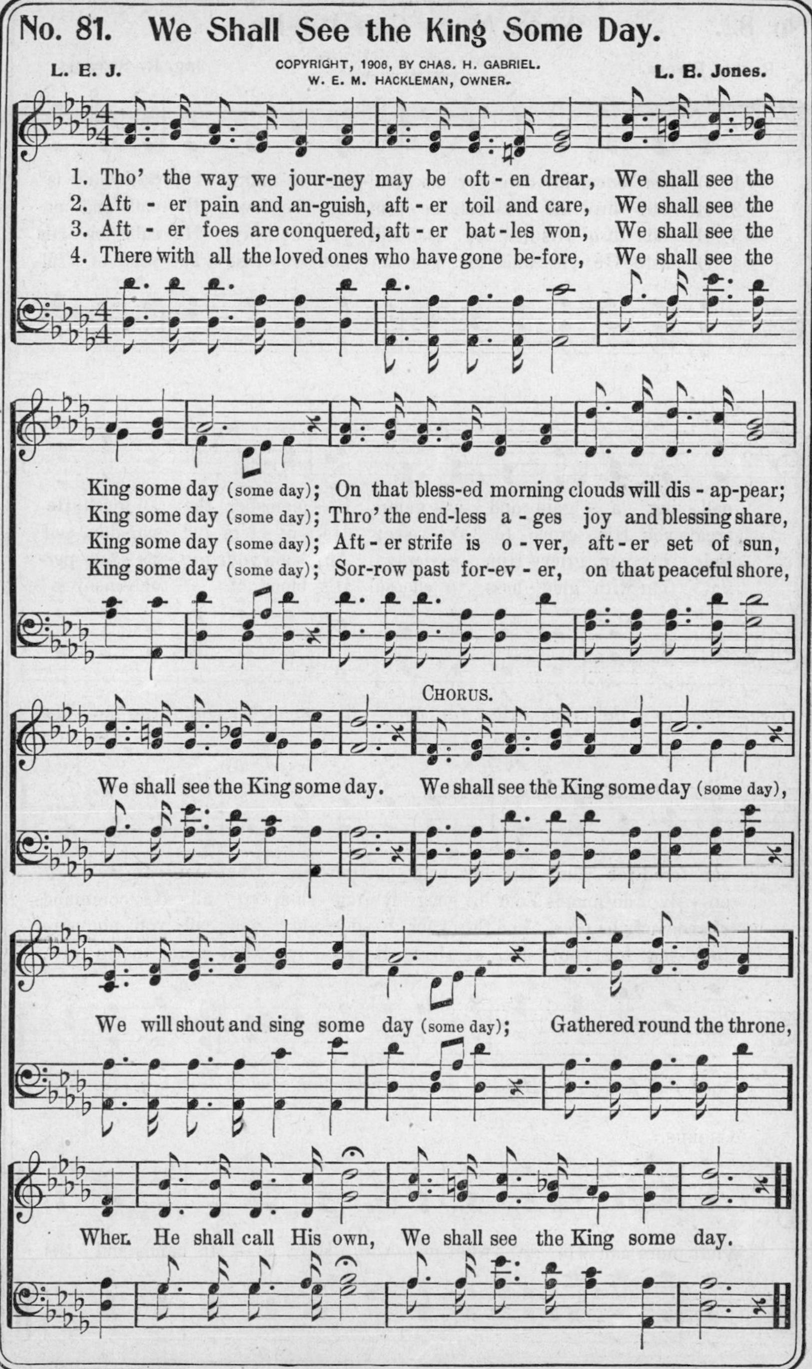
No. 81. We Shall See the King Some Day.
L. E. J.
COPYRIGHT, 1906, BY CHAS. H. GABRIEL.
W. E. M. HACKLEMAN, OWNER.
L. E. Jones.
1. Tho' the way we jour-ney may be oft - en drear, We shall see the
2. Aft - er pain and an-guish, aft - er toil and care, We shall see the
3. Aft - er foes are conquered, aft - er bat - les won, We shall see the
4. There with all the loved ones who have gone be-fore, We shall see the
King some day (some day); On that bless-ed morning clouds will dis - ap-pear;
King some day (some day); Thro' the end-less a - ges joy and blessing share,
King some day (some day); Aft - er strife is o - ver, aft - er set of sun,
King some day (some day); Sor-row past for-ev - er, on that peaceful shore,
We shall see the King some day.
CHORUS.
We shall see the King some day (some day),
We will shout and sing some day (some day);
Gathered round the throne,
When He shall call His own,
We shall see the King some day.

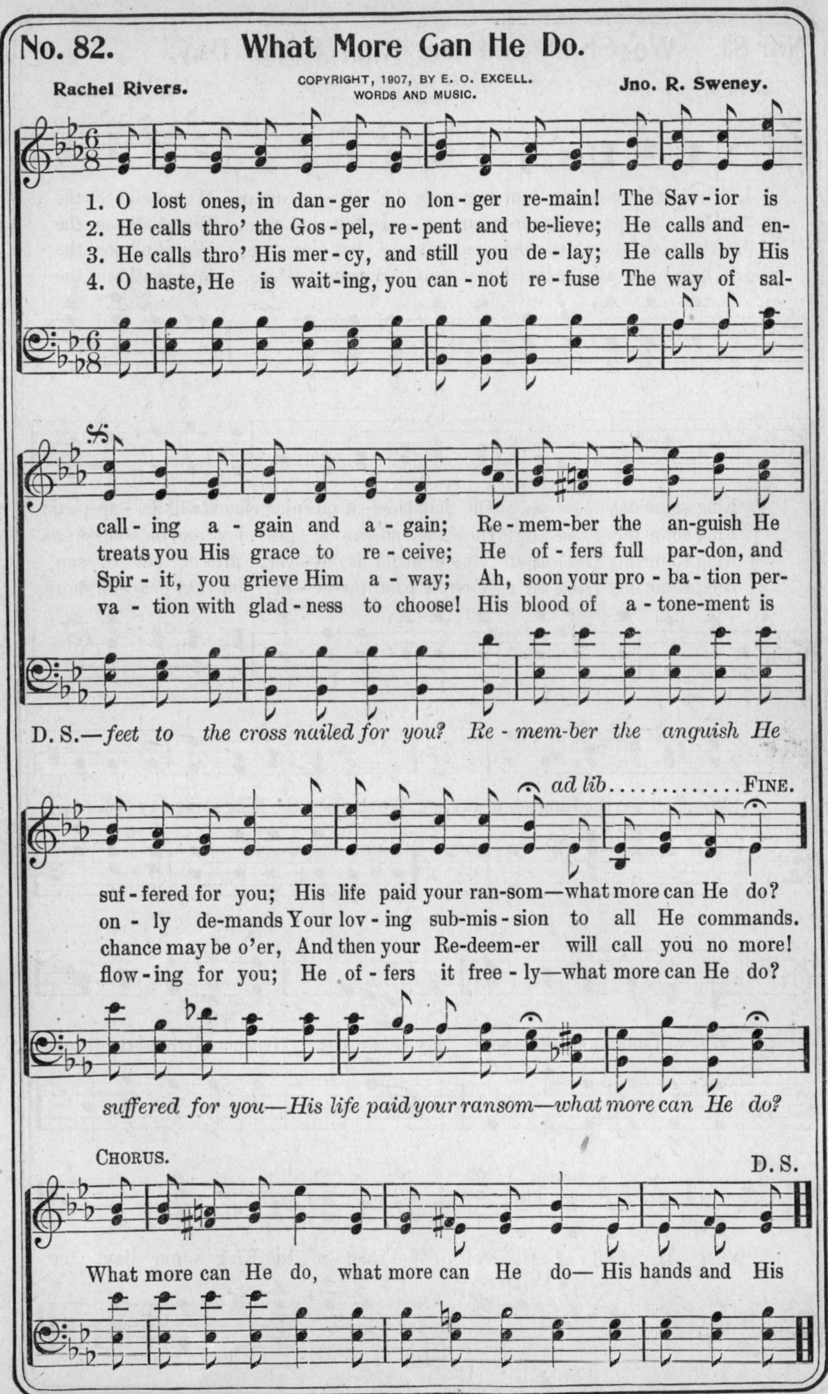
No. 82. What More Can He Do.
Rachel Rivers.
COPYRIGHT, 1907, BY E. O. EXCELL. WORDS AND MUSIC.
Jno. R. Sweney.
1. O lost ones, in dan-ger no lon-ger re-main! The Sav-ior is
2. He calls thro' the Gos-pel, re-pent and be-lieve; He calls and en-
3. He calls thro' His mer-cy, and still you de-lay; He calls by His
4. O haste, He is wait-ing, you can-not re-fuse The way of sal-
call-ing a-gain and a-gain; Re-mem-ber the an-guish He
treats you His grace to re-ceive; He of-fers full par-don, and
Spir-it, you grieve Him a-way; Ah, soon your pro-ba-tion per-
va-tion with glad-ness to choose! His blood of a-tone-ment is
D. S.—feet to the cross nailed for you? Re-mem-ber the anguish He
ad lib............ FINE.
suf-fered for you; His life paid your ran-som—what more can He do?
on-ly de-mands Your lov-ing sub-mis-sion to all He commands.
chance may be o'er, And then your Re-deem-er will call you no more!
flow-ing for you; He of-fers it free-ly—what more can He do?
suffered for you—His life paid your ransom—what more can He do?
CHORUS.
D. S.
What more can He do, what more can He do— His hands and His

No. 83. No Cross For Me?

Fanny J. Crosby. — Jno. R. Sweney.

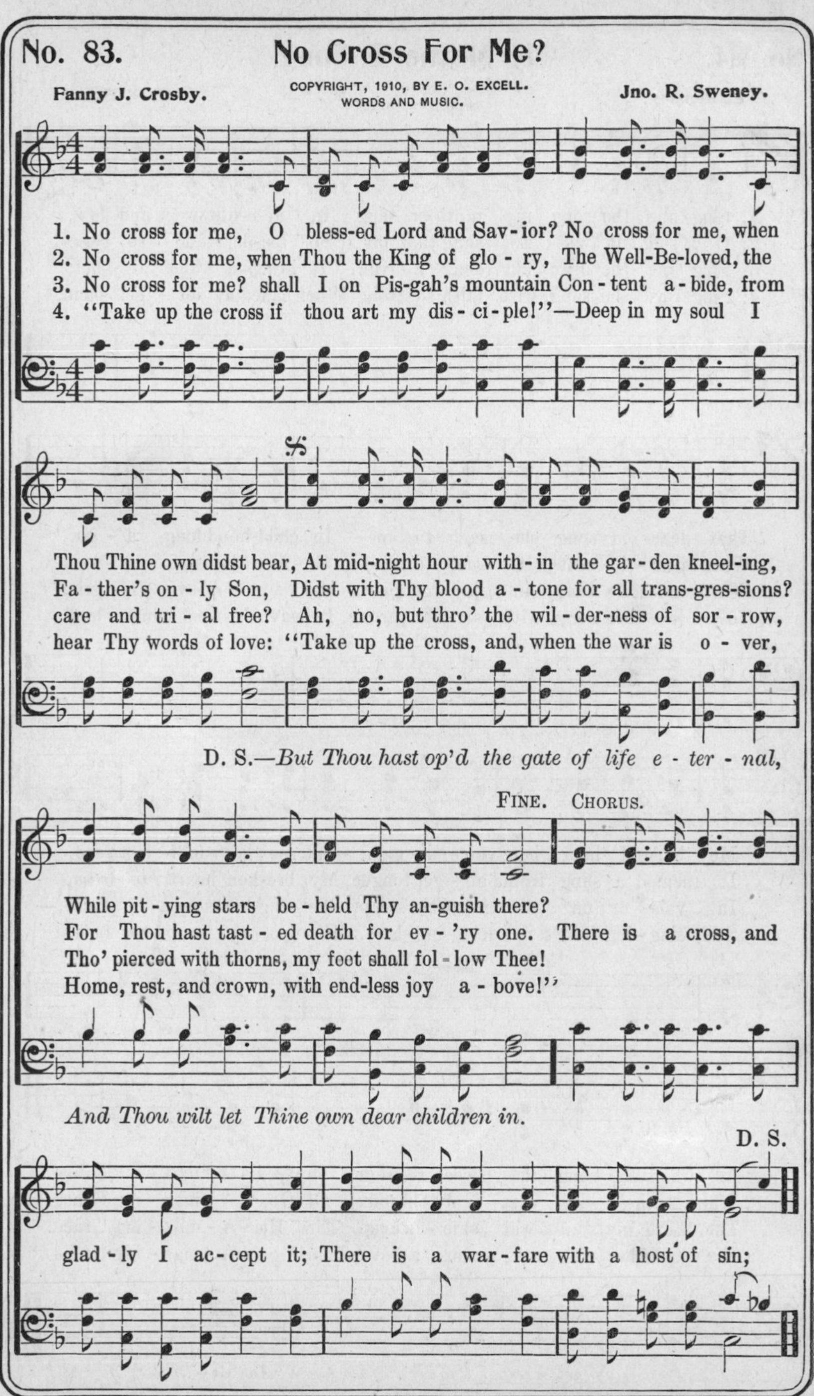

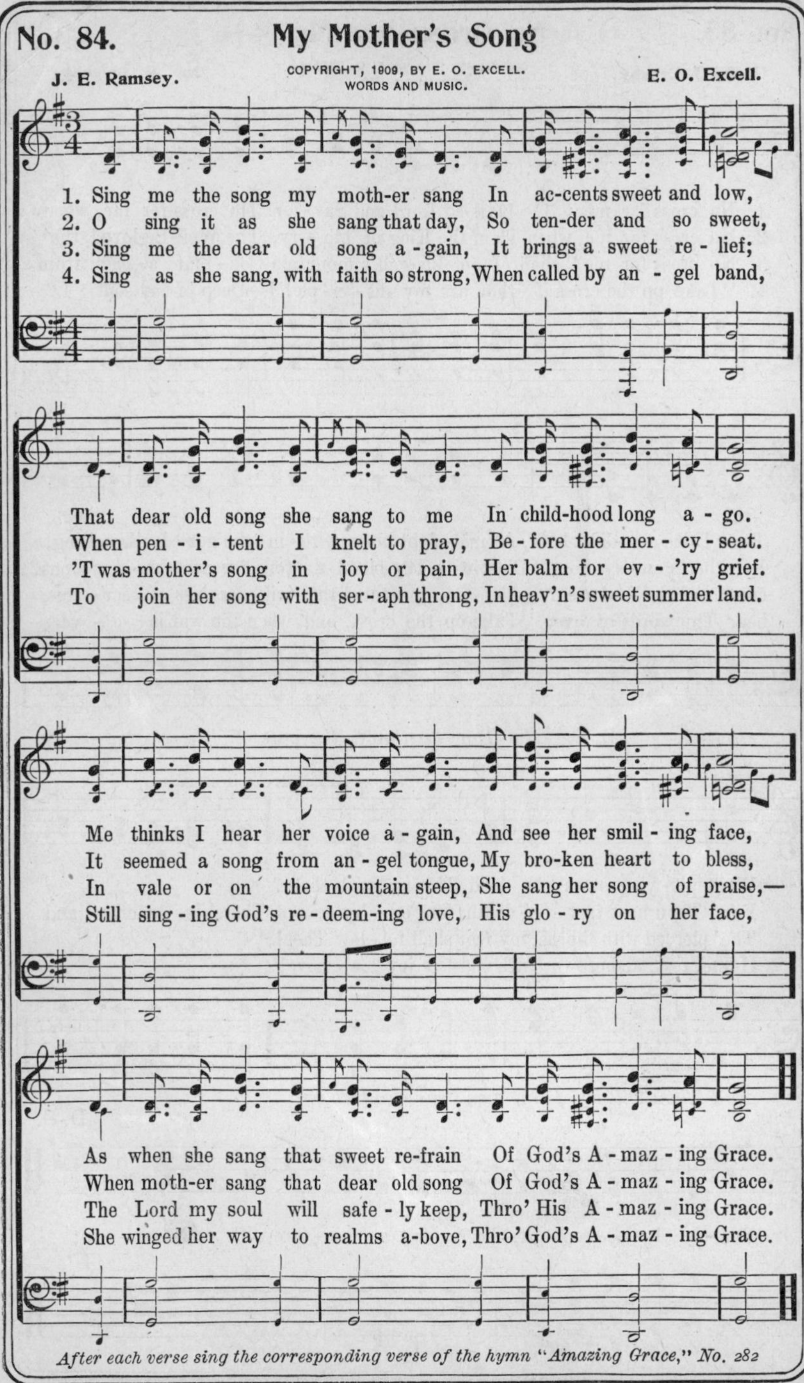
No. 84.
My Mother's Song
J. E. Ramsey.
COPYRIGHT, 1909, BY E. O. EXCELL.
WORDS AND MUSIC.
E. O. Excell.
1. Sing me the song my moth-er sang In ac-cents sweet and low,
2. O sing it as she sang that day, So ten-der and so sweet,
3. Sing me the dear old song a-gain, It brings a sweet re-lief;
4. Sing as she sang, with faith so strong, When called by an-gel band,
That dear old song she sang to me In child-hood long a-go.
When pen-i-tent I knelt to pray, Be-fore the mer-cy-seat.
'T was mother's song in joy or pain, Her balm for ev-'ry grief.
To join her song with ser-aph throng, In heav'n's sweet summer land.
Me thinks I hear her voice a-gain, And see her smil-ing face,
It seemed a song from an-gel tongue, My bro-ken heart to bless,
In vale or on the mountain steep, She sang her song of praise,—
Still sing-ing God's re-deem-ing love, His glo-ry on her face,
As when she sang that sweet re-frain Of God's A-maz-ing Grace.
When moth-er sang that dear old song Of God's A-maz-ing Grace.
The Lord my soul will safe-ly keep, Thro' His A-maz-ing Grace.
She winged her way to realms a-bove, Thro' God's A-maz-ing Grace.
After each verse sing the corresponding verse of the hymn "Amazing Grace," No. 282

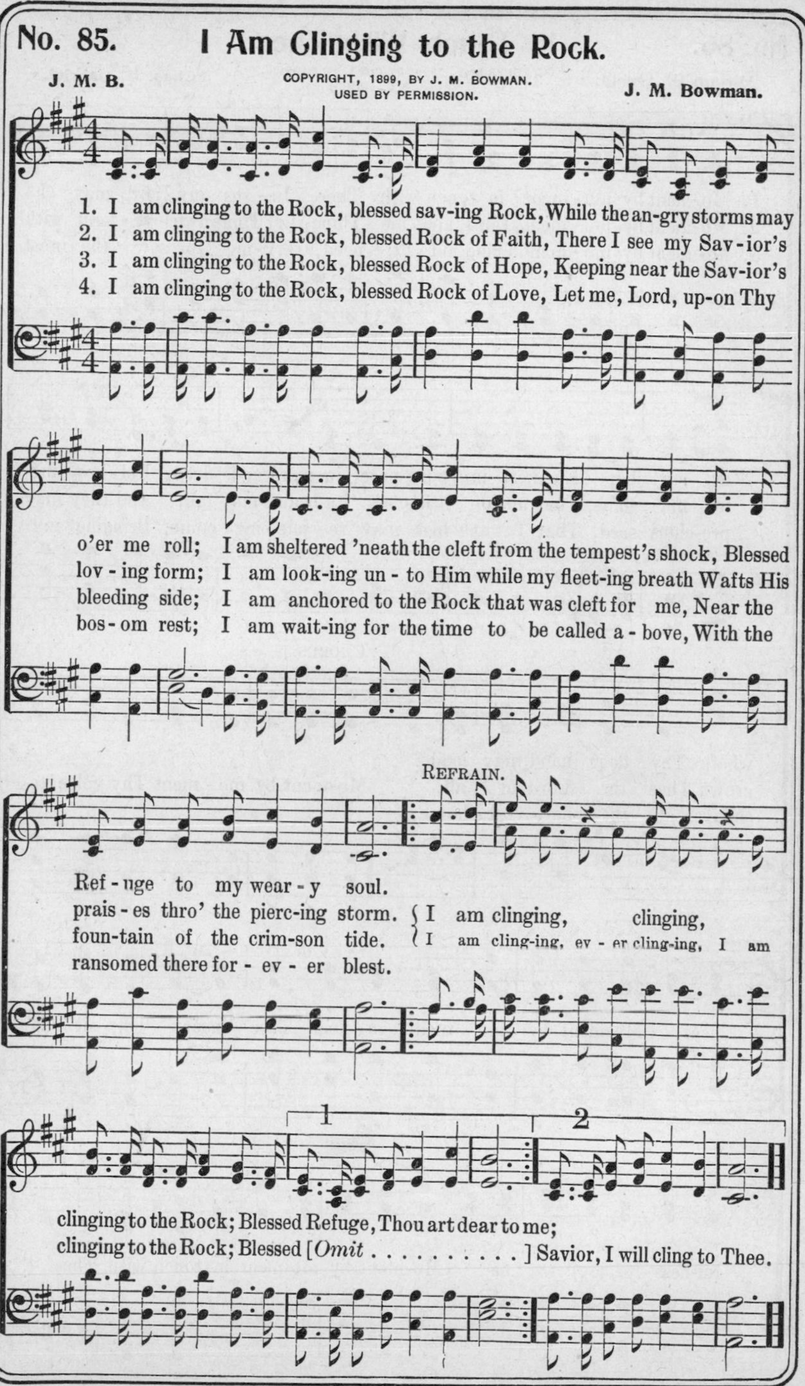
No. 85. I Am Clinging to the Rock.
J. M. B.
COPYRIGHT, 1899, BY J. M. BOWMAN.
USED BY PERMISSION.
J. M. Bowman.
1. I am clinging to the Rock, blessed sav-ing Rock, While the an-gry storms may o'er me roll; I am sheltered 'neath the cleft from the tempest's shock, Blessed Ref-uge to my wear-y soul.
2. I am clinging to the Rock, blessed Rock of Faith, There I see my Sav-ior's lov-ing form; I am look-ing un-to Him while my fleet-ing breath Wafts His prais-es thro' the pierc-ing storm.
3. I am clinging to the Rock, blessed Rock of Hope, Keeping near the Sav-ior's bleeding side; I am anchored to the Rock that was cleft for me, Near the foun-tain of the crim-son tide.
4. I am clinging to the Rock, blessed Rock of Love, Let me, Lord, up-on Thy bos-om rest; I am wait-ing for the time to be called a-bove, With the ransomed there for-ev-er blest.
REFRAIN.
I am clinging, clinging,
I am cling-ing, ev-er cling-ing, I am clinging to the Rock; Blessed Refuge, Thou art dear to me;
clinging to the Rock; Blessed [Omit . . . .] Savior, I will cling to Thee.
1
2

No. 86. In Touch With Thee.
Miriam E. Arnold.
COPYRIGHT, 1906, BY CHAS. H. GABRIEL.
E. O. EXCELL, OWNER.
Chas. H. Gabriel.
1. Mo-ment by mo-ment in touch with Thee, Je-sus my Lord, may I
2. Mo-ment by mo-ment, Lord, keep me Thine, Let Thine own love-light with
3. Mo-ment by mo-ment Thine aid I need, Try-ing to sow the most
ev-er be; Ear-nest in pur-pose, in word and deed, Fol-low-ing
in me shine, That up-on oth-ers its beams may fall, And they may
pre-cious seed, That I at last may re-joic-ing come, Bringing my
where Thy dear hand may lead.
crown Thee the Lord of all.
sheaves at the har-vest-home.
CHORUS.
Mo-ment by mo-ment Thy voice to
hear, Mo-ment by mo-ment to feel Thee near! Oh, it is
ful-ness of joy to be Mo-ment by mo-ment in touch with Thee!

No. 87. Triumph By and By!
C. R. Blackall.
USED BY PERMISSION OF MRS. H. R. PALMER, OWNER OF COPYRIGHT.
H. R. Palmer.
1. The prize is set be-fore us— To win, our Lord im-plores us, The eye of God is o'er us From on high! His lov-ing tones are fall-ing, While sin is dark, ap-pall-ing; 'Tis Je-sus gen-tly calling—He is nigh (He is nigh).
2. We'll fol-low where He lead-eth, We'll pas-ture where He feed-eth, We'll yield to Him who pleadeth From on high. Then naught from Him shall sever, Our hopes shall brighten ever, And faith shall fail us never—He is nigh (He is nigh).
3. Our home is bright a-bove us, No tri-als dark to move us, But Je-sus dear to love us There on high; We'll give Him best en-deav-or, And praise His name forever; His precious words can never, Never die (Never die).
CHORUS.
By and by we shall meet Him, By and by we shall greet Him, And with
1
Je-sus reign in glo-ry By and by (by and by);
2
Jesus reign in glo-ry by and by.

No. 88. Keep the Heart Singing.
C. H. G.
COPYRIGHT, 1902, BY CHAS. H. GABRIEL.
COPYRIGHT, 1907, BY E. O. EXCELL.
Chas. H. Gabriel.
1. We may light - en toil and care, Or a heav - y bur-den share, With a
2. If His love is in the soul, And we yield to His con-trol, Sweetest
3. How a word of love will cheer, Kin-dle hope, and ban-ish fear, Soothe a
word, a kind-ly deed, or sun - ny smile; We may gir - dle day and night
mu - sic will the lone-ly hours be - guile; We may drive the clouds a-way,
pain, or take a - way the sting of guile; Oh, how much we all may do,
FINE.
With a ha - lo of de-light, If we keep the heart singing all the while.
Cheer and bless the darkest day, If we keep the heart singing all the while.
In the world we trav-el thro', If we keep the heart singing all the while.
CHORUS.
Keep the heart singing all the while; . . . . Make the world brighter with a
sing - ing, singing all the while; bright-er,
smile; . . . . . . Keep the song ringing! lone - ly hours we may be-guile,
bright-er with a smile;
D. S.

No. 89. Safe in the Fold.
Fanny J. Crosby.
COPYRIGHT, 1910, BY E. O. EXCELL. WORDS AND MUSIC.
Jno. R. Sweney.
1. O Je-sus, my Rock, My Ref-uge, my All, In Thee will I trust, On Thee will I call, And praise Thee for-ev-er For blessings un-told; Thy right hand up-holds me, I'm safe in the fold.
2. Tho' stormy the way, Tho' thunders may roll, The rainbow of peace Still shines in my soul; The sky may be cloud-y, The night may be cold, Yet, un-der Thy watch-care, I'm safe in the fold.
3. I'm safe in the fold, All glo-ry to Thee! I look for a morn That's dawn-ing for me; A beau-ti-ful mansion, The streets paved with gold, And there I shall ev-er Be safe in the fold.
CHORUS.
Safe ..... in the fold, ... Safe ..... in the fold; ..... Thy right hand up-holds me, I'm safe ...... in the fold ...
Safe in the fold, Safe in the fold, I'm safe in the fold, Safe in the fold; Thy right hand up-holds me, Thy right hand up-holds me, I'm safe, I am safe

No. 90. O Wanderer, Come Home.
Eben E. Rexford.
COPYRIGHT, 1910, BY E. O. EXCELL. WORDS AND MUSIC.
Samuel W. Beazley.
1. O why have you wan-dered so far from the right way? Come
2. O think of the love that for - ev - er is call - ing, Come
3. O grieve not the heart that for - ev - er is yearn-ing, Come
4. O turn from the path-way of doubt and of dan - ger, Come
home, ... come home; The path you should tread is a
home, ... come home; The road is so rough, and the
home, ... come home; God keeps in heav'n's win-dow a
home, ... come home; And be to thy Fa - ther no
Come home:
D. S.—waits at the por - tals of
FINE.
CHORUS.
safe way, a bright way, Come home, . . come home.
dark-ness is fall-ing, Come home, . . come home. O wan - der - er,
light al - ways burning, Come home, . . come home.
lon - ger a stran-ger, Come home, . . come home.
Come home,
heav-en to greet you, Come home, ... come home.
D. S.
come, hear the Fa - ther en-treat you, Come home, . . . come home; He
Come home.

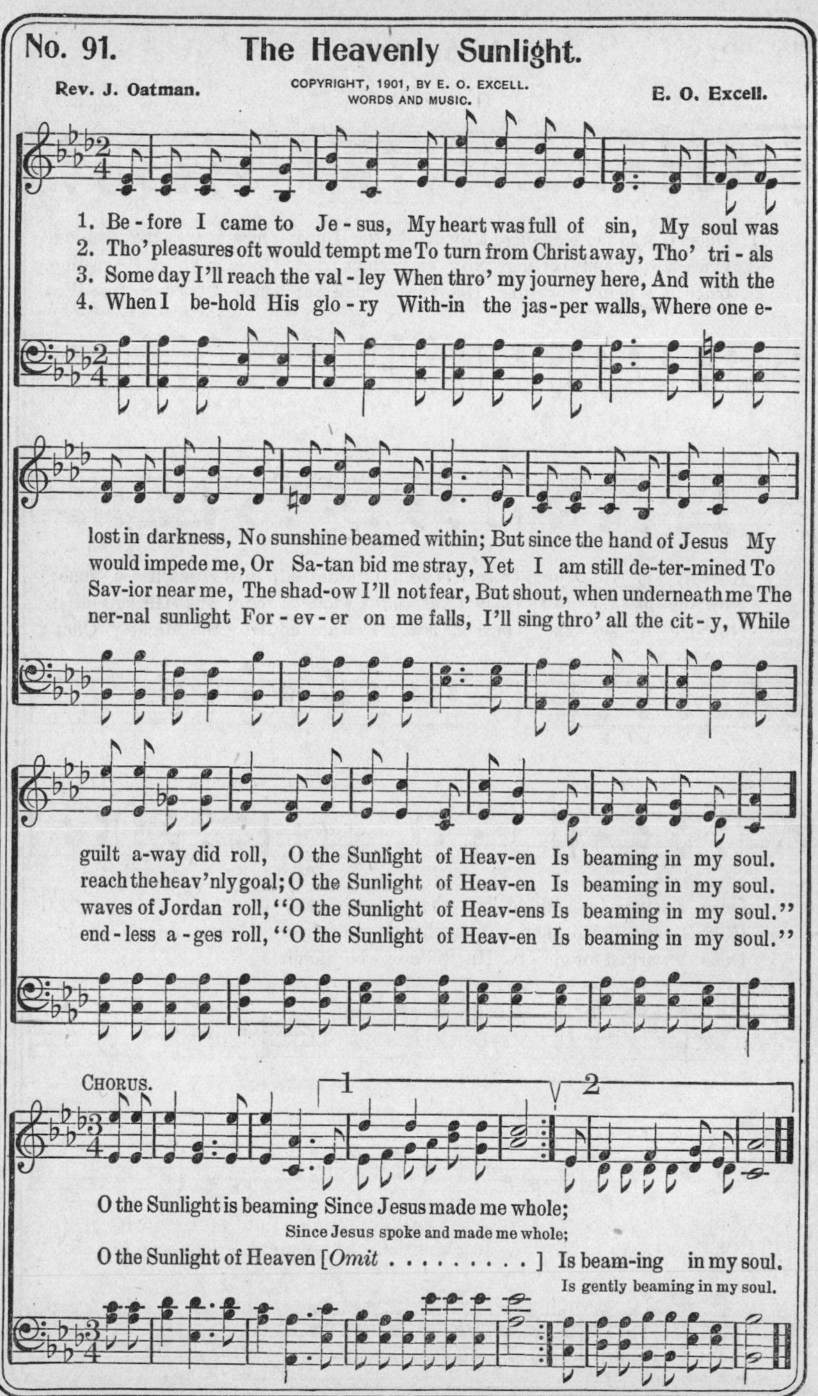
No. 91. The Heavenly Sunlight.
Rev. J. Oatman.
COPYRIGHT, 1901, BY E. O. EXCELL. WORDS AND MUSIC.
E. O. Excell.
1. Be - fore I came to Je - sus, My heart was full of sin, My soul was lost in darkness, No sunshine beamed within; But since the hand of Jesus My guilt a-way did roll, O the Sunlight of Heav-en Is beaming in my soul.
2. Tho' pleasures oft would tempt me To turn from Christ away, Tho' tri - als would impede me, Or Sa-tan bid me stray, Yet I am still de-ter-mined To reach the heav'nly goal; O the Sunlight of Heav-en Is beaming in my soul.
3. Some day I'll reach the val - ley When thro' my journey here, And with the Sav-ior near me, The shad-ow I'll not fear, But shout, when underneath me The waves of Jordan roll, "O the Sunlight of Heav-ens Is beaming in my soul."
4. When I be-hold His glo - ry With-in the jas-per walls, Where one e-ner-nal sunlight For - ev - er on me falls, I'll sing thro' all the cit - y, While end - less a - ges roll, "O the Sunlight of Heav-en Is beaming in my soul."
CHORUS.
O the Sunlight is beaming Since Jesus made me whole;
Since Jesus spoke and made me whole;
O the Sunlight of Heaven [Omit . . . .] Is beam-ing in my soul.
Is gently beaming in my soul.

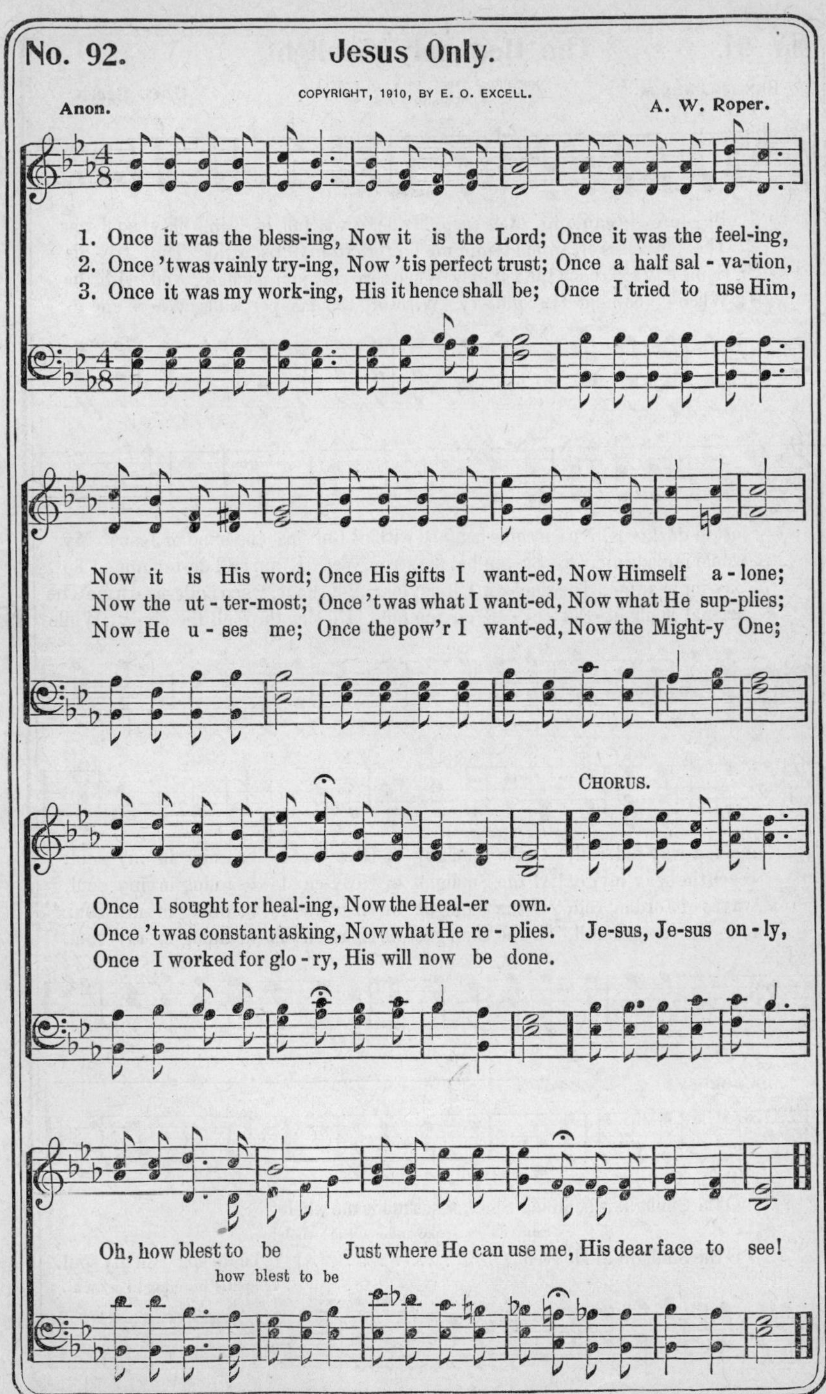
No. 92. Jesus Only.
COPYRIGHT, 1910, BY E. O. EXCELL.
Anon.
A. W. Roper.
1. Once it was the bless-ing, Now it is the Lord; Once it was the feel-ing,
2. Once 'twas vainly try-ing, Now 'tis perfect trust; Once a half sal - va-tion,
3. Once it was my work-ing, His it hence shall be; Once I tried to use Him,
Now it is His word; Once His gifts I want-ed, Now Himself a - lone;
Now the ut - ter-most; Once 'twas what I want-ed, Now what He sup-plies;
Now He u - ses me; Once the pow'r I want-ed, Now the Might-y One;
Once I sought for heal-ing, Now the Heal-er own.
Once 'twas constant asking, Now what He re - plies.
Once I worked for glo - ry, His will now be done.
CHORUS.
Je-sus, Je-sus on - ly,
Oh, how blest to be Just where He can use me, His dear face to see!
how blest to be

No. 93.
Satisfied.
A. H. Ackley.
WORDS AND MUSIC COPYRIGHT, 1909, BY B. D. ACKLEY.
F. G. FISCHER, OWNER.
B. D. Ackley.
1. When I have fin - ished my pil - grim - age here, When shall have vanished temp - ta - tion and fear, As in the arms of His love I a - bide,
2. When I am troub - led by grief and de - spair, Grace nev - er fail - ing a - waits me up there; Will - ing to trust Him what - ev - er be - tide,
3. When I have trav - eled the way with my Lord, Count - ing the mile - posts by faith in His word, Liv - ing and dy - ing with Him at my side,
CHORUS.
I shall be sat - is - fied. I.......... shall be sat - is - fied, I............ shall be sat - is - fied;
I shall be sat - is - fied, I shall be sat - is - fied, I shall be sat - is - fied, I shall be sat - is - fied;
rit.
Sheltered a - bove by His in - fin - ite love, I shall be sat - is - fied.

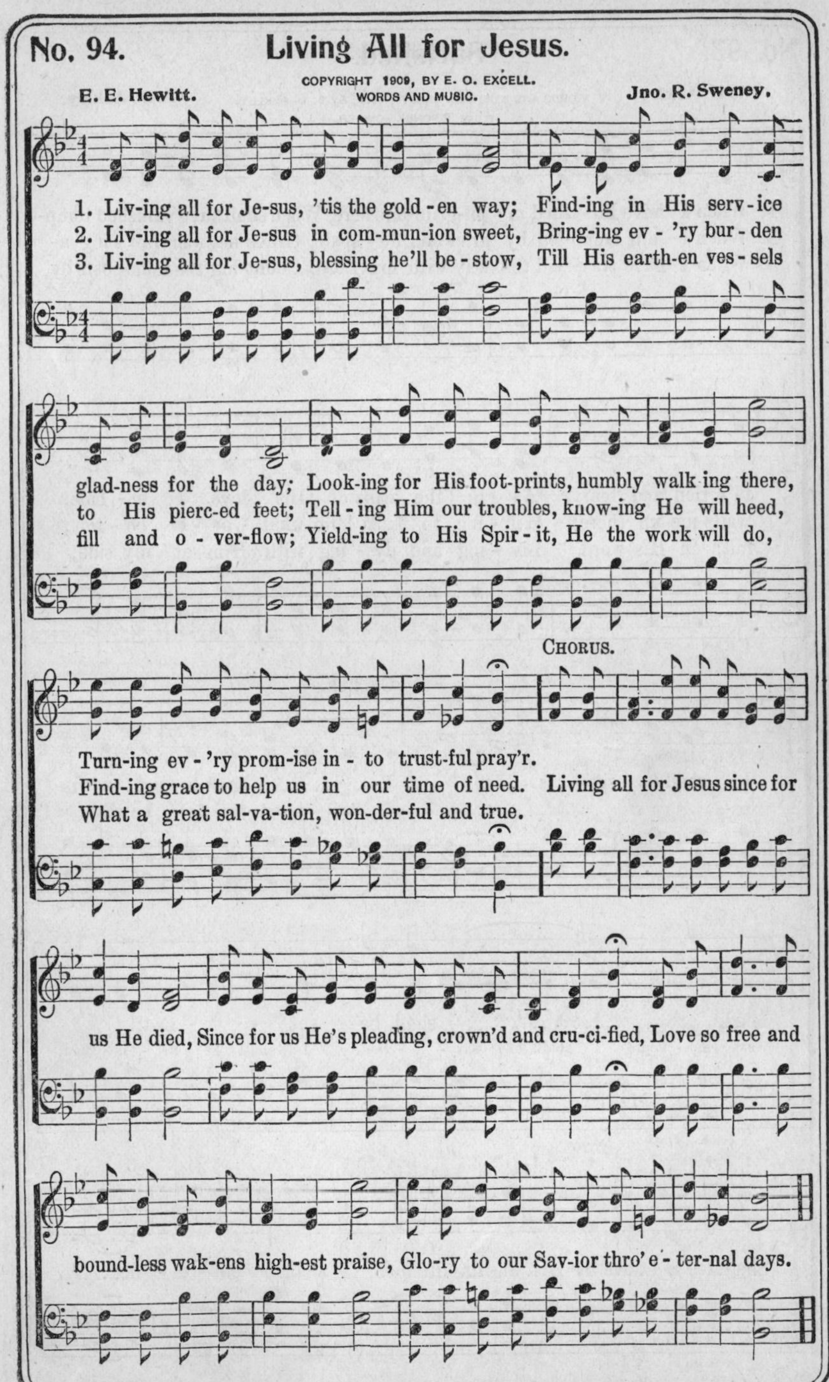
No. 94. Living All for Jesus.
COPYRIGHT 1909, BY E. O. EXCELL.
WORDS AND MUSIC.
E. E. Hewitt.
Jno. R. Sweney.
1. Liv-ing all for Je-sus, 'tis the gold-en way; Find-ing in His serv-ice glad-ness for the day; Look-ing for His foot-prints, humbly walk-ing there, Turn-ing ev-'ry prom-ise in-to trust-ful pray'r.
2. Liv-ing all for Je-sus in com-mun-ion sweet, Bring-ing ev-'ry bur-den to His pierc-ed feet; Tell-ing Him our troubles, know-ing He will heed, Find-ing grace to help us in our time of need.
3. Liv-ing all for Je-sus, blessing he'll be-stow, Till His earth-en ves-sels fill and o-ver-flow; Yield-ing to His Spir-it, He the work will do, What a great sal-va-tion, won-der-ful and true.
CHORUS.
Living all for Jesus since for us He died, Since for us He's pleading, crown'd and cru-ci-fied, Love so free and bound-less wak-ens high-est praise, Glo-ry to our Sav-ior thro' e-ter-nal days.

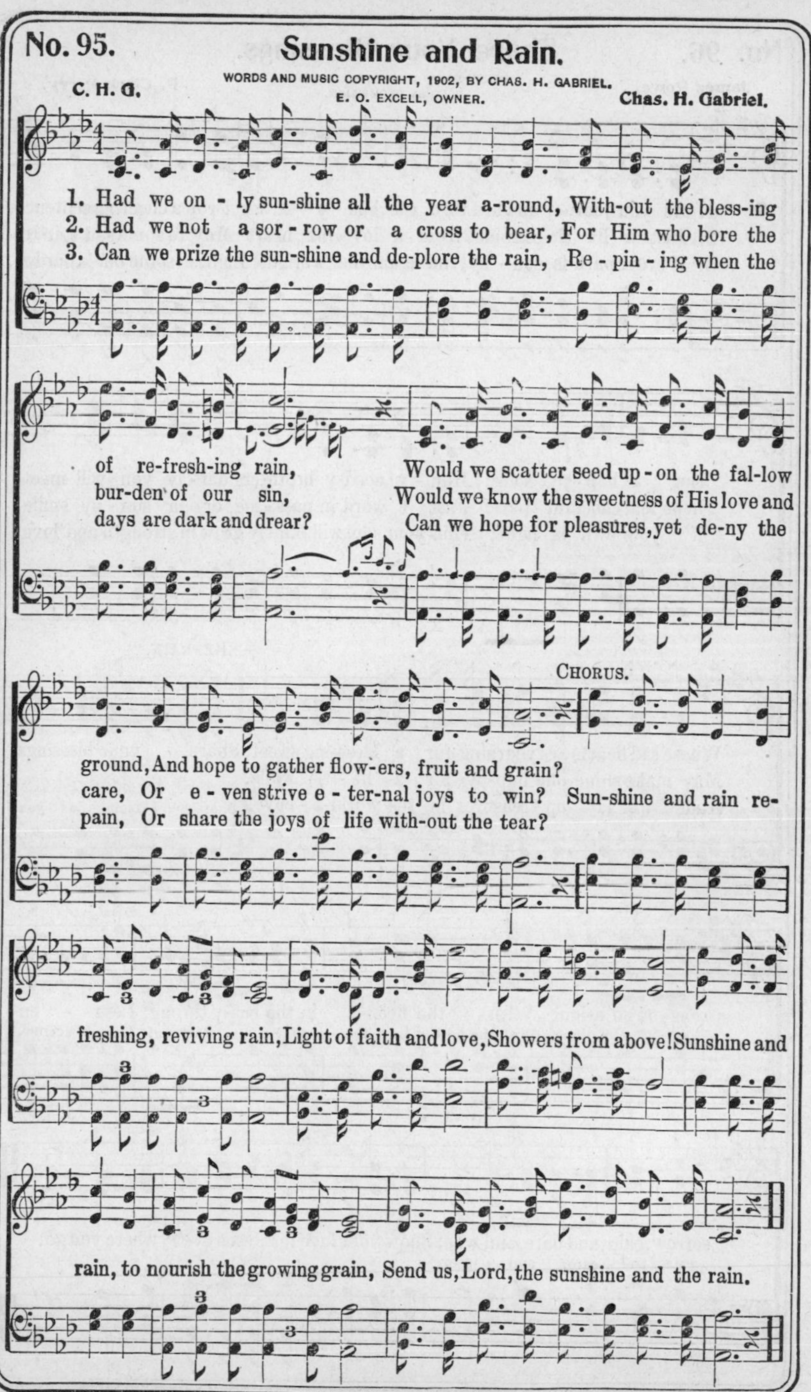
No. 95.
Sunshine and Rain.
WORDS AND MUSIC COPYRIGHT, 1902, BY CHAS. H. GABRIEL.
E. O. EXCELL, OWNER.
C. H. G.
Chas. H. Gabriel.
1. Had we on - ly sun-shine all the year a-round, With-out the bless-ing of re-fresh-ing rain, Would we scatter seed up-on the fal-low ground, And hope to gather flow-ers, fruit and grain?
2. Had we not a sor - row or a cross to bear, For Him who bore the bur-den of our sin, Would we know the sweetness of His love and care, Or e - ven strive e - ter-nal joys to win?
3. Can we prize the sun-shine and de-plore the rain, Re - pin - ing when the days are dark and drear? Can we hope for pleasures, yet de-ny the pain, Or share the joys of life with-out the tear?
CHORUS.
Sun-shine and rain re-freshing, reviving rain, Light of faith and love, Showers from above! Sunshine and rain, to nourish the growing grain, Send us, Lord, the sunshine and the rain.

No. 96. Share Your Blessings.
James Rowe.
PERRY BROS. MUSIC CO., OWNERS.
USED BY PERMISSION.
F. Clark Perry.
1. As you journey onward thro' the bus - y throng, Drop a cheering sentence,
2. Just a lit - tle sentence from a lov - ing heart May to some sad spir-it
3. If your path is sun - ny, make another's bright; Lighten some one's burden,
sing a hap - py song; Man - y need-y broth-ers dai - ly you will meet,
hope and cheer im - part; Just a word in pass - ing, or a sun - ny smile,
if your own is light; Thus your soul will dai - ly grow in strength and love,
REFRAIN.
Whose sad hearts are yearning for a bless-ing sweet. Share your blessings,
May make some one hap-py for a lit - tle while.
And will lay up treasures in the world a - bove. Share your blessings, as you
as you go a-long, With the need-y in the bus-y throng; Less - en
go a - long, With the need-y in the bus - y throng; Less-en sorrow,
sorrow, pain, and care, and woe; Show your love for Jesus ev-'rywhere you go.
pain, and care, and woe;

No. 97. In Heavenly Love Abiding.
Anna L. Waring.
COPYRIGHT, 1910, BY E. O. EXCELL.
E. O. Sellers.
UNISON.
1. In heav'n-ly love a - bid - ing, No change my heart shall fear;
2. Wher-ev - er He may guide me, No want shall turn me back;
3. Green pas-tures are be - fore me, Which yet I have not seen;
And safe is such con - fid - ing, For noth - ing changes here.
My Shep - herd is be - side me, And noth - ing can I lack.
Bright skies will soon be o'er me, Where dark - est clouds have been.
The storm may roar with - out me, My heart may low be laid,
His wis - dom ev - er wak - eth, His sight is nev - er dim,
My hope I can - not meas-ure, My path to life is free,
But God is round a - bout me, And can I be dis - mayed?
He knows the way He tak - eth, And I will walk with Him;
My Sav - ior has my treas-ure, And He will walk with me;
PARTS.
But God is round a - bout me, And can I be dismayed (dismayed)?
He knows the way He tak - eth, And I will walk with Him (with Him).
My Sav - ior has my treas - ure, And He will walk with me (with me).

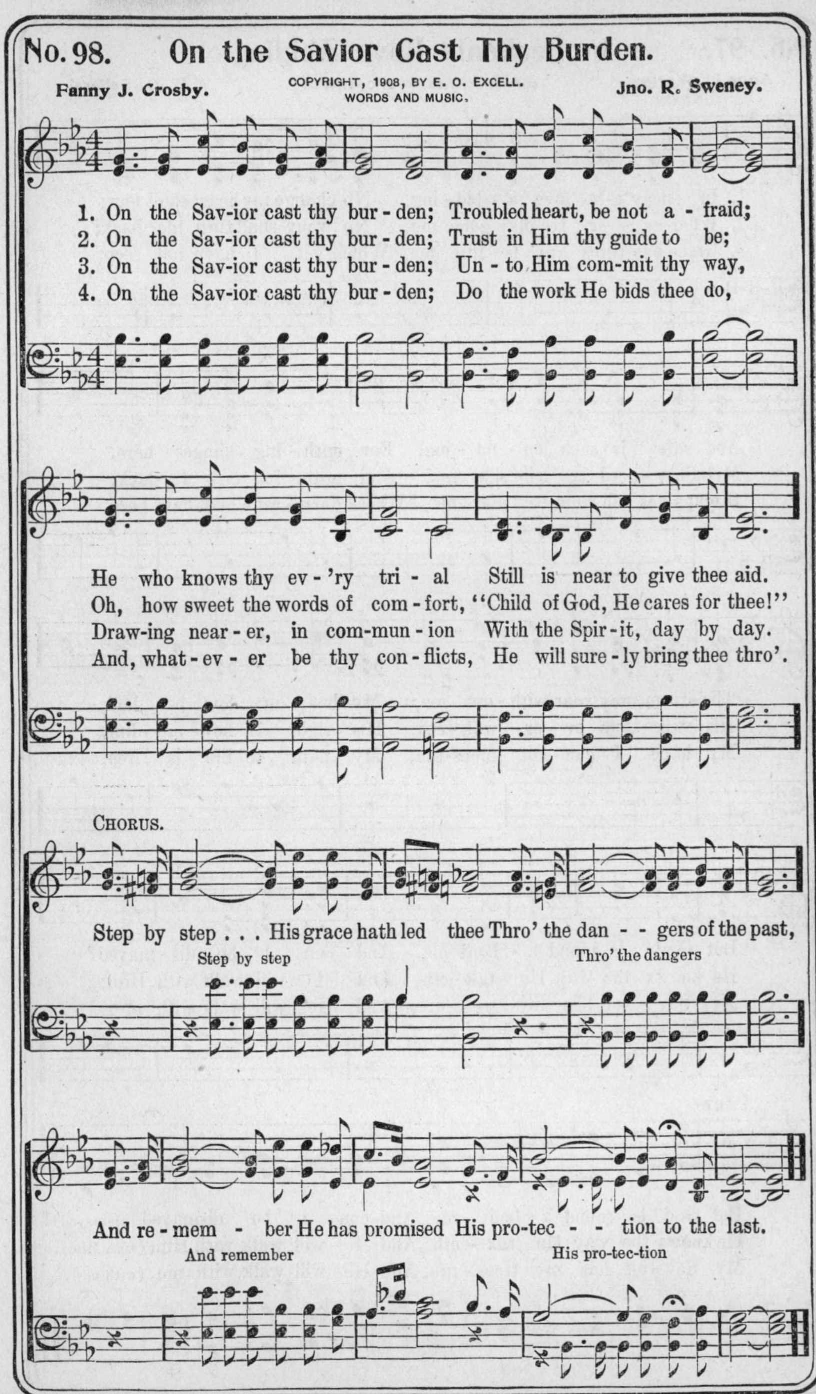
No. 98. On the Savior Cast Thy Burden.
Fanny J. Crosby.
COPYRIGHT, 1908, BY E. O. EXCELL. WORDS AND MUSIC.
Jno. R. Sweney.
1. On the Sav-ior cast thy bur - den; Troubled heart, be not a - fraid;
2. On the Sav-ior cast thy bur - den; Trust in Him thy guide to be;
3. On the Sav-ior cast thy bur - den; Un - to Him com-mit thy way,
4. On the Sav-ior cast thy bur - den; Do the work He bids thee do,
He who knows thy ev - 'ry tri - al Still is near to give thee aid.
Oh, how sweet the words of com - fort, "Child of God, He cares for thee!"
Draw-ing near-er, in com-mun - ion With the Spir - it, day by day.
And, what - ev - er be thy con - flicts, He will sure - ly bring thee thro'.
CHORUS.
Step by step . . . His grace hath led thee Thro' the dan - - gers of the past,
Step by step
Thro' the dangers
And re - mem - ber He has promised His pro - tec - - tion to the last.
And remember
His pro-tec-tion

No. 99.
Divine Peace.
Andrew Bonar.
COPYRIGHT, 1910, BY E. O. EXCELL.
E. O. Sellers.
1. Peace like the riv - er's gen-tle flow; Peace like the morning's si-lent glow;
2. Peace thro' the night and thro' the day; Peace thro' all windings of our way;
3. O King of peace, this peace be - stow Up-on a stranger here be - low;
4. Peace from the Father and the Son; Peace from the Spir-it, all His own;
From day to day, in love sup-plied, An endless and un-ebb-ing tide.
In pain, and toil, and wear-i - ness, A deep and ev - er - last-ing peace.
O God of peace, Thy peace im-part To ev-'ry troubled, trembling heart.
Peace that shall nev - er-more be lost, Of Father, Son, and Ho - ly Ghost.
Refrain.
Peace, upon peace, like wave on wave, This is the por-tion that I crave;
The peace of God which passeth thought, The peace of Christ which changeth not.

No. 100.
Let Us Be Strong.
Jennie E. Hussey.
COPYRIGHT, 1905, BY CHAS. H. GABRIEL.
E. O. EXCELL, OWNER.
Chas. H. Gabriel.
1. There's an e - vil in our land, And a foe we must withstand, Let us be
2. There are du - ties to be done Ere the world for Christ is won, Let us be
3. Then for God, and home, and right, Pressing forward in His might, Let us be
strong, ... let us be strong in the Lord! There's a work that we must do;
strong, ... let us be strong in the Lord! Then to cleanse the haunts of sin,
strong, ... let us be strong in the Lord! For the work is His we know;
Let us be strong,
That we may be just and true, Let us be strong, let us be strong and courageous!
Truth and right to ush-er in, Let us be strong, let us be strong and courageous!
Where He leads us we will go; Let us be strong, let us be strong and courageous!
CHORUS.
1
Let us be strong (Let us be strong) to fight the wrong (to fight the wrong), Pressing a-
Un-til we join (Un - til we join) the victor's song (the victor's song); [Omit.]
2
long . . . . . with the conq'ring throng,
Pressing along
Let us be strong . . . . and courageous!
Let us be strong

No. 101. Just a Little Nearer.
N. A. McAuley.
COPYRIGHT, 1910, BY E. O. EXCELL. WORDS AND MUSIC.
Chas. H. Gabriel.
1. Are you grow-ing more like Je-sus ev - 'ry day (ev - 'ry day)? Is His bless-ed Spir - it shin - ing on your way (on your way)? Does the path-way bright-er grow As you strive His will to know? Are you grow-ing more like Je - sus ev - 'ry day?
2. Are you liv - ing more like Je-sus ev - 'ry day (ev - 'ry day)? Help-ing those who walk be-side you in the way (in the way)? Do you bring the Sav - ior near By a life of hope and cheer? Are you liv - ing more like Je - sus ev - 'ry day?
3. Are you do - ing more for Je-sus ev - 'ry day (ev - 'ry day)? Tell-ing out the sav - ing sto - ry while you may (while you may)? Do you strive in love to win Pre - cious souls now lost in sin? Are you do - ing more for Je - sus ev - 'ry day?
D. S.—lit - tle clos - er to Him I do so much a - dore, Just a lit - tle near-er to my Sav-ior's side.
FINE. CHORUS.
Grow-ing just a lit - tle stronger as I trust Him more, trust Him more and more,
As be-neath the shadow of His wings I hide; I safe - ly hide; Just a
D. S.

No. 102. Lift Him Up.
S. R. Amy.
WORDS AND MUSIC COPYRIGHT, 1906, BY E. O. EXCELL.
INTERNATIONAL COPYRIGHT SECURED.
J. M. Dungan.
1. Your brother has a bur-den that is hard to bear; He fell be-fore the
2. In God's own image, with a pre-cious soul to save, His strength turned into
3. If you will give him courage and his soul is won, Your heart will leap with
tempt-er in a sin-ful snare, And he looks to you to help him; he has
weakness, who was once so brave, He is struggling for a foot-hold, and would
glad-ness when the work is done; One more star to shine in heav-en, O what
drained the bitter cup: In the name of Christ your Savior, lift him up, lift him up.
fain renounce the cup: In the name of Christ your Savior, lift him up, lift him up.
joy will fill your cup! In the name of Christ your Savior, lift him up, lift him up.
CHORUS.
Lift him up, ... lift up your brother, Lift him up, lift him up;
Lift him up,
Lift him up, lift him up;
In the name . . . . of Christ your Savior, Lift him up, lift him up.
In the name, in the name of Christ your Sav-ior,
Lift him up,

No. 103. I Will Not Forget Thee.
C. H. G.
COPYRIGHT, 1889, BY E. O. EXCELL.
WORDS AND MUSIC.
Chas. H. Gabriel.
1. Sweet is the promise—"I will not forget thee," Nothing can mo-lest or
2. Trust-ing the promise—"I will not forget thee," Onward will I go with
3. When at the gold-en por-tals I am standing, All my trib-u-la-tions,
turn my soul a-way; E'en tho' the night be dark with-in the val-ley,
songs of joy and love; Tho' earth de-spise me, tho' my friends forsake me,
all my sorrows past, How sweet to hear the bless-ed proc-la-ma-tion,
Just be-yond is shining one e-ter-nal day.
I shall be remembered in my home above.
"Enter, faithful servant, welcome home at last!"
CHORUS.
I . . . . . . will not forget thee or
I will not forget thee, I will nev-er
leave thee; In my hands I'll hold thee, in my arms I'll fold thee; I. . . . . will
leave thee;
I will not for-get
not for-get thee or leave thee; I am thy Re-deem-er, I will care for thee.
thee, for-get

No. 104. "We Shall Be Like Him."
Flora Kirkland.
COPYRIGHT, 1906, BY GEO. C. STEBBINS.
Geo. C. Stebbins.
1. "We shall be like Him," the Son of God most ho-ly, "We shall be like Him," sweet
2. "We shall be like Him," this promise lights the future, Shedding soft radiance up-
3. "We shall be like Him," the glo-ri-fied Re-deem-er; His lov-ing-kind-ness this
promise of His grace! Christian, press forward! some bright, some glad to-morrow
on our pathway dim. He who redeemed us, the Lamb once slain on Cal-v'ry,
add-ed grace bestows! We shall be-hold Him no more with clouded vi-sion,
"We shall be like Him," for we shall see His face.
Shines now in glo-ry;—and we shall be like Him.
Bright-er and bright-er to faith the prospect grows.
REFRAIN.
"We shall be like Him, We shall be like Him, For we shall see Him as He is; We shall be like Him, we shall be like Him, For we shall see Him as He is."
"We shall be like Him, We shall be like Him, For we shall see Him as He is; We shall be like Him, we shall be like Him, For we shall see Him as He is."

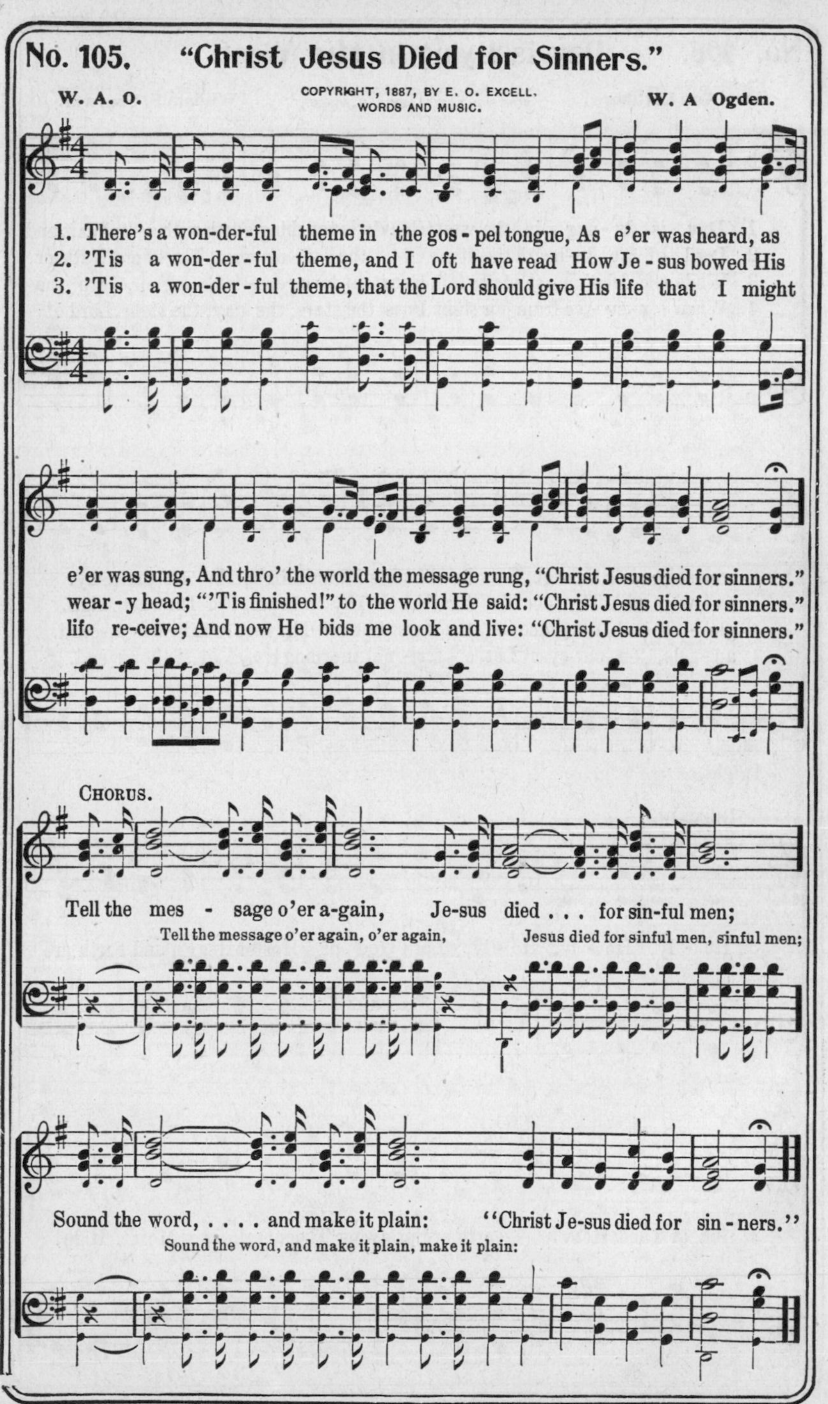
No. 105. "Christ Jesus Died for Sinners."
W. A. O.
COPYRIGHT, 1887, BY E. O. EXCELL.
WORDS AND MUSIC.
W. A Ogden.
1. There's a won-der-ful theme in the gos - pel tongue, As e'er was heard, as
2. 'Tis a won-der - ful theme, and I oft have read How Je - sus bowed His
3. 'Tis a won-der - ful theme, that the Lord should give His life that I might
e'er was sung, And thro' the world the message rung, "Christ Jesus died for sinners."
wear - y head; "'Tis finished!" to the world He said: "Christ Jesus died for sinners."
life re-ceive; And now He bids me look and live: "Christ Jesus died for sinners."
Chorus.
Tell the mes - sage o'er a-gain, Je-sus died . . . for sin-ful men;
Tell the message o'er again, o'er again,
Jesus died for sinful men, sinful men;
Sound the word, ... and make it plain: "Christ Je-sus died for sin - ners."
Sound the word, and make it plain, make it plain:

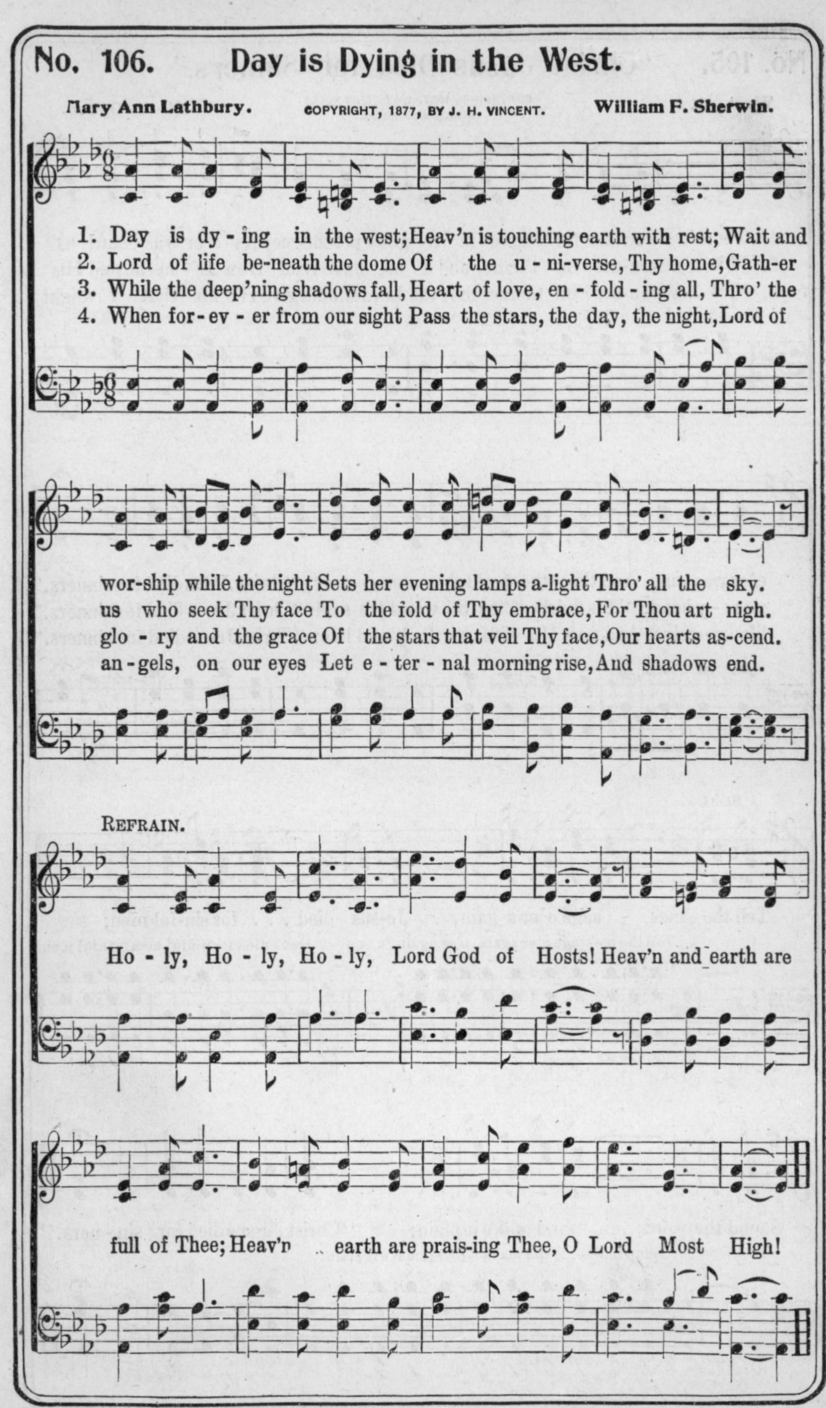

No. 106. Day is Dying in the West.
Mary Ann Lathbury. COPYRIGHT, 1877, BY J. H. VINCENT. William F. Sherwin.
1. Day is dy - ing in the west; Heav'n is touching earth with rest; Wait and
2. Lord of life be-neath the dome Of the u - ni-verse, Thy home, Gath-er
3. While the deep'ning shadows fall, Heart of love, en - fold - ing all, Thro' the
4. When for - ev - er from our sight Pass the stars, the day, the night, Lord of
wor-ship while the night Sets her evening lamps a-light Thro' all the sky.
us who seek Thy face To the fold of Thy embrace, For Thou art nigh.
glo - ry and the grace Of the stars that veil Thy face, Our hearts as-cend.
an - gels, on our eyes Let e - ter - nal morning rise, And shadows end.
REFRAIN.
Ho - ly, Ho - ly, Ho - ly, Lord God of Hosts! Heav'n and earth are
full of Thee; Heav'n earth are prais-ing Thee, O Lord Most High!

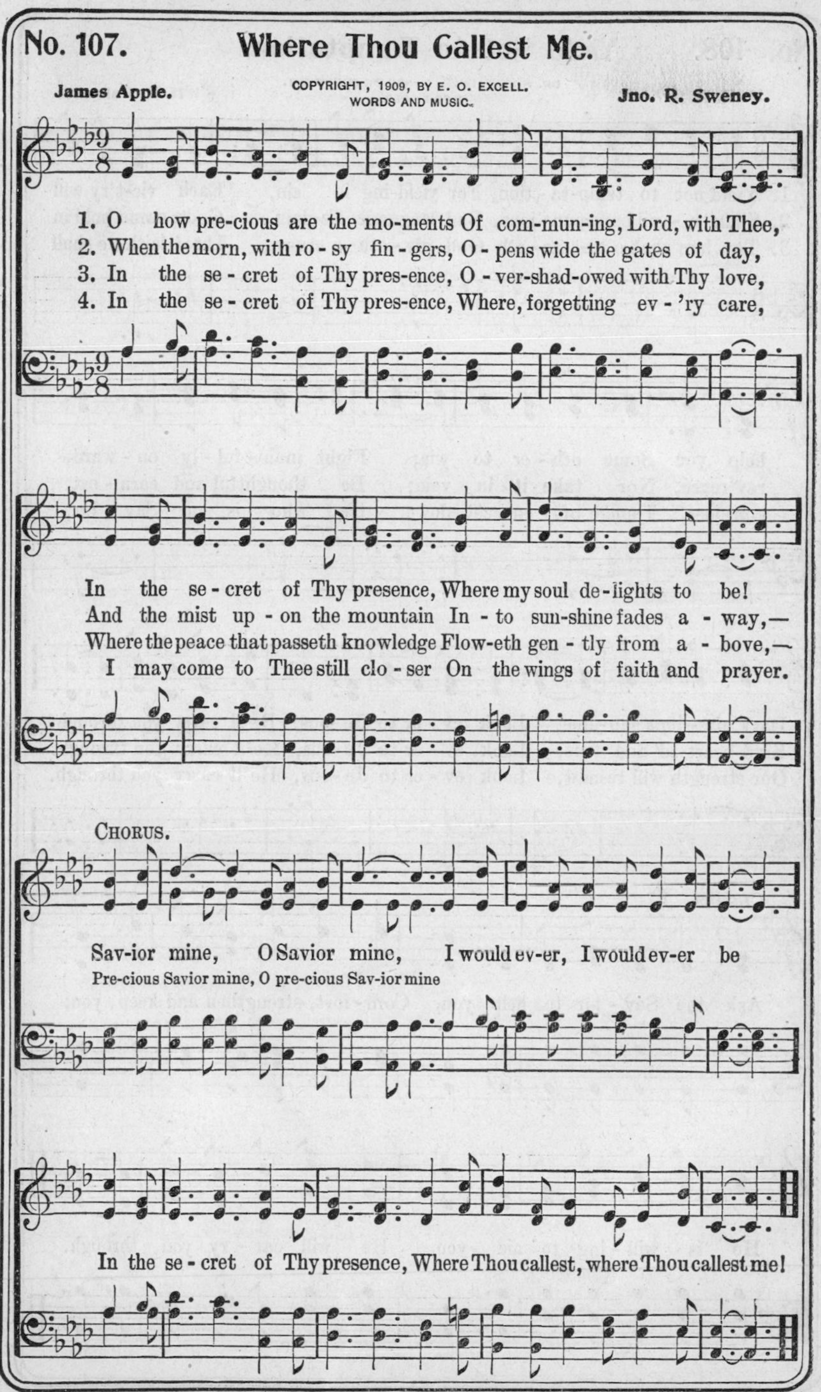
No. 107. Where Thou Gallest Me.
James Apple.
COPYRIGHT, 1909, BY E. O. EXCELL.
WORDS AND MUSIC.
Jno. R. Sweney.
1. O how pre-cious are the mo-ments Of com-mun-ing, Lord, with Thee,
2. When the morn, with ro - sy fin - gers, O - pens wide the gates of day,
3. In the se - cret of Thy pres-ence, O - ver-shad-owed with Thy love,
4. In the se - cret of Thy pres-ence, Where, forgetting ev - 'ry care,
In the se - cret of Thy presence, Where my soul de-lights to be!
And the mist up - on the mountain In - to sun-shine fades a - way,—
Where the peace that passeth knowledge Flow-eth gen - tly from a - bove,—
I may come to Thee still clo - ser On the wings of faith and prayer.
CHORUS.
Sav-ior mine, O Savior mine, I would ev-er, I would ev-er be
Pre-cious Savior mine, O pre-cious Sav-ior mine
In the se - cret of Thy presence, Where Thou callest, where Thou callest me!

No. 108. Yield Not to Temptation.

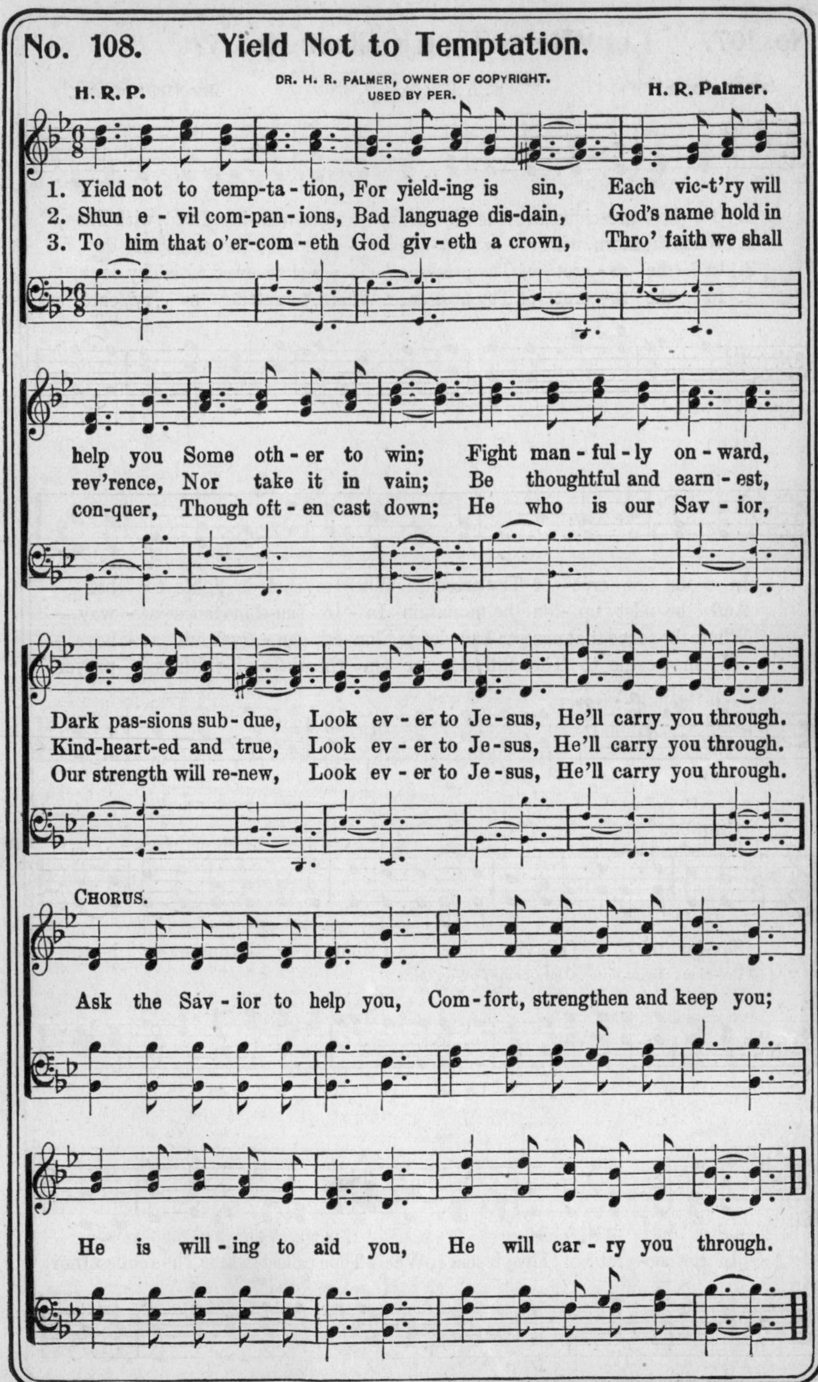

No. 109. Let the Cheering Sunbeams Fly.
J. W. Carpenter.
COPYRIGHT, 1904, BY CARPENTER & BURCHIT.
W. E. M. HACKLEMAN, OWNER.
Dr. J. A. Burchit.
1. You have known the Mas - ter, bless - ed Mas - ter, You have known His mer - cy and His love; You have caught the sunbeams, cheering sunbeams, Gen-tly fall-ing from the skies a - bove (so gen - tly).
2. You have seen the sun-beams, cheer-ing sun-beams, Chas - ing shad-ows from the cloud - ed sky; You have seen the dawn-ing, wondrous dawn-ing, Coming, glorious, when the sunbeams fly (bright sun-beams).
3. You have seen the sun-beams, cheer-ing sun-beams, Foll'wing show-ers on the fields new-sown; You have seen the har - vest, gold - en har - vest, Safe-ly garnered, with the ear full-grown (blest har - vest).
CHORUS.
Scatter the sunbeams, cheering, bright sunbeams; Darkened hearts for sunlight cry; . . Bear the news of mer - cy, Tell the news of Je - sus, Let the cheering sunbeams fly.
Scat - ter sun - beams, cheer - ing sun-beams; Hearts for sun - light cry; . . Bear the news of mer - cy, Tell the love of Je - sus,
Dark - ened hearts for light are cry - ing;

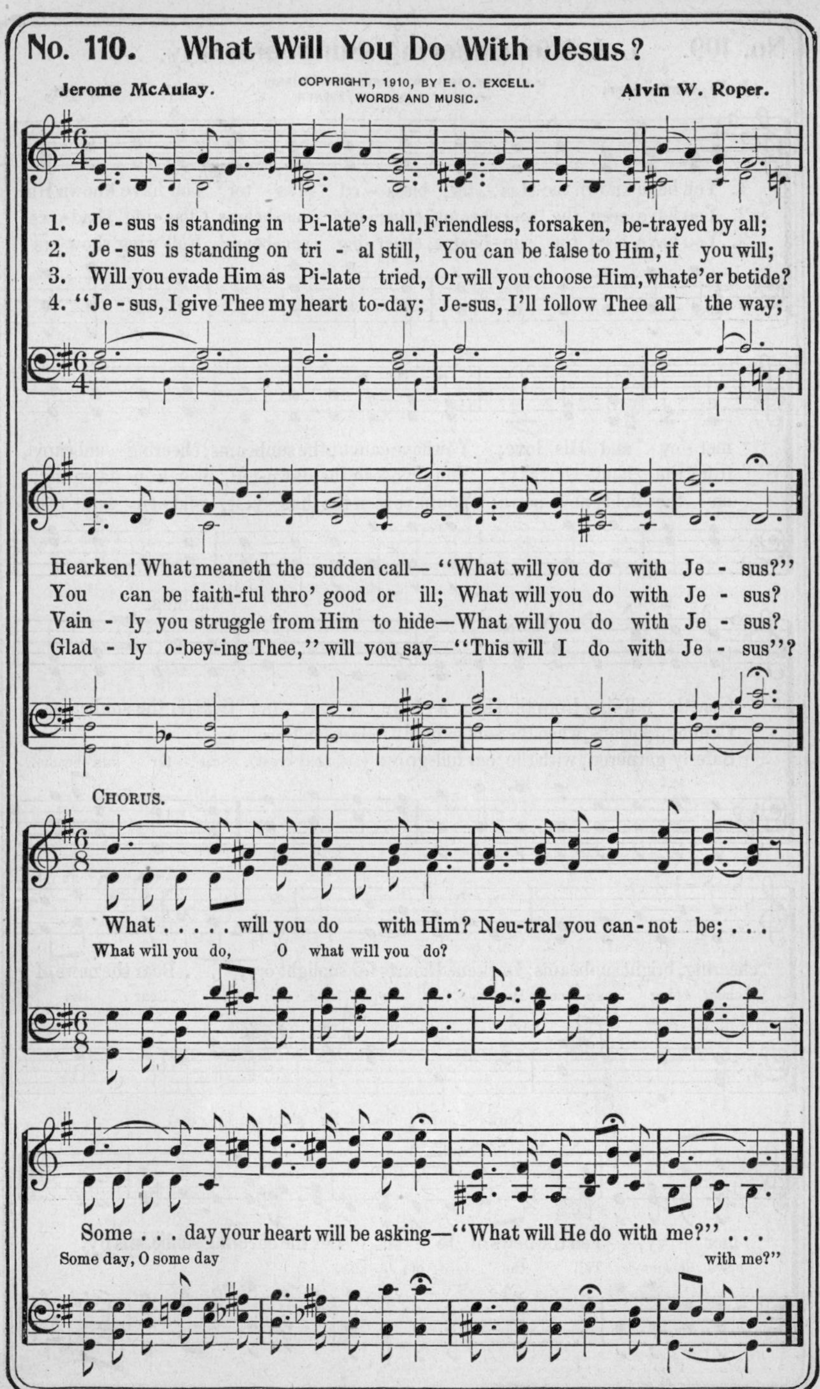
No. 110. What Will You Do With Jesus?
Jerome McAulay.
COPYRIGHT, 1910, BY E. O. EXCELL. WORDS AND MUSIC.
Alvin W. Roper.
1. Je - sus is standing in Pi-late's hall, Friendless, forsaken, be-trayed by all;
2. Je - sus is standing on tri - al still, You can be false to Him, if you will;
3. Will you evade Him as Pi-late tried, Or will you choose Him, whate'er betide?
4. "Je - sus, I give Thee my heart to-day; Je-sus, I'll follow Thee all the way;
Hearken! What meaneth the sudden call— "What will you do with Je - sus?"
You can be faith-ful thro' good or ill; What will you do with Je - sus?
Vain - ly you struggle from Him to hide—What will you do with Je - sus?
Glad - ly o-bey-ing Thee," will you say—"This will I do with Je - sus"?
CHORUS.
What . . . . . will you do with Him? Neu-tral you can-not be; . . .
What will you do, O what will you do?
Some . . . day your heart will be asking—"What will He do with me?" . . .
Some day, O some day
with me?"

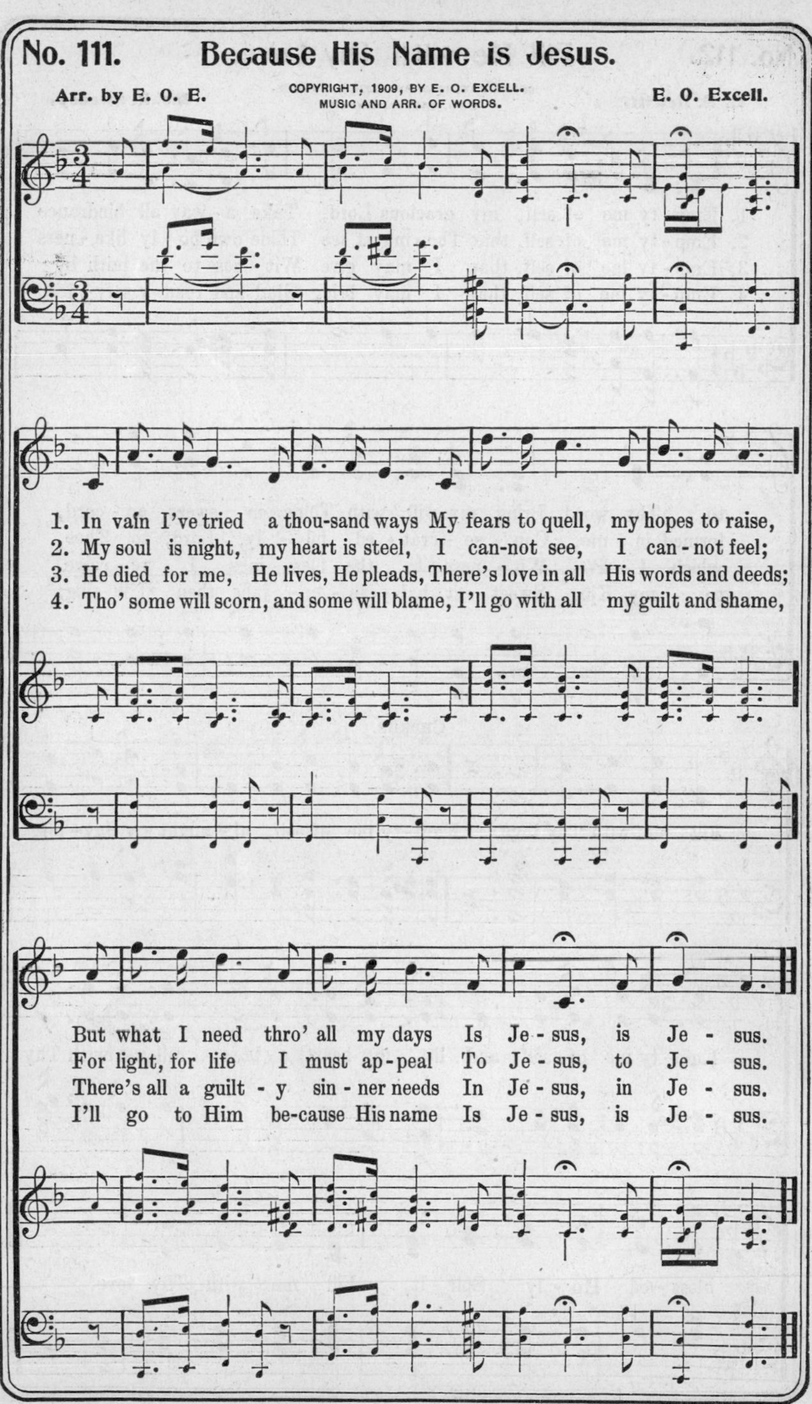
No. 111. Because His Name is Jesus.
Arr. by E. O. E.
COPYRIGHT, 1909, BY E. O. EXCELL.
MUSIC AND ARR. OF WORDS.
E. O. Excell.
1. In vain I've tried a thou-sand ways My fears to quell, my hopes to raise,
2. My soul is night, my heart is steel, I can-not see, I can-not feel;
3. He died for me, He lives, He pleads, There's love in all His words and deeds;
4. Tho' some will scorn, and some will blame, I'll go with all my guilt and shame,
But what I need thro' all my days Is Je-sus, is Je-sus.
For light, for life I must ap-peal To Je-sus, to Je-sus.
There's all a guilt-y sin-ner needs In Je-sus, in Je-sus.
I'll go to Him be-cause His name Is Je-sus, is Je-sus.

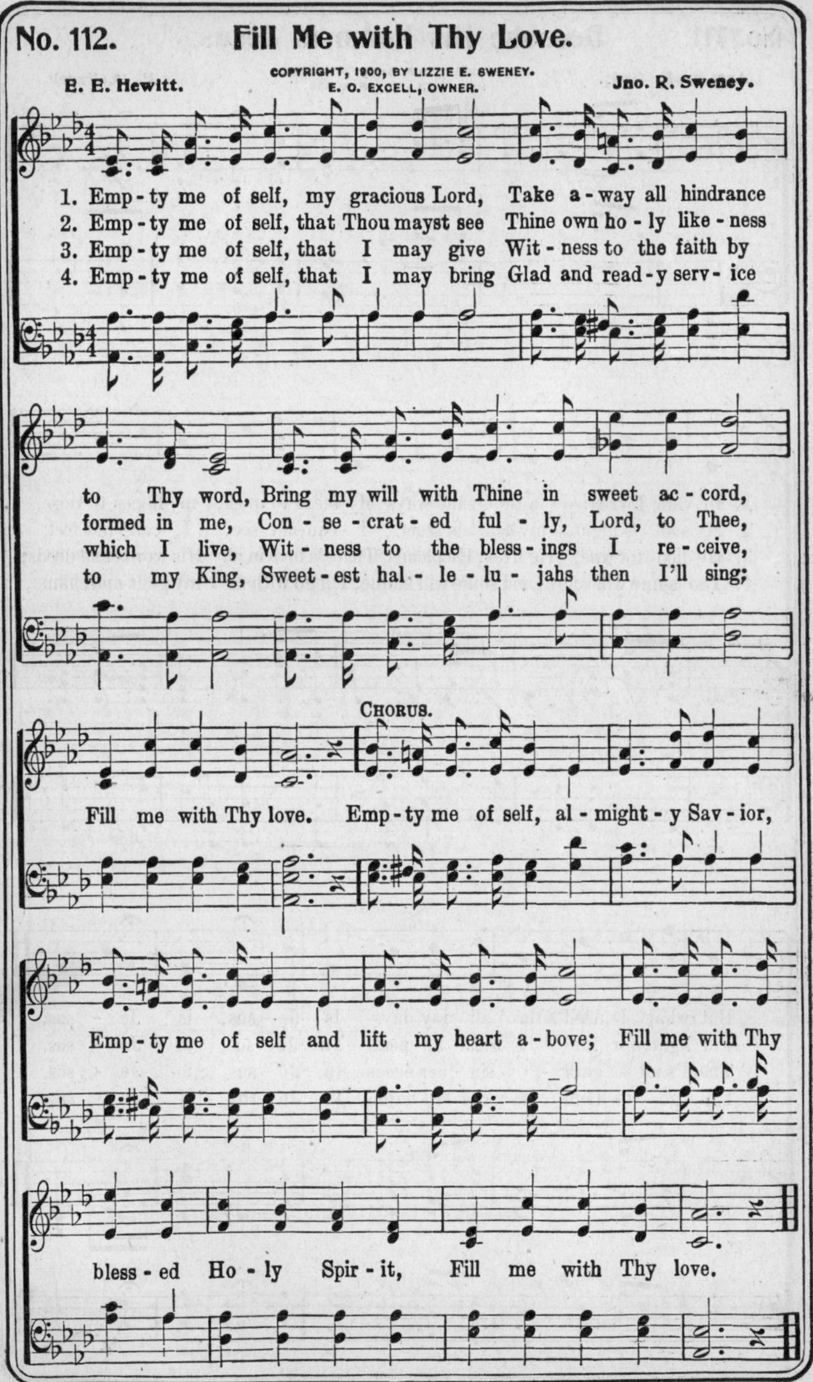
No. 112. Fill Me with Thy Love.
COPYRIGHT, 1900, BY LIZZIE E. SWENEY.
E. O. EXCELL, OWNER.
E. E. Hewitt.
Jno. R. Sweney.
1. Emp-ty me of self, my gracious Lord, Take a-way all hindrance to Thy word, Bring my will with Thine in sweet ac-cord,
2. Emp-ty me of self, that Thou mayst see Thine own ho-ly like-ness formed in me, Con-se-crat-ed ful-ly, Lord, to Thee,
3. Emp-ty me of self, that I may give Wit-ness to the faith by which I live, Wit-ness to the bless-ings I re-ceive,
4. Emp-ty me of self, that I may bring Glad and read-y serv-ice to my King, Sweet-est hal-le-lu-jahs then I'll sing;
Fill me with Thy love.
CHORUS.
Emp-ty me of self, al-might-y Sav-ior, Emp-ty me of self and lift my heart a-bove; Fill me with Thy bless-ed Ho-ly Spir-it, Fill me with Thy love.

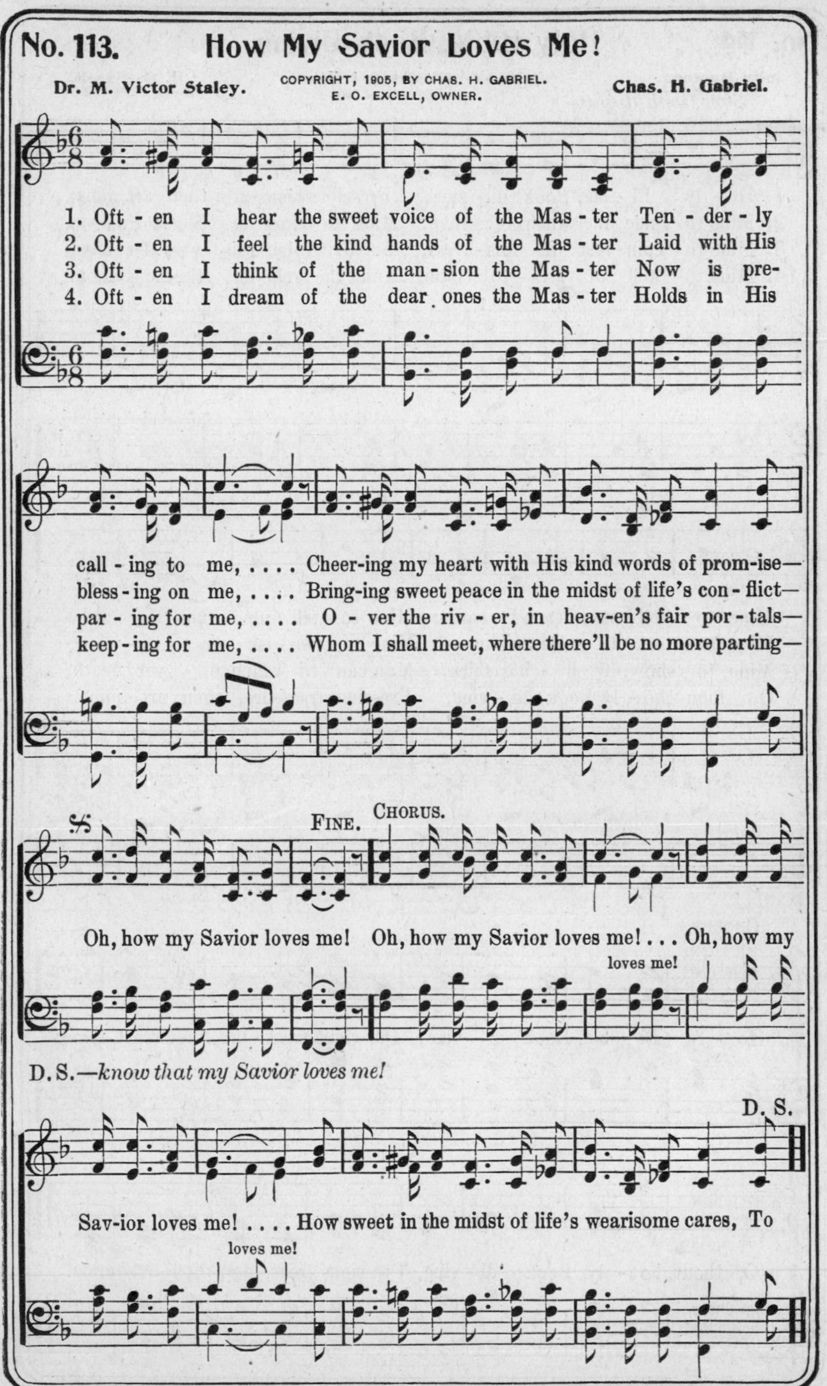
No. 113. How My Savior Loves Me!
Dr. M. Victor Staley.
COPYRIGHT, 1905, BY CHAS. H. GABRIEL.
E. O. EXCELL, OWNER.
Chas. H. Gabriel.
1. Oft - en I hear the sweet voice of the Mas - ter Ten - der - ly
2. Oft - en I feel the kind hands of the Mas - ter Laid with His
3. Oft - en I think of the man - sion the Mas - ter Now is pre-
4. Oft - en I dream of the dear ones the Mas - ter Holds in His
call - ing to me, ... Cheer-ing my heart with His kind words of prom-ise—
bless - ing on me, ... Bring-ing sweet peace in the midst of life's con - flict—
par - ing for me, ... O - ver the riv - er, in heav-en's fair por - tals—
keep - ing for me, ... Whom I shall meet, where there'll be no more parting—
FINE.
CHORUS.
Oh, how my Savior loves me! Oh, how my Savior loves me! . . . Oh, how my
loves me!
D. S.—know that my Savior loves me!
D. S.
Sav-ior loves me! . . . . How sweet in the midst of life's wearisome cares, To
loves me!

No. 114. Holy Bible, Book Divine.
John Burton.
COPYRIGHT 1900, BY E. O. EXCELL.
E. O. Excell.
Slow, with dignity.
1. Ho - ly Bi - ble, Book di - vine, Pre-cious treas-ure, thou art mine:
2. Mine to chide me when I rove; Mine to show a Sav-ior's love;
3. Mine to com-fort in dis-tress, Suf-f'ring in this wil - der - ness;
4. Mine to tell of joys to come, And the reb - el sin-ner's doom:
rit.
Mine to tell me whence I came; Mine to tell me what I am;
Mine thou art to guide and guard; Mine to pun - ish or re - ward;
Mine to show, by liv - ing faith, Man can tri - umph o - ver death;
O thou ho - ly Book di - vine, Pre-cious treas-ure, thou art mine.
CHORUS.
Ho - ly Bi - ble, Book di - vine, Pre-cious treas - ure, thou art mine;
O thou ho - ly Book di - vine, Pre-cious treas - ure, thou art mine!

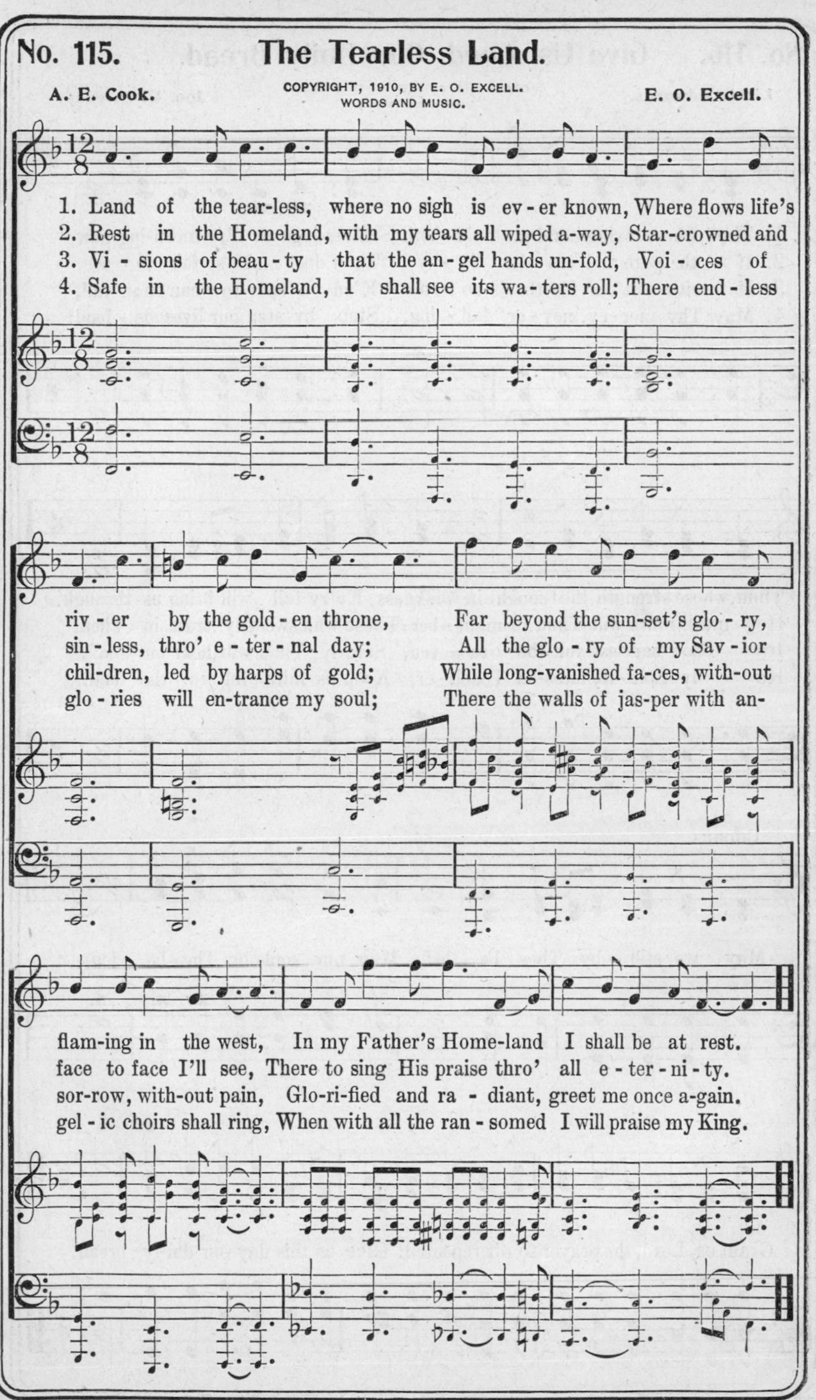
No. 115. The Tearless Land.
A. E. Cook.
COPYRIGHT, 1910, BY E. O. EXCELL.
WORDS AND MUSIC.
E. O. Excell.
1. Land of the tear-less, where no sigh is ev - er known, Where flows life's
2. Rest in the Homeland, with my tears all wiped a-way, Star-crowned and
3. Vi - sions of beau - ty that the an - gel hands un-fold, Voi - ces of
4. Safe in the Homeland, I shall see its wa - ters roll; There end - less
riv - er by the gold - en throne, Far beyond the sun-set's glo - ry,
sin - less, thro' e - ter - nal day; All the glo - ry of my Sav - ior
chil-dren, led by harps of gold; While long-vanished fa-ces, with-out
glo - ries will en-trance my soul; There the walls of jas-per with an-
flam-ing in the west, In my Father's Home-land I shall be at rest.
face to face I'll see, There to sing His praise thro' all e - ter - ni - ty.
sor-row, with-out pain, Glo-ri-fied and ra - diant, greet me once a-gain.
gel - ic choirs shall ring, When with all the ran - somed I will praise my King.

No. 116. Give Us, Lord, Our Daily Bread.
Lizzie Edwards.
COPYRIGHT, 1910, BY E. O. EXCELL. WORDS AND MUSIC.
Jno. R. Sweney.
1. Thou, whose loving hand pro-vid-eth Bless-ings ev-'ry morn-ing new,
2. If the pure and ten-der lil-y Thou dost make so fair to see,
3. If with-out our Fa-ther's no-tice E'en a spar-row can-not fall,
4. May Thy mer-cy, nev-er fail-ing, Step by step our lives de-fend;
Thou, whose strength, tho' sought in weakness, Ev'ry toil will bring us through:
How much more wilt Thou re-mem-ber Those who sweet-ly trust in Thee!
If Thou car-est for the ra-ven, Sure-ly Thou wilt hear our call.
Ho-ly Spir-it, bless-ed Teach-er, Keep us faith-ful to the end.
CHORUS.
May we still by Thee be led, May our souls by Thee be fed;
Grant us, Lord, the prayer so oft repeated: Give us this day our dai-ly bread.

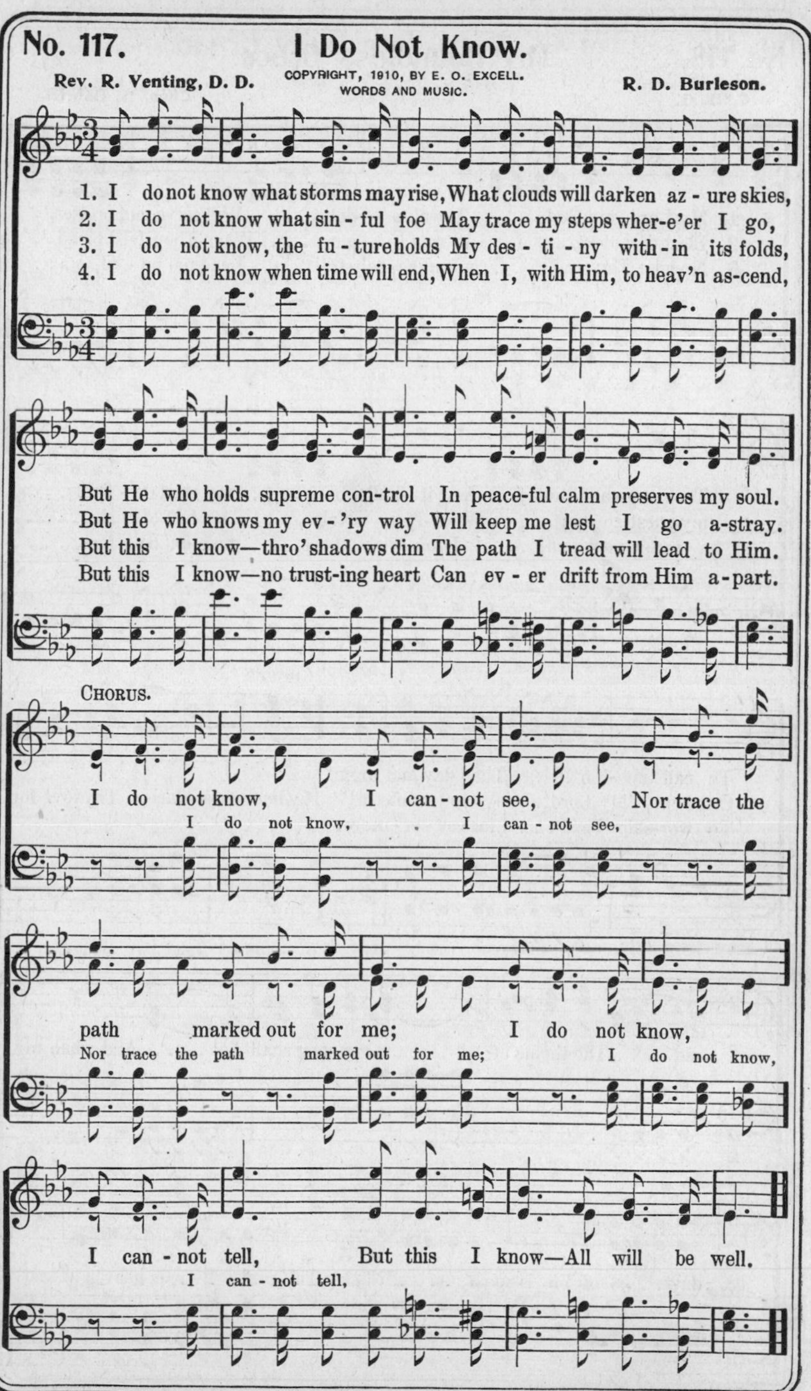
No. 117. I Do Not Know.
Rev. R. Venting, D. D.
COPYRIGHT, 1910, BY E. O. EXCELL. WORDS AND MUSIC.
R. D. Burleson.
1. I do not know what storms may rise, What clouds will darken az - ure skies,
2. I do not know what sin - ful foe May trace my steps wher-e'er I go,
3. I do not know, the fu - ture holds My des - ti - ny with - in its folds,
4. I do not know when time will end, When I, with Him, to heav'n as-cend,
But He who holds supreme con-trol In peace-ful calm preserves my soul.
But He who knows my ev - 'ry way Will keep me lest I go a-stray.
But this I know—thro' shadows dim The path I tread will lead to Him.
But this I know—no trust-ing heart Can ev - er drift from Him a-part.
CHORUS.
I do not know, I can - not see, Nor trace the
I do not know, I can - not see,
path marked out for me; I do not know,
Nor trace the path marked out for me; I do not know,
I can - not tell, But this I know—All will be well.
I can - not tell,

No. 118.
Thy Boundless Grace.
COPYRIGHT, 1910, BY E. O. EXCELL.
WORDS AND MUSIC.
C. H. G.
Chas. H. Gabriel.
1. My Lord, my God, . . . I will a - dore, ... Will serve and praise . . Thee more and more, . . And it shall be . . . . . my chief de - light . . . . To call up - on . . . . Thee day and night.
2. Blest day of grace . . . it was to me . . . . .When Thou didst plead . . my guest to be; . . . . . When I, so false, . . . so full of sin, ... Cried out, "My Lord, . . my God, come in!"
3. Now let Thy will, . . . not mine, con-trol; . . . . Lead me un - til, ... a ran-somed soul, . . . I join with those . . . gone on be - fore, ... To wor-ship Thee . . . for - ev - er - more.
CHORUS.
Thy boundless grace, Thy love for me . . . . The theme of all . . . . . my song shall be! . . . . And when my day . . . . of life is past, ... I'll sing Thy praise . . . in heav'n at last.

No. 119.
Happy Song-Land.
C. A. H.
COPYRIGHT, 1903, BY E. O. EXCELL.
C. A. Havens.
Melody prominent.
1. Song-land fair, O - ver there, Free from sorrow, free from care; Angels bright,
2. Toils are o'er, Near the shore, Near the blessed ev - er - more; Hand in hand,
Robed in white, Dwell in peace and pure de - light; By and by, Shadows nigh,
Near the strand, Near the shining Sum - mer Land; Where we go, Fountains flow,
Rest - ing comes in home on high; We shall join in prais - es there, In that hap - py
In the noontide's sunny glow; Joyful ransomed souls are there, In that happy
D. S.—We shall join in praises there, In that happy
FINE.
REFRAIN.
rit.
Song-land fair. Ho - ly, hap - py Song-land fair, Radiant mansions 'wait us there;
Song-land fair.
D. S.
By and by, Shad - ows nigh, Rest - ing comes in home on high;

No. 120. His Love for Me.
F. M. Eastwood.
WORDS AND MUSIC COPYRIGHT, 1908, BY E. O. EXCELL.
INTERNATIONAL COPYRIGHT SECURED.
Fred H. Byshe.
1. You have heard of the sto - ry of Je - - sus— Of His grace flow-ing bound-less and free, But there's no one can tell you the ful - ness Of His won - der - ful love for me. . . .
2. You have heard how He blessed lit - tle chil - - dren: "Come, all ye that are wear - y," said He; So I came, and He gave me the bless - ing Of His won - der - ful love for me. . . .
3. You have heard how the blind, as they sought Him, Found their sight when He bade them to see; So my sin - blind - ed eyes have been o - pened By His won - der - ful love for me. . . .
4. You have heard how He spake to the tem - - pest—How the words "Peace, be still!" calmed the sea; So my soul found the peace that it longed for In His won - der - ful love for me. . . .
CHORUS.
His love for me, His love for me! High as the heav'n, deep as the sea; Love that will last thro' e - ter - ni - ty, His love for me, His love for me!

No. 121. From Every Stormy Wind.
H. Stowell.
S. Wilder.
Solo Obligato.
1. From ev - 'ry storm - y wind that blows, From ev - 'ry
2. There is a place where Je - sus sheds The oil of
Accompanying voices pp.
3. There is a scene where spir - its blend, Where friend holds
4. Oh, let my hand for - get her skill, My tongue be
swell - ing tide of woes, There is a calm, a
glad - ness on our heads; A place than all be-
fel - low - ship with friend; Tho' sun - dered far, by
si - lent, cold, and still, This bound - ing heart for-
sure re - treat: 'T is found be - neath the mer - cy-seat.
sides more sweet: It is the blood - bought mer - cy-seat.
faith they meet A - round one com - mon mer - cy - seat.
get to beat, If I for - get the mer - cy - seat!

No. 122. More Like the Master.
COPYRIGHT, 1906, BY CHAS. H. GABRIEL.
E. O. EXCELL, OWNER.
C. H. G.
Chas. H. Gabriel.
1. More like the Mas - ter I would ev - er be, More of His meek-ness, more hu - mil - i - ty; More zeal to la - bor, more cour-age to be true, More con - se - cra - tion for work He bids me do.
2. More like the Mas - ter is my dai - ly pray'r, More strength to car - ry cross - es I must bear; More earn - est ef - fort to bring His king - dom in, More of His Spir - it, the wan - der - er to win.
3. More like the Mas - ter I would live and grow, More of His love to oth - ers I would show; More self - de - ni - al, like His in Gal - i - lee, More like the Mas - ter I long to ev - er be.
CHORUS.
Take Thou my heart . . . . . . I would be Thine a - lone; . . . . . Take Thou my heart . . . . and make it all Thine own; . . . Purge me from sin, ... O
Take my heart, O take my heart, I would be Thine a - lone; Take my heart, O take my heart and make it all Thine own; Purge Thou me from ev - 'ry sin, O

More Like the Master.
Lord I now im-plore, Wash me and keep me Thine for-ev-er-more.
Lord I now implore Wash and keep me Thine forevermore.
No. 123. He is My Portion Forever.
COPYRIGHT, 1900 BY LIZZIE E. SWENEY.
E. O EXCELL, OWNER.
Lizzie Edwards.
Jno. R. Sweney.
1. All, all to Je-sus, I con-se-crate a-new, He is my por-tion for-ev-er;
2. All, all to Je-sus, my trusting heart can say, He is my por-tion for-ev-er;
3. Tho' He may try me this blessed truth I know, He is my por-tion for-ev-er;
4. All, all to Je-sus, I cheer-ful-ly re-sign, He is my por-tion for-ev-er;
FINE.
On-ly His glo-ry hence-forth will I pur-sue, He is my por-tion for-ev-er.
Led by His mer-cy I'm walk-ing ev-'ry day, He is my por-tion for-ev-er.
He will not leave me, His promise tells me so, He is my por-tion for-ev-er.
I have the wit-ness that He, my Lord, is mine, He is my por-tion for-ev-er.
D.S.-Mine is a treasure no moth nor rust de-stroys; Je-sus, my portion for-ev-er.
REFRAIN.
D. S.
Take, take the world with all its gilded toys, Take, take the world, I covet not its joys,

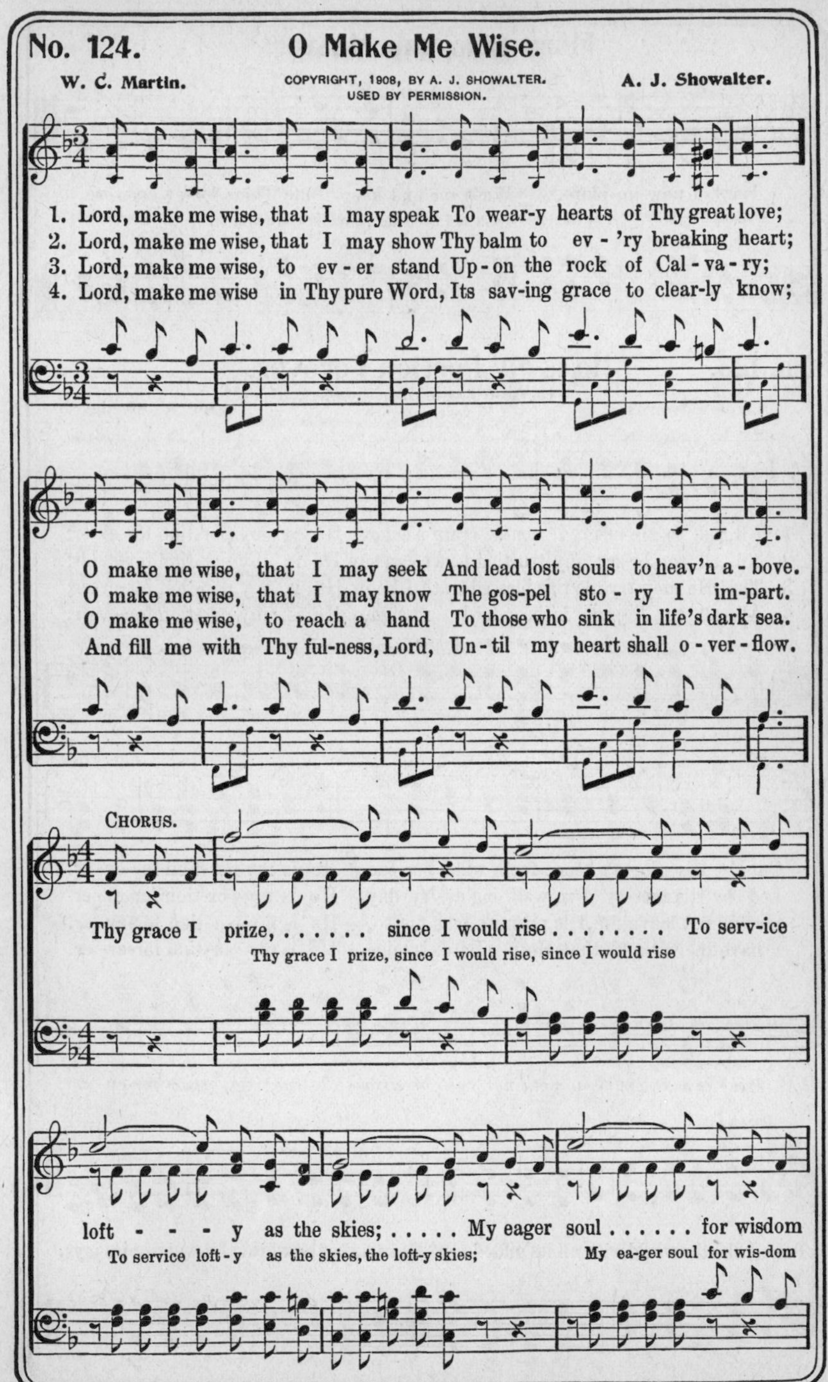
No. 124. O Make Me Wise.
W. C. Martin.
COPYRIGHT, 1908, BY A. J. SHOWALTER. USED BY PERMISSION.
A. J. Showalter.
1. Lord, make me wise, that I may speak To wear-y hearts of Thy great love;
2. Lord, make me wise, that I may show Thy balm to ev - 'ry breaking heart;
3. Lord, make me wise, to ev - er stand Up-on the rock of Cal - va - ry;
4. Lord, make me wise in Thy pure Word, Its sav-ing grace to clear-ly know;
O make me wise, that I may seek And lead lost souls to heav'n a - bove.
O make me wise, that I may know The gos-pel sto - ry I im-part.
O make me wise, to reach a hand To those who sink in life's dark sea.
And fill me with Thy ful-ness, Lord, Un-til my heart shall o - ver - flow.
CHORUS.
Thy grace I prize, ... since I would rise . . . . To serv-ice
Thy grace I prize, since I would rise, since I would rise
loft - - - y as the skies; . . . . . My eager soul . . . . . . for wisdom
To service loft - y as the skies, the loft-y skies; My ea-ger soul for wis-dom

O Make Me Wise.
rit.
cries, ... O make me wise, ... O make me wise. . . . .
cries, for wisdom cries, O make me wise, O make me wise, O make me wise.
No. 125.
Anywhere With Jesus.
COPYRIGHT, 1903, BY E. O. EXCELL. WORDS AND MUSIC.
INTERNATIONAL COPYRIGHT SECURED.
John R. Clements.
E. O. Excell.
1. I'll go an - y-where, my Sav - ior, If Thou wilt make it clear; I will
2. I'll do an - y-thing, my Sav - ior, That hon-or brings to Thee; I will
3. I'll be an - y-thing, my Sav - ior, In sta-tion high or low; I will
4. I'll hold ev'ry-thing, my Sav - ior, A sa-cred trust of Thine; And the
CHORUS.
tell sal - va-tion's sto - ry To lost ones far and near.
fol - low close Thy lead - ing, Wher-e'er it tak - eth me. An - y-where, my
toil, or wait, or suf - fer, If Thou dost will it so.
tal - ents to me giv - en, I'll count them not as mine.
Sav-ior, Anywhere with Thee, Anywhere and ev'rywhere, As Thou leadest me.

No. 126. The Joyful Song.
Fanny J. Crosby.
COPYRIGHT, 1894, BY JNO. R. SWENEY.
USED BY PERMISSION OF L. E. SWENEY, EXECUTRIX.
Adam Geibel.
1. Be - hold! a roy - al ar - my, With ban - ner, sword and shield, Are
2. And now the foe, ad - vanc - ing, That val - iant host as - sails, And
3. Oh, when the war is end - ed, When strife and con - flict cease, When
march-ing forth to con-quer, On life's great bat-tle-field; Its ranks are filled with
yet they nev-er fal - ter, Their courage nev - er fails; Their Leader calls, "Be
all are safe-ly gath-ered With-in the vale of peace, Be - fore the King e-
sol - diers, U - ni-ted, bold and strong, Who fol-lowed their Com-mand-er,
faith-ful!" They pass the word a - long, They see His sig - nal flash - ing,
ter - nal, That vast and might-y throng Shall praise His name for - ev - er,
And sing their joy - ful song.
And shout the joy - ful song.
And this shall be their song:
CHORUS. In unison.
Vic - to - ry, vic - to - ry, Thro' Him that re-
deemed us! Vic - to - ry, vic - to - ry, Thro' Je - sus Christ our Lord!

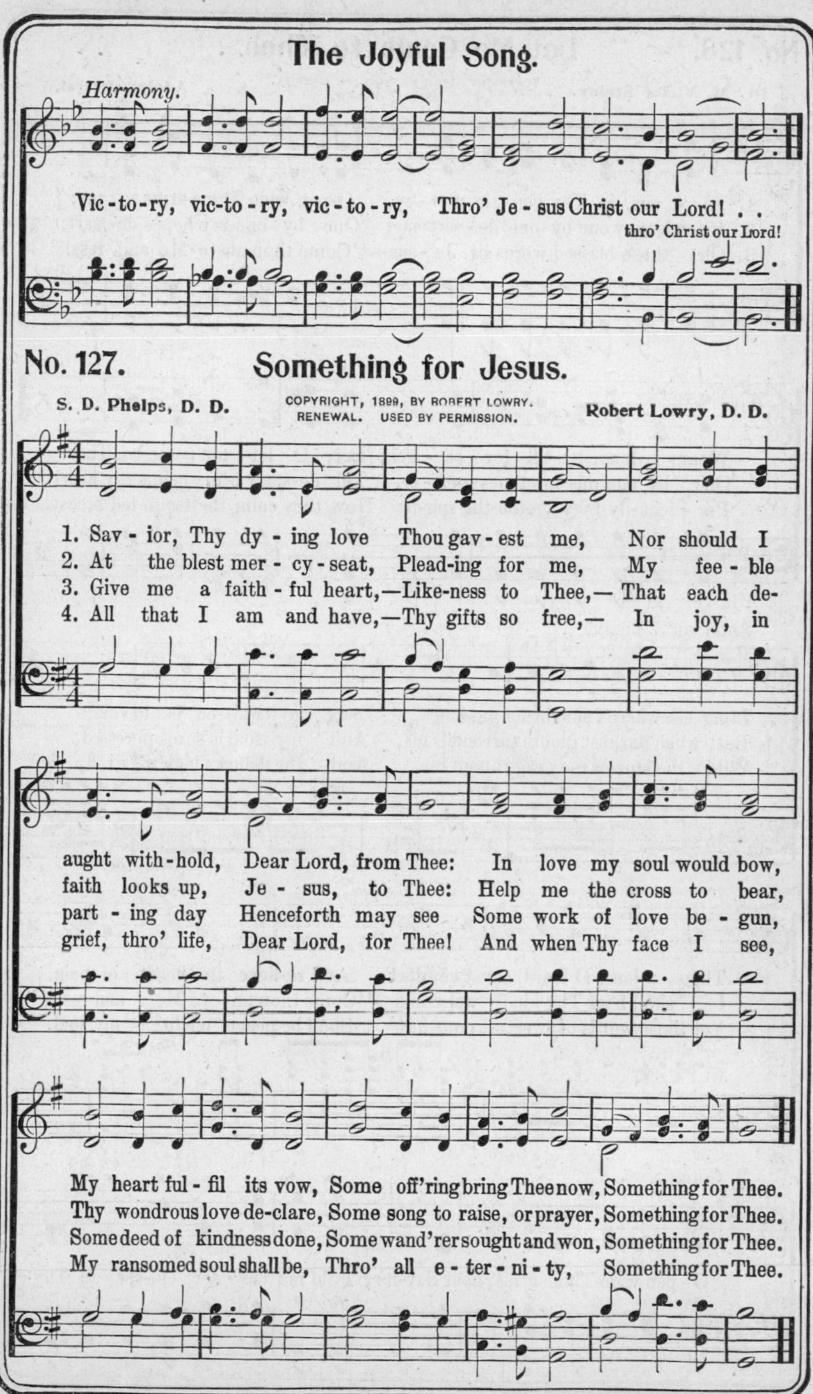
The Joyful Song.
Harmony.
Vic-to-ry, vic-to-ry, vic-to-ry, Thro' Je-sus Christ our Lord! . .
thro' Christ our Lord!
No. 127.
Something for Jesus.
S. D. Phelps, D. D.
COPYRIGHT, 1899, BY ROBERT LOWRY. RENEWAL. USED BY PERMISSION.
Robert Lowry, D. D.
1. Sav-ior, Thy dy-ing love Thou gav-est me, Nor should I aught with-hold, Dear Lord, from Thee: In love my soul would bow, My heart ful-fil its vow, Some off'ring bring Thee now, Something for Thee.
2. At the blest mer-cy-seat, Plead-ing for me, My fee-ble faith looks up, Je-sus, to Thee: Help me the cross to bear, Thy wondrous love de-clare, Some song to raise, or prayer, Something for Thee.
3. Give me a faith-ful heart,—Like-ness to Thee,—That each de-part-ing day Henceforth may see Some work of love be-gun, Some deed of kindness done, Some wand'rer sought and won, Something for Thee.
4. All that I am and have,—Thy gifts so free,—In joy, in grief, thro' life, Dear Lord, for Thee! And when Thy face I see, My ransomed soul shall be, Thro' all e-ter-ni-ty, Something for Thee.

No. 128. Let Me Come to Thee.
Dr. M. Victor Staley.
COPYRIGHT, 1902, BY CHAS. H. GABRIEL.
E. O. EXCELL, OWNER.
Adolph Jesreal.
1. Je - sus, in Thy gen - tle mer - cy, O - pen wide Thine arms to me;
2. Friends may one by one de - sert me; One by one my hopes de - part;
3. Oh, those blessed words of Je - sus—"Come thou un - to Me and rest!"
Wear - y, lone, by all for - sa - ken, Let, O let me come to Thee!
One by one mis - for - tunes gath - er, Till de - spair o'erwhelms my heart:
Per - fect - ly they soothe the spir - it; How they calm the troub - led breast!
Solo or Unison.
Long elsewhere I sought for guidance, Long have wait - ed, but in vain;
But, when darkest gloom surrounds me, And my soul is sore oppressed,
Wild the storms may rage about me, And the billows high may roll,
R. H.
Thou a - lone, O Lord, canst comfort And re - lieve this heart of pain.
I shall hear Thy kindly wel - come—"Come thou un - to Me and rest!"
Yet those words of sweetest com - fort Shall be peace un - to my soul.
Chorus.
O - pen wide Thine arms, dear Sav - ior, Fold me clo - ser, clo - ser to Thy

Let Me Come to Thee.
heart; . . . . . E'en when weary and discouraged, Bid me not from Thee depart.
closer to Thy heart;
No. 129. My Father Knows My Need.
Mrs. W. H. Keesler.
COPYRIGHT, 1906, BY CHAS. H. GABRIEL.
E. O. EXCELL, OWNER.
Chas. H. Gabriel.
1. My Fa-ther knows my need, And I can trust His love: He may not
2. My Fa-ther knows my need, He will sup-ply it all; He hears His
3. My Fa-ther knows my need, His love no tongue can tell; And if some-
4. My Fa-ther knows my need, I fear no dread a-larms, For round a-
al-ways deign to give me The things which most I crave.
chil-dren when they cry, and He answers when they call.
times He does de-ny me, I know for me 'tis well.
bout and un-der-neath me Are Ev-er-last-ing Arms.
CHORUS.
My Fa-ther
knows, ... O yes, He knows, . . And with my soul 'tis well.
My Fa-ther knows, He knows, And with my soul 'tis well.

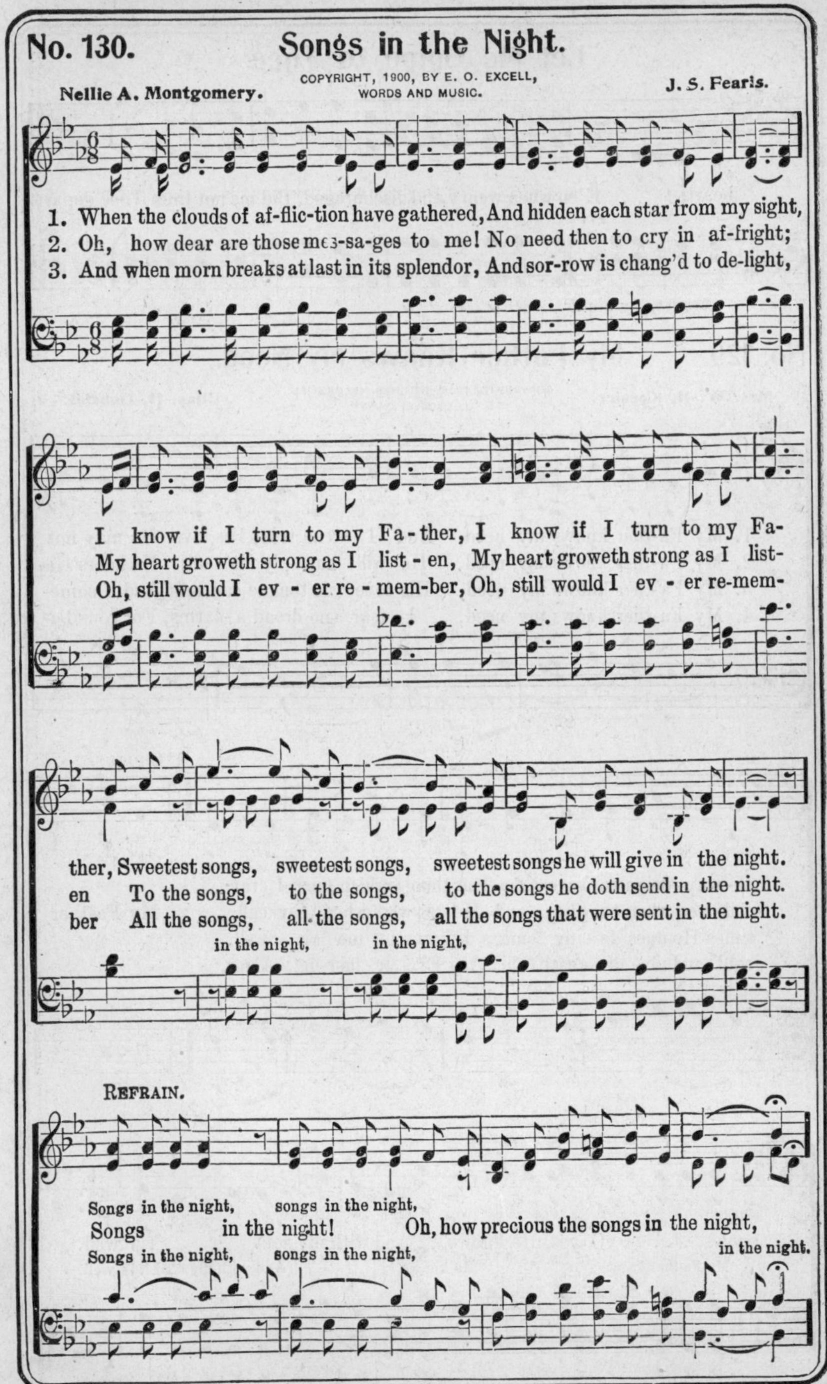
No. 130. Songs in the Night.
COPYRIGHT, 1900, BY E. O. EXCELL, WORDS AND MUSIC.
Nellie A. Montgomery.
J. S. Fearis.
1. When the clouds of af-flic-tion have gathered, And hidden each star from my sight,
2. Oh, how dear are those mes-sa-ges to me! No need then to cry in af-fright;
3. And when morn breaks at last in its splendor, And sor-row is chang'd to de-light,
I know if I turn to my Fa-ther, I know if I turn to my Fa-
My heart groweth strong as I list-en, My heart groweth strong as I list-
Oh, still would I ev-er re-mem-ber, Oh, still would I ev-er re-mem-
ther, Sweetest songs, sweetest songs, sweetest songs he will give in the night.
en To the songs, to the songs, to the songs he doth send in the night.
ber All the songs, all the songs, all the songs that were sent in the night.
in the night, in the night,
REFRAIN.
Songs in the night, songs in the night,
Songs in the night! Oh, how precious the songs in the night,
Songs in the night, songs in the night,
in the night.

Songs in the Night.
My heart...... run-neth o-ver, For the songs He doth send in the night.
My heart run-neth o - ver, runs o - ver,
No. 131. I Have Trusted.
Fanny J. Crosby.
COPYRIGHT, 1910, BY E. O. EXCELL.
WORDS AND MUSIC.
Jno. R. Sweney.
1. I have trust-ed my Re-deem-er, And my faith is trust-ing yet;
2. I have trust-ed my Re-deem-er When all oth-er re-fuge failed;
3. I have trust-ed my Re-deem-er, Hal-le-lu-jah to His name!
4. I have trust-ed my Re-deem-er, I will trust Him till I die,
FINE.
He has res-cued me from dan-gers That my heart will ne'er for-get.
I have plead-ed His pro-tec-tion, And thro' grace I have prevailed.
He has taught me how to trust Him, And His prom-ise how to claim.
And I'll shout and give Him glo-ry In His king-dom by and by.
D.S.—And to sing His lov-ing-kind-ness Shall my ev-'ry power em-ploy.
CHORUS.
D. S.
I have trust-ed Him in sor-row, I have trust-ed Him in joy;

No. 132.
Like As a Father.
COPYRIGHT, 1910, BY E. O. EXCELL.
WORDS AND MUSIC.
Helen L. Dungan.
J. M. Dungan.
1. O the love of the Fa-ther is ten-der and true, And will give ev-'ry
2. Yes, He suf-fered the sin-less on Cal-va-ry's tree, To pro-vide life e-
3. You should give to Him glad-ly your will and your heart, Walking close by His
bless-ing that's promised to you; Gives you par-don and peace thro' His
ter-nal for you and for me: O re-ject not His of-f'ring nor
side, and from Him nev-er part; He will guide you and bless you, what-
Son cru-ci-fied,—That your sins be for-giv-en He suf-fered and died.
turn Him a-side; 'T was for you that He suffered—yes, suf-fered and died.
ev-er be-tide, For He suf-fered to save you—yes, suf-fered and died.
CHORUS.
Like as a fa-ther pit-i-eth his chil-dren, How sweet the
com-fort comes when eyes with tears are dim; Like as a fa-ther

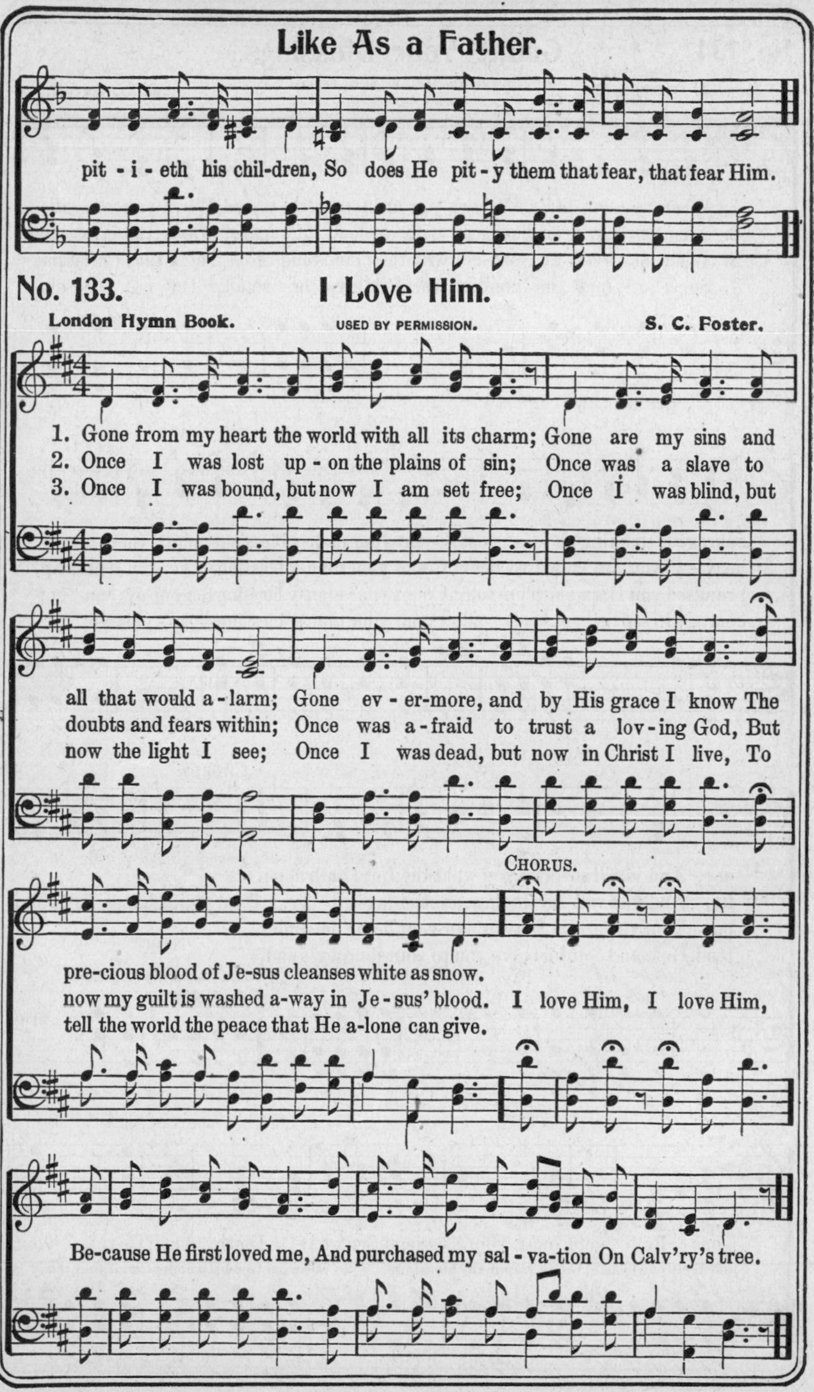

Like As a Father.
pit - i - eth his chil-dren, So does He pit - y them that fear, that fear Him.
No. 133.
I Love Him.
London Hymn Book.
USED BY PERMISSION.
S. C. Foster.
1. Gone from my heart the world with all its charm; Gone are my sins and
2. Once I was lost up - on the plains of sin; Once was a slave to
3. Once I was bound, but now I am set free; Once I was blind, but
all that would a - larm; Gone ev - er-more, and by His grace I know The
doubts and fears within; Once was a - fraid to trust a lov - ing God, But
now the light I see; Once I was dead, but now in Christ I live, To
CHORUS.
pre-cious blood of Je-sus cleanses white as snow.
now my guilt is washed a-way in Je - sus' blood. I love Him, I love Him,
tell the world the peace that He a-lone can give.
Be-cause He first loved me, And purchased my sal - va-tion On Calv'ry's tree.

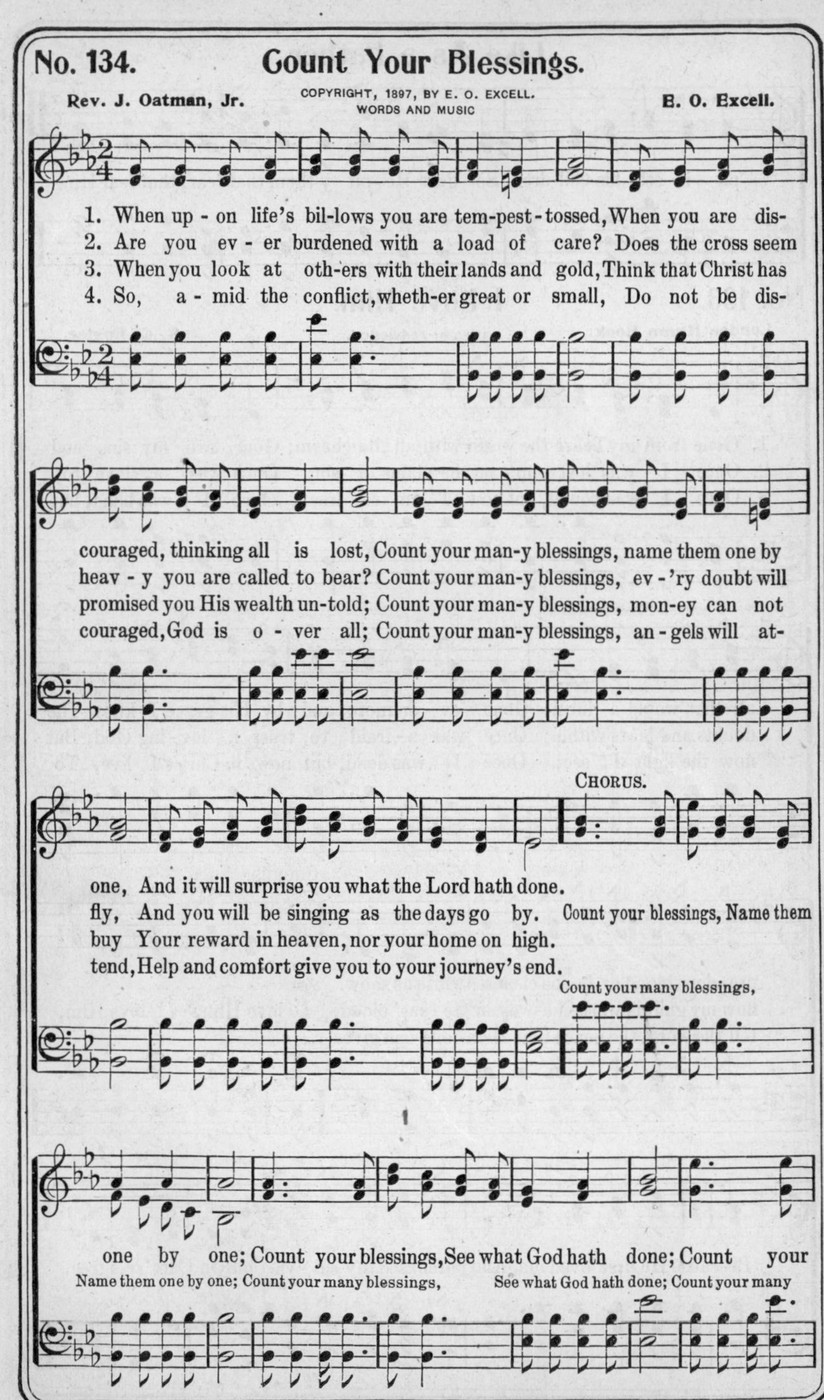
No. 134. Count Your Blessings.
Rev. J. Oatman, Jr.
COPYRIGHT, 1897, BY E. O. EXCELL.
WORDS AND MUSIC
E. O. Excell.
1. When up - on life's bil-lows you are tem-pest-tossed, When you are dis-
2. Are you ev - er burdened with a load of care? Does the cross seem
3. When you look at oth-ers with their lands and gold, Think that Christ has
4. So, a - mid the conflict, wheth-er great or small, Do not be discouraged, thinking all is lost, Count your man-y blessings, name them one by
heav - y you are called to bear? Count your man-y blessings, ev - 'ry doubt will
promised you His wealth un-told; Count your man-y blessings, mon-ey can not
couraged, God is o - ver all; Count your man-y blessings, an - gels will at-
CHORUS.
one, And it will surprise you what the Lord hath done.
fly, And you will be singing as the days go by.
buy Your reward in heaven, nor your home on high.
tend, Help and comfort give you to your journey's end.
Count your blessings, Name them
Count your many blessings,
one by one; Count your blessings, See what God hath done; Count your
Name them one by one; Count your many blessings, See what God hath done; Count your many

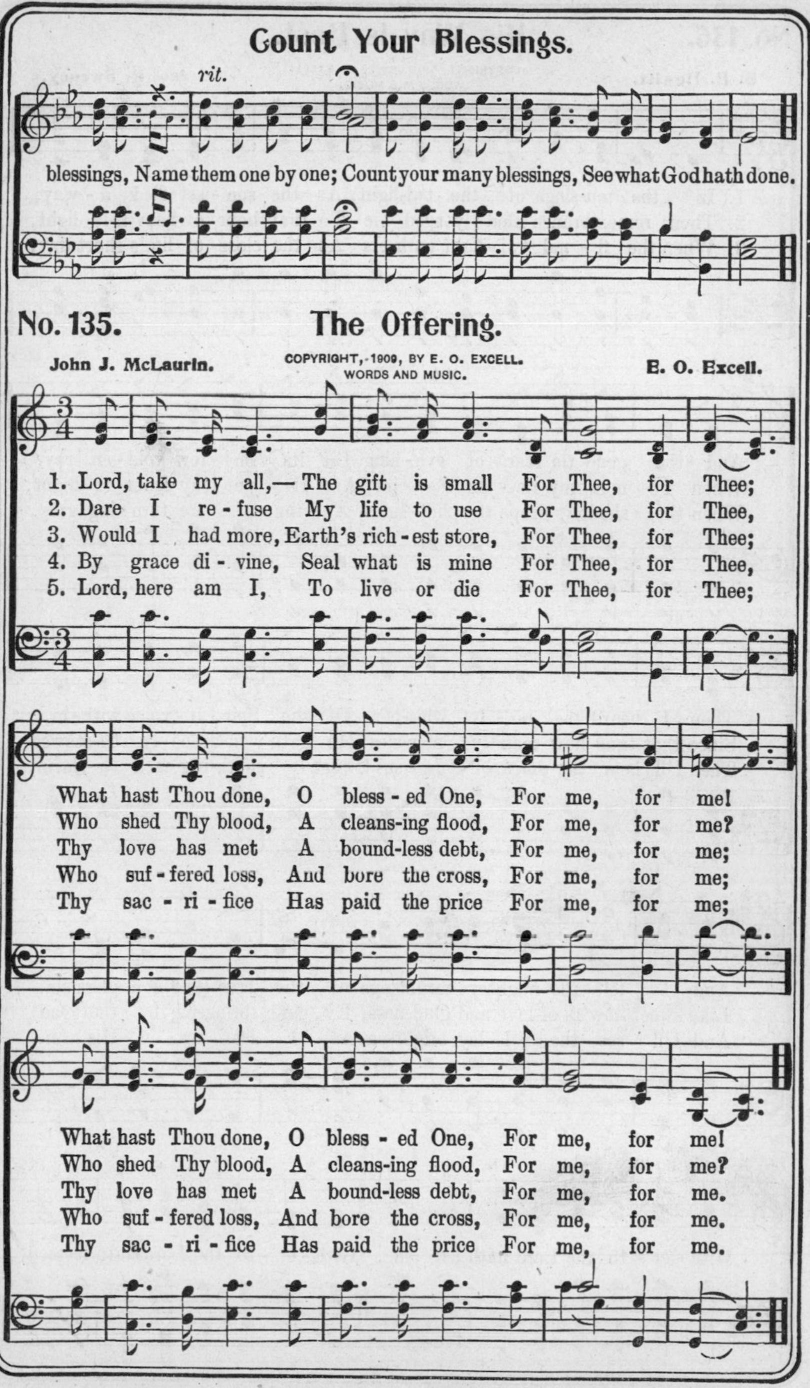

Count Your Blessings.
rit.
blessings, Name them one by one; Count your many blessings, See what God hath done.
No. 135.
The Offering.
John J. McLaurin.
COPYRIGHT, 1909, BY E. O. EXCELL.
WORDS AND MUSIC.
E. O. Excell.
1. Lord, take my all,— The gift is small For Thee, for Thee;
2. Dare I re - fuse My life to use For Thee, for Thee,
3. Would I had more, Earth's rich - est store, For Thee, for Thee;
4. By grace di - vine, Seal what is mine For Thee, for Thee,
5. Lord, here am I, To live or die For Thee, for Thee;
What hast Thou done, O bless - ed One, For me, for me!
Who shed Thy blood, A cleans-ing flood, For me, for me?
Thy love has met A bound-less debt, For me, for me;
Who suf - fered loss, And bore the cross, For me, for me;
Thy sac - ri - fice Has paid the price For me, for me;
What hast Thou done, O bless - ed One, For me, for me!
Who shed Thy blood, A cleans-ing flood, For me, for me?
Thy love has met A bound-less debt, For me, for me.
Who suf - fered loss, And bore the cross, For me, for me.
Thy sac - ri - fice Has paid the price For me, for me.

No. 136. His Way is Best.
COPYRIGHT, 1910, BY E. O EXCELL. WORDS AND MUSIC.
E. E. Hewitt.
Jno. R. Sweney.
1. In the mu-sings of the twi-light, As the sun - set died a - way,
2. Then remembrance kind - ly sped me To that hour of heav'n-ly light,
3. When the fi - nal twi - light gath-ers At the close of life's short day,
And the gen - tle star of eve - ning Lit its mel - low gold - en ray,
When I met my ris - en Sav - ior, And He put my fears to flight;
When the shadows drape the hill - sides, And the skies are turn - ing gray,
Then I heard the ho - ly whis-per Of the Spir - it - voice with - in,
Since that time how man - y mer-cies He hath won-drous - ly be-stowed,
Then I'll hear the voice of Je - sus Sweet-ly sooth-ing each a - larm,
And I felt the might-y throbbings of the love that con-quers sin.
Like sweet flow'rs of love and glad-ness, Ev - er spring-ing by the road'
And I'll see the val - ley bright-en As I lean up - on His arm.
CHORUS.
Hith - er - to the Lord hath led me, Hith - er - to the Lord hath blessed,

His Way is Best.
And I'll trust Him still to lead me, For I know His way is best.
No. 137. Open My Eyes, That I May See.
C. H. S.
COPYRIGHT, 1895, BY CLARA M. SCOTT. OWNED BY THE EVANGELICAL PUBLISHING CO., CHICAGO.
Chas. H. Scott.
1. O-pen my eyes, that I may see Glimpses of truth Thou hast for me;
2. O-pen my ears, that I may hear Voi-ces of truth Thou send-est clear;
3. O-pen my mouth, and let me bear Glad-ly the warm truth ev-'ry-where;
Place in my hands the won-der-ful key That shall un-clasp, and set me free.
And while the wave-notes fall on my ear, Ev-'ry-thing false will dis-ap-pear.
O-pen my heart, and let me pre-pare Love with Thy children thus to share.
Si-lent-ly now I wait for Thee, Read-y, my God, Thy will to see;
O-pen my eyes, ears, heart, il-lum-ine me, Spir-it di-vine!

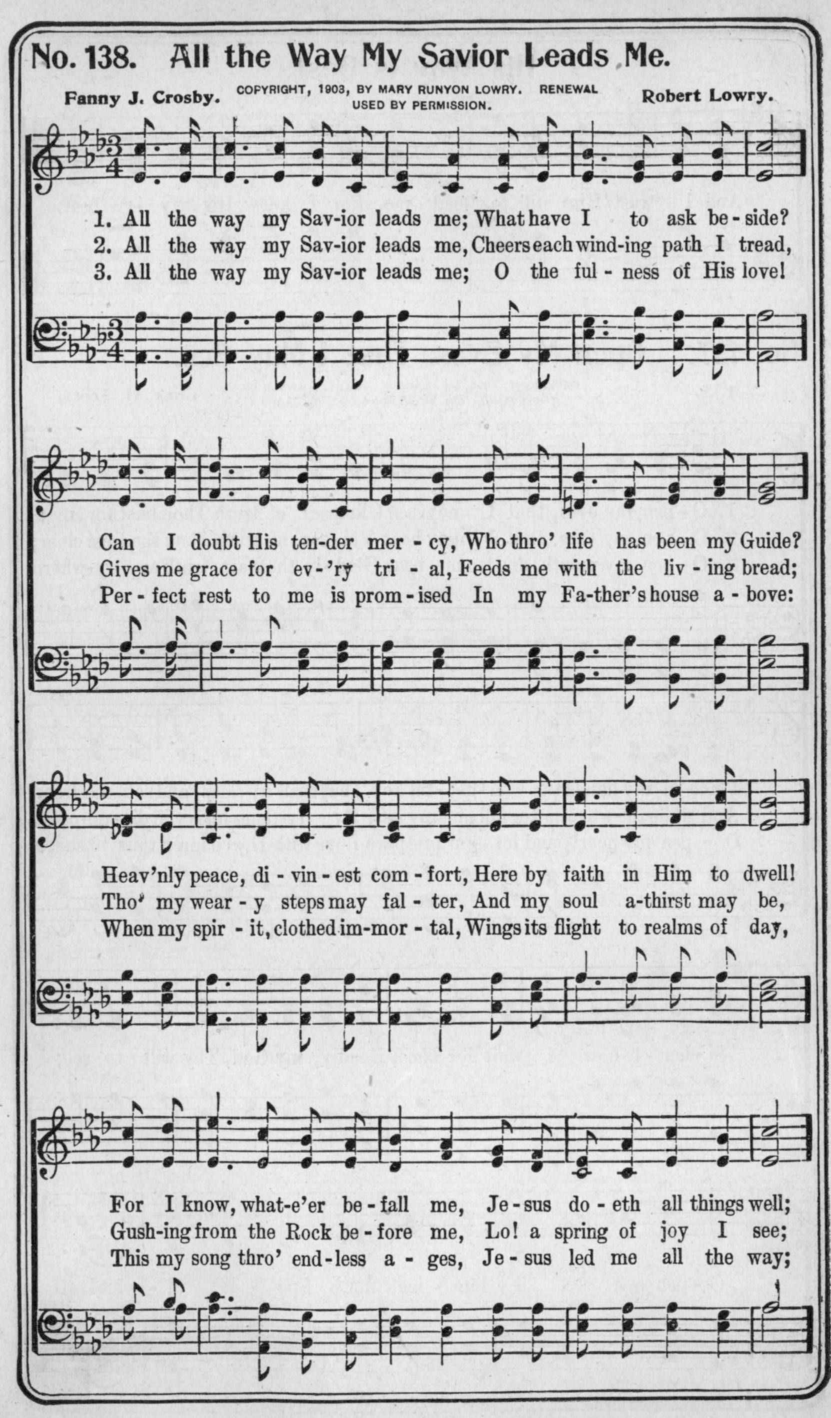
No. 138. All the Way My Savior Leads Me.
Fanny J. Crosby.
COPYRIGHT, 1903, BY MARY RUNYON LOWRY. RENEWAL
USED BY PERMISSION.
Robert Lowry.
1. All the way my Sav-ior leads me; What have I to ask be-side?
2. All the way my Sav-ior leads me, Cheers each wind-ing path I tread,
3. All the way my Sav-ior leads me; O the ful-ness of His love!
Can I doubt His ten-der mer - cy, Who thro' life has been my Guide?
Gives me grace for ev-'ry tri - al, Feeds me with the liv - ing bread;
Per-fect rest to me is prom-ised In my Fa-ther's house a - bove:
Heav'nly peace, di - vin - est com - fort, Here by faith in Him to dwell!
Tho' my wear - y steps may fal - ter, And my soul a-thirst may be,
When my spir - it, clothed im-mor - tal, Wings its flight to realms of day,
For I know, what-e'er be-fall me, Je-sus do-eth all things well;
Gush-ing from the Rock be - fore me, Lo! a spring of joy I see;
This my song thro' end-less a - ges, Je-sus led me all the way;

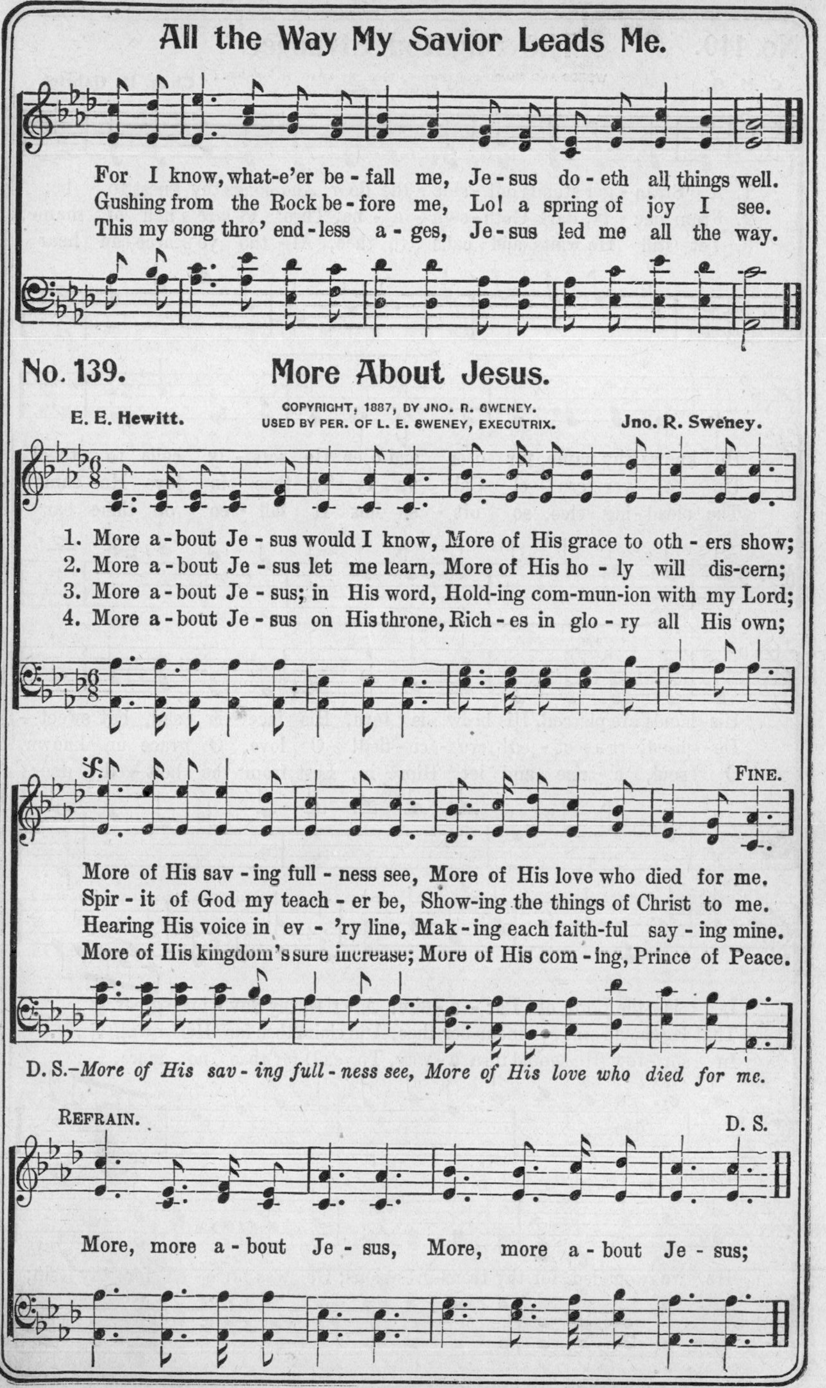
All the Way My Savior Leads Me.
For I know, what-e'er be-fall me, Je-sus do-eth all things well.
Gushing from the Rock be-fore me, Lo! a spring of joy I see.
This my song thro' end-less a-ges, Je-sus led me all the way.
No. 139.
More About Jesus.
E. E. Hewitt.
COPYRIGHT, 1887, BY JNO. R. SWENEY.
USED BY PER. OF L. E. SWENEY, EXECUTRIX.
Jno. R. Sweney.
1. More a-bout Je-sus would I know, More of His grace to oth-ers show;
2. More a-bout Je-sus let me learn, More of His ho-ly will dis-cern;
3. More a-bout Je-sus; in His word, Hold-ing com-mun-ion with my Lord;
4. More a-bout Jesus on His throne, Rich-es in glo-ry all His own;
FINE.
More of His sav-ing full-ness see, More of His love who died for me.
Spir-it of God my teach-er be, Show-ing the things of Christ to me.
Hearing His voice in ev-'ry line, Mak-ing each faith-ful say-ing mine.
More of His kingdom's sure increase; More of His com-ing, Prince of Peace.
D. S.–More of His sav-ing full-ness see, More of His love who died for me.
REFRAIN.
D. S.
More, more a-bout Je-sus, More, more a-bout Je-sus;

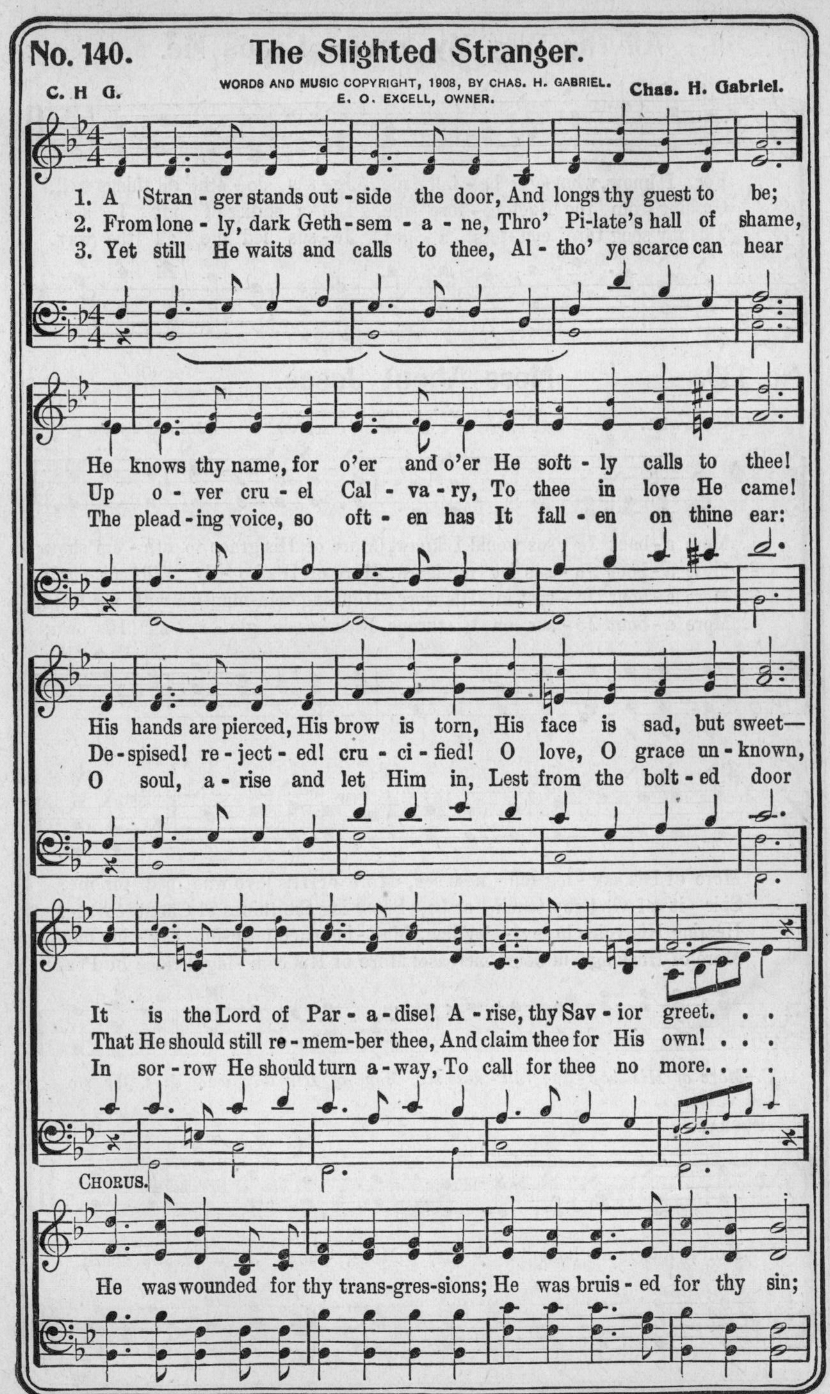
No. 140. The Slighted Stranger.
C. H. G.
WORDS AND MUSIC COPYRIGHT, 1908, BY CHAS. H. GABRIEL. E. O. EXCELL, OWNER.
Chas. H. Gabriel.
1. A Stran - ger stands out - side the door, And longs thy guest to be;
2. From lone - ly, dark Geth - sem - a - ne, Thro' Pi-late's hall of shame,
3. Yet still He waits and calls to thee, Al - tho' ye scarce can hear
He knows thy name, for o'er and o'er He soft - ly calls to thee!
Up o - ver cru - el Cal - va - ry, To thee in love He came!
The plead - ing voice, so oft - en has It fall - en on thine ear:
His hands are pierced, His brow is torn, His face is sad, but sweet—
De - spised! re - ject - ed! cru - ci - fied! O love, O grace un - known,
O soul, a - rise and let Him in, Lest from the bolt - ed door
It is the Lord of Par - a - dise! A - rise, thy Sav - ior greet. . . .
That He should still re - mem - ber thee, And claim thee for His own! . . .
In sor - row He should turn a - way, To call for thee no more. . . .
CHORUS.
He was wounded for thy trans - gres - sions; He was bruis - ed for thy sin;

The Slighted Stranger.
Yet He stands at thy heart's door pleading, Why, O why not let Him in?
No. 141. Jesus My King.
COPYRIGHT, 1909, BY E. O. EXCELL.
WORDS AND MUSIC.
E. E. Hewitt.
Jno. R. Sweney.
1. My life, my all, to Thee I bring, Je-sus, my King, Je-sus, my King!
2. With love en-kin-dled lips I sing, Je-sus, my King, Je-sus, my King!
3. Rich blessing will Thy kingdom bring, Je-sus, my King, Je-sus, my King!
4. What loy-al hom-age can I bring, Je-sus, my King, Je-sus, my King!
I come full par-don to poss-ess, To Thee my King of Right-eous-ness,
A King and priest up-on Thy throne, Make my al-le-giance Thine a-lone;
As dew up-on the sum-mer flow'rs, As on the grass re-fresh-ing show'rs,
Thy kingdom rul-eth o-ver all, Be-fore Thy face, the an-gels fall,
And like a riv-er's glad increase, For rest of heart, my King of Peace.
Thy blood a-ton-ing ev-'ry day, My will, now governed by Thy sway.
So may Thy precious word dis-till, The world with grace and gladness fill.
Thy glo-ries light the realms a-bove, And yet, Thou car-est for my love.

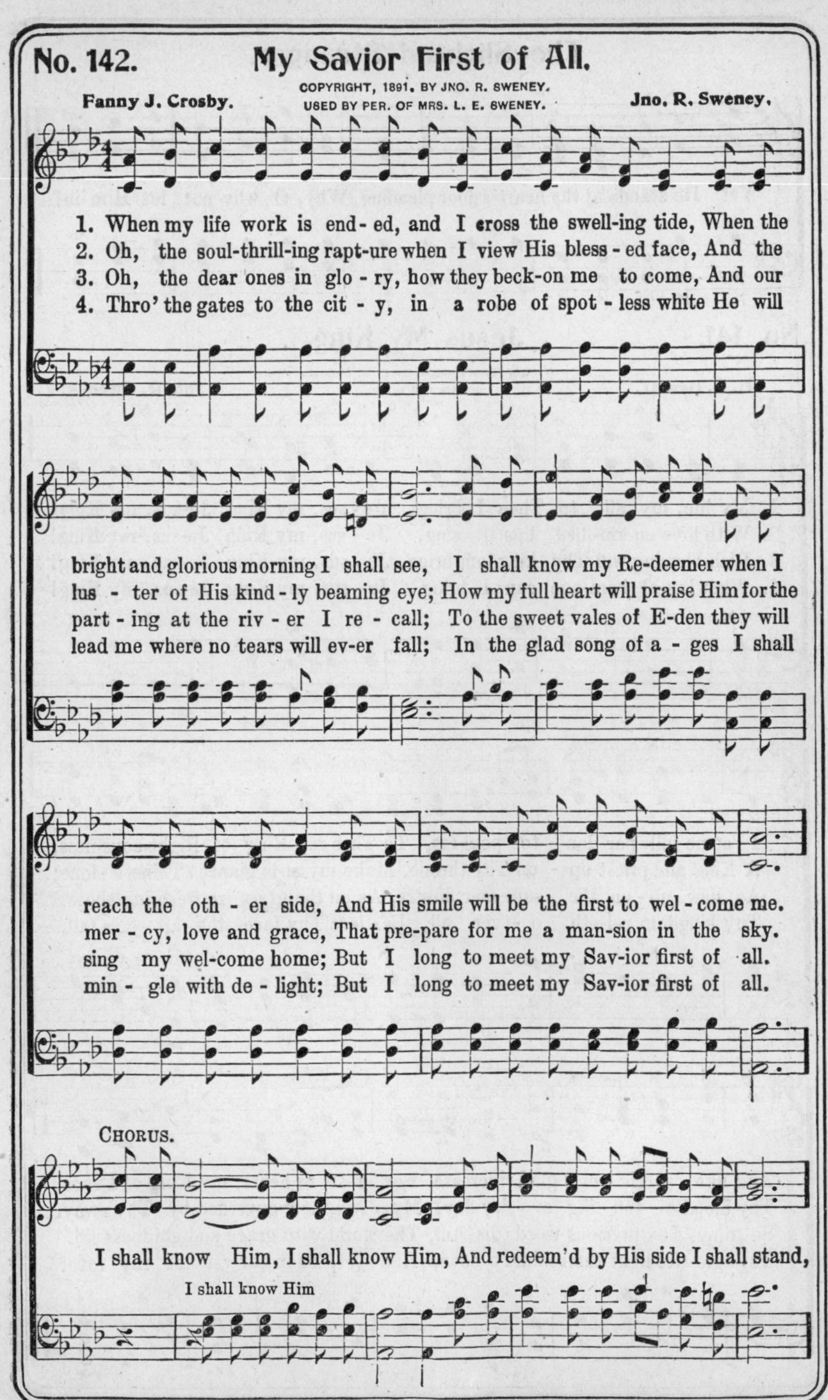
No. 142.
My Savior First of All.
COPYRIGHT, 1891, BY JNO. R. SWENEY.
USED BY PER. OF MRS. L. E. SWENEY.
Fanny J. Crosby.
Jno. R. Sweney.
1. When my life work is end- ed, and I cross the swell-ing tide, When the
2. Oh, the soul-thrill-ing rapt-ure when I view His bless - ed face, And the
3. Oh, the dear ones in glo - ry, how they beck-on me to come, And our
4. Thro' the gates to the cit - y, in a robe of spot - less white He will
bright and glorious morning I shall see, I shall know my Re-deemer when I
lus - ter of His kind - ly beaming eye; How my full heart will praise Him for the
part - ing at the riv - er I re - call; To the sweet vales of E-den they will
lead me where no tears will ev-er fall; In the glad song of a - ges I shall
reach the oth - er side, And His smile will be the first to wel - come me.
mer - cy, love and grace, That pre-pare for me a man-sion in the sky.
sing my wel-come home; But I long to meet my Sav-ior first of all.
min - gle with de - light; But I long to meet my Sav-ior first of all.
CHORUS.
I shall know Him, I shall know Him, And redeem'd by His side I shall stand,
I shall know Him

My Savior First of All.
I shall know Him, I shall know Him By the print of the nails in His hand.
I shall know Him,
No. 143. The Song-Land of My Soul.
COPYRIGHT, 1902, BY E. O. EXCELL.
Jessie Brown Pounds. WORDS AND MUSIC Victor H. Benke.
1. There are storms the world o'er sweeping, I can hear their thund'ring roll;
2. There is war the world o'er spreading; I can hear its cries of dole;
3. I can hear the glad E - van - gels, Of a bet - ter day to be,
But my God His calm is keep-ing, In the song - land of my soul.
But no strife I need be dread-ing, In the song - land of my soul.
In my song - land with the an - gels, There my Fa - ther dwells with me.
CHORUS.
In the song-land, blessed song - land! In the song - land of my soul;
In the song-land, bless-ed song-land! In the blessed song-land of my soul.
God His ho - ly calm is keep-ing, In the song - land of my soul.
In the bless-ed song-land of my soul.

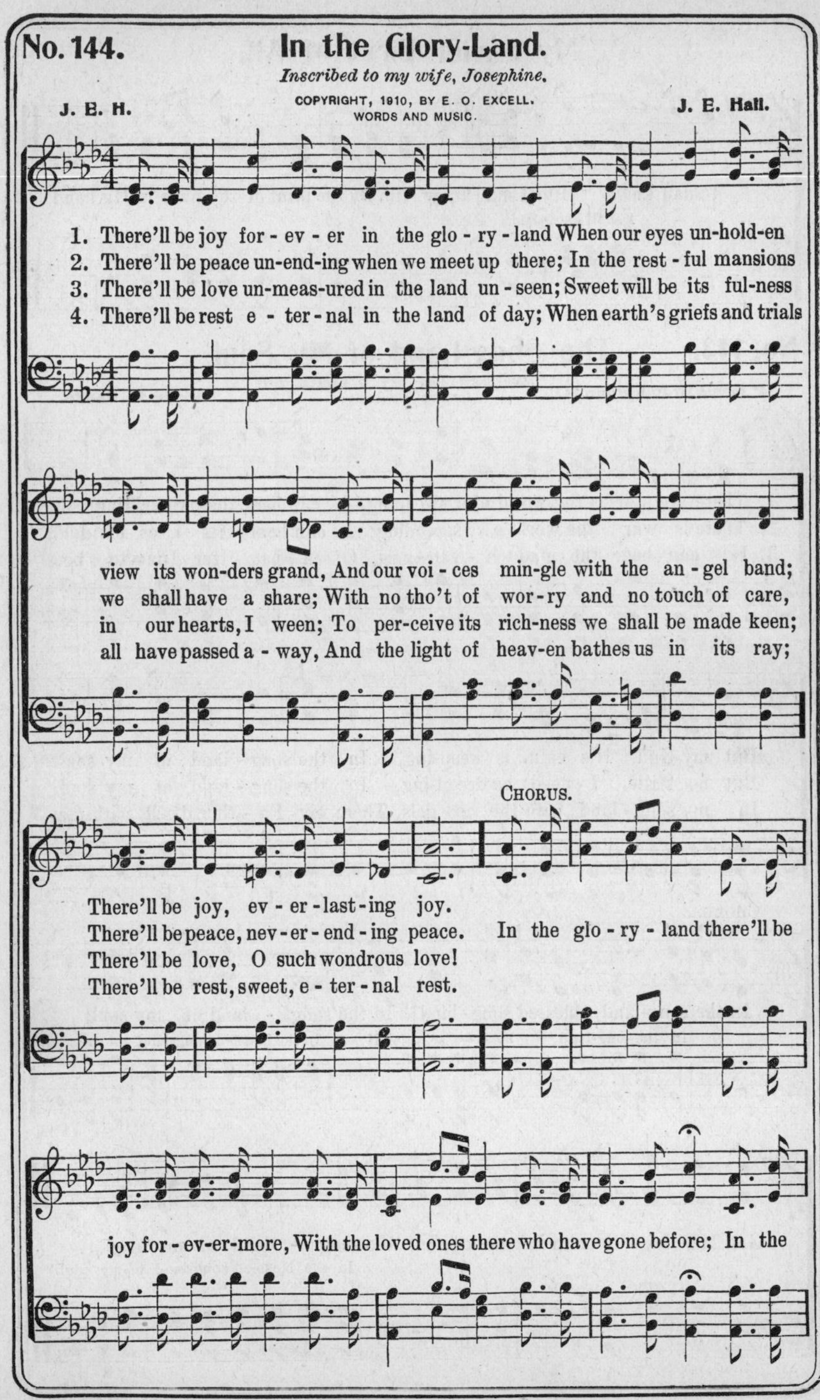
No. 144.
In the Glory-Land.
Inscribed to my wife, Josephine.
J. E. H.
COPYRIGHT, 1910, BY E. O. EXCELL.
WORDS AND MUSIC.
J. E. Hall.
1. There'll be joy for-ev-er in the glo-ry-land When our eyes un-hold-en view its won-ders grand, And our voi-ces min-gle with the an-gel band;
2. There'll be peace un-end-ing when we meet up there; In the rest-ful mansions we shall have a share; With no tho't of wor-ry and no touch of care,
3. There'll be love un-meas-ured in the land un-seen; Sweet will be its ful-ness in our hearts, I ween; To per-ceive its rich-ness we shall be made keen;
4. There'll be rest e-ter-nal in the land of day; When earth's griefs and trials all have passed a-way, And the light of heav-en bathes us in its ray;
There'll be joy, ev-er-last-ing joy.
There'll be peace, nev-er-end-ing peace.
There'll be love, O such wondrous love!
There'll be rest, sweet, e-ter-nal rest.
CHORUS.
In the glo-ry-land there'll be joy for-ev-er-more, With the loved ones there who have gone before; In the

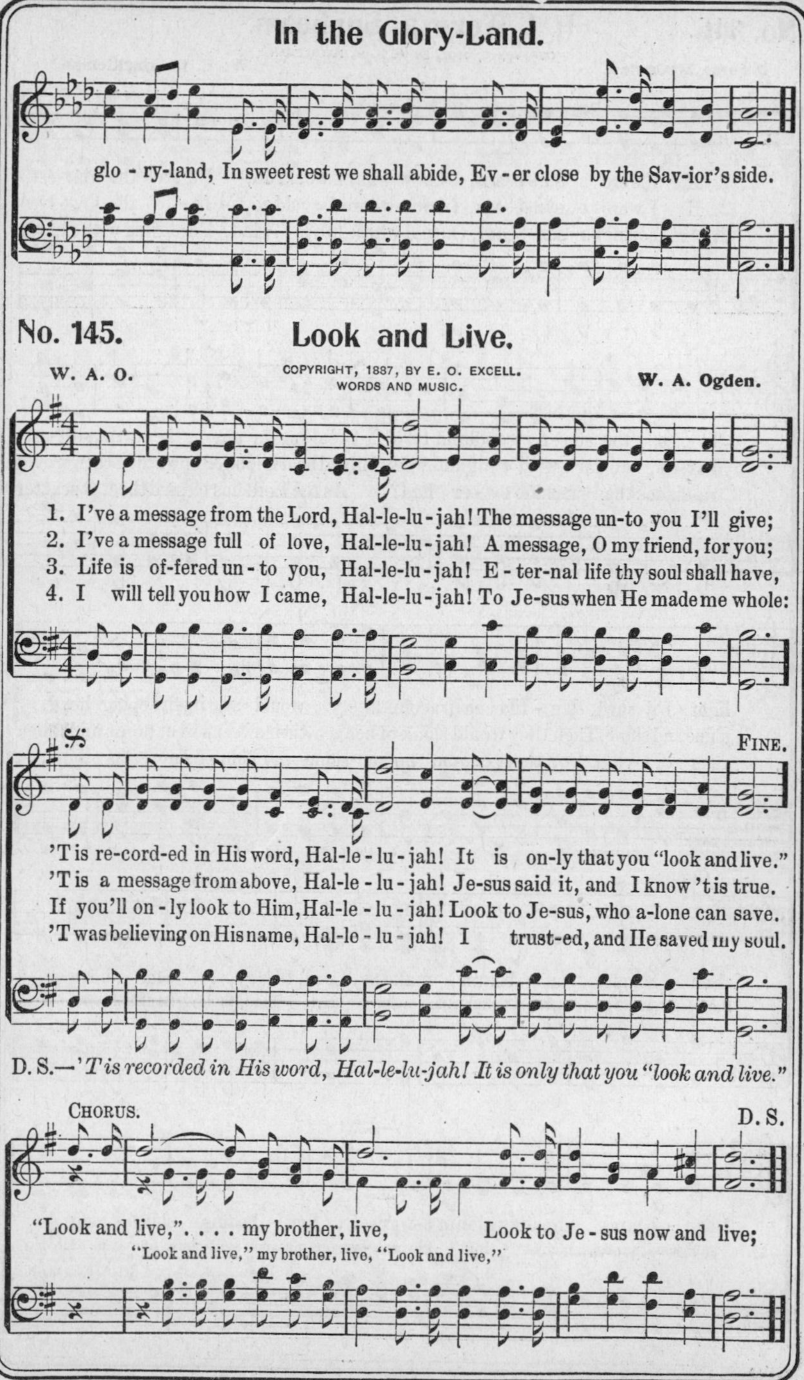
In the Glory-Land.
glo - ry-land, In sweet rest we shall abide, Ev - er close by the Sav-ior's side.
No. 145.
Look and Live.
W. A. O.
COPYRIGHT, 1887, BY E. O. EXCELL.
WORDS AND MUSIC.
W. A. Ogden.
1. I've a message from the Lord, Hal-le-lu-jah! The message un-to you I'll give;
2. I've a message full of love, Hal-le-lu-jah! A message, O my friend, for you;
3. Life is of-fered un-to you, Hal-le-lu-jah! E-ter-nal life thy soul shall have,
4. I will tell you how I came, Hal-le-lu-jah! To Je-sus when He made me whole:
FINE.
'T is re-cord-ed in His word, Hal-le-lu-jah! It is on-ly that you "look and live."
'T is a message from above, Hal-le-lu-jah! Je-sus said it, and I know 't is true.
If you'll on-ly look to Him, Hal-le-lu-jah! Look to Je-sus, who a-lone can save.
'T was believing on His name, Hal-le-lu-jah! I trust-ed, and He saved my soul.
D. S.—'T is recorded in His word, Hal-le-lu-jah! It is only that you "look and live."
CHORUS.
D. S.
"Look and live," . . . . my brother, live, Look to Je - sus now and live;
"Look and live," my brother, live, "Look and live,"

No. 146. If I Were a Sunbeam.
COPYRIGHT, 1907, BY W. E. M. HACKLEMAN.
Jerome McCauley.
W. E. M. Hackleman.
1. If I were a sun-beam, I know what I would do,— I'd seek the whit-est lil - ies the sun - ny woodland thro'; Steal-ing in among them, the soft-est light I'd shed, Un - til each graceful lil - y would raise its drooping head.
2. If I were a sun-beam, I know where I would go,— In - to the low - ly hov-els, all dark with want and woe; Till sad hearts looked upward, I then would shine and shine, Then they would think of heaven, their sweet, sweet home and mine.
3. Art thou not a sun-beam, O child whose life is glad, En-dowed with clearer ra-diance than sunshine ev - er had? As the Lord has blessed thee, O scatter rays di - vine, For there can be no sun-shine so help - ful now as thine.
CHORUS.
Sun - beams, sun - beams, make us, Lord, to-day, . . Sun - beams, sun - beams, chas-ing gloom a-way; . . Sun - beams shin - ing
Sunbeams, sunbeams, sunbeams, sunbeams, make us, Lord, to-day, Sunbeams, sunbeams, sunbeams, sunbeams, chas - ing gloom a - way; Sunbeams, sunbeams, sunbeams shin-ing

If I Were a Sunbeam.
in each saddened heart, O the heav'nly sun-beams make the dark de-part.
No. 147, I've Found a Friend.
Rev J. G. Small.
COPYRIGHT, 1903, BY E. O. EXCELL.
INTERNATIONAL COPYRIGHT SECURED.
Aug. Halter.
1. I've found a Friend, O such a Friend! He loved me ere I knew Him;
2. I've found a Friend, O such a Friend! He bled, He died to save me;
3. I've found a Friend, O such a Friend! So kind, and true, and ten - der,
He drew me with the cords of love, And thus He bound me to Him.
And not a - lone the gift of love, But His own life He gave me.
So wise a Coun-sel - or and Guide, So might-y a De-fend - er.
CHORUS.
I love to sing of such a Friend, Whose love no pow'r can sev - er;
rit.
My heart, my strength, my life, my all, Are His, and His for-ev - er.

No. 148.
Heaven in the Soul.
Alice Elrod.
COPYRIGHT, 1906, BY CHAS. H. GABRIEL.
E. O. EXCELL, OWNER.
Chas. H. Gabriel.
1. I have found a joy and sweetness Tongue can nev - er - more ex - press;
2. Je - sus walks and talks be - side me, Makes the way all bright and clear,
3. Oh, 'tis sweet to dwell with Je - sus, Walk with Him in robes of white,
'Tis a qui - et, ho - ly rap - ture Sent from God— a peace-ful rest.
Smooths the rug - ged, sto - ny path-way, So I walk with - out a fear.
Just to lean up - on His bos - om As He floods our souls with light.
Lo! I heard the Mas - ter call - ing O'er the bil - lows' an - gry roll,
Praise Him, praise Him for sal - va - tion, For a heart made pure and whole;
Tho' the storms may 'round me gath - er, And may al - most hide the goal,
Then I gave my heart to Je - sus, And I've heav'n in my soul.
I'm so glad I came to Je - sus, For I've heav'n in my soul.
Yet I'll trust it all to Je - sus, And keep heav'n in my soul.
CHORUS.
Yes, I've heav'n in my soul, Peace and joy be - yond con - trol; Tho' the

Heaven in the Soul.
1
2
storm-y bil-lows roll, I have heav'n in my soul; I'll keep heav'n in my soul.
No. 149.
For Thee, O Lord.
Ada Blenkhorn.
COPYRIGHT, 1895, BY CHAS. H. GABRIEL.
E. O. EXCELL, OWNER.
Chas. H. Gabriel.
1. Give me a song, O Lord, give me a song for Thee, Filled with sweet
2. Give me a word, O Lord, give me a word for Thee; Fraught with the
3. Give me a prayer, O Lord, give me a prayer for Thee; Mount-ing the
mu - sic of heav'n-ly spheres,—Faith's song of tri-umph o'er doubts and fears;
gift of Thy per - fect peace, Bid - ding all doubt-ing and tur - moil cease,
sky up - on faith's broad wings, Flood-ing the world with the joy it brings,
Give me a song, give me a song, Give me a song, O Lord, for Thee.
Give me a word, give me a word, Give me a word, O Lord, for Thee.
Give me a prayer, give me a prayer, Give me a prayer, O Lord, for Thee.

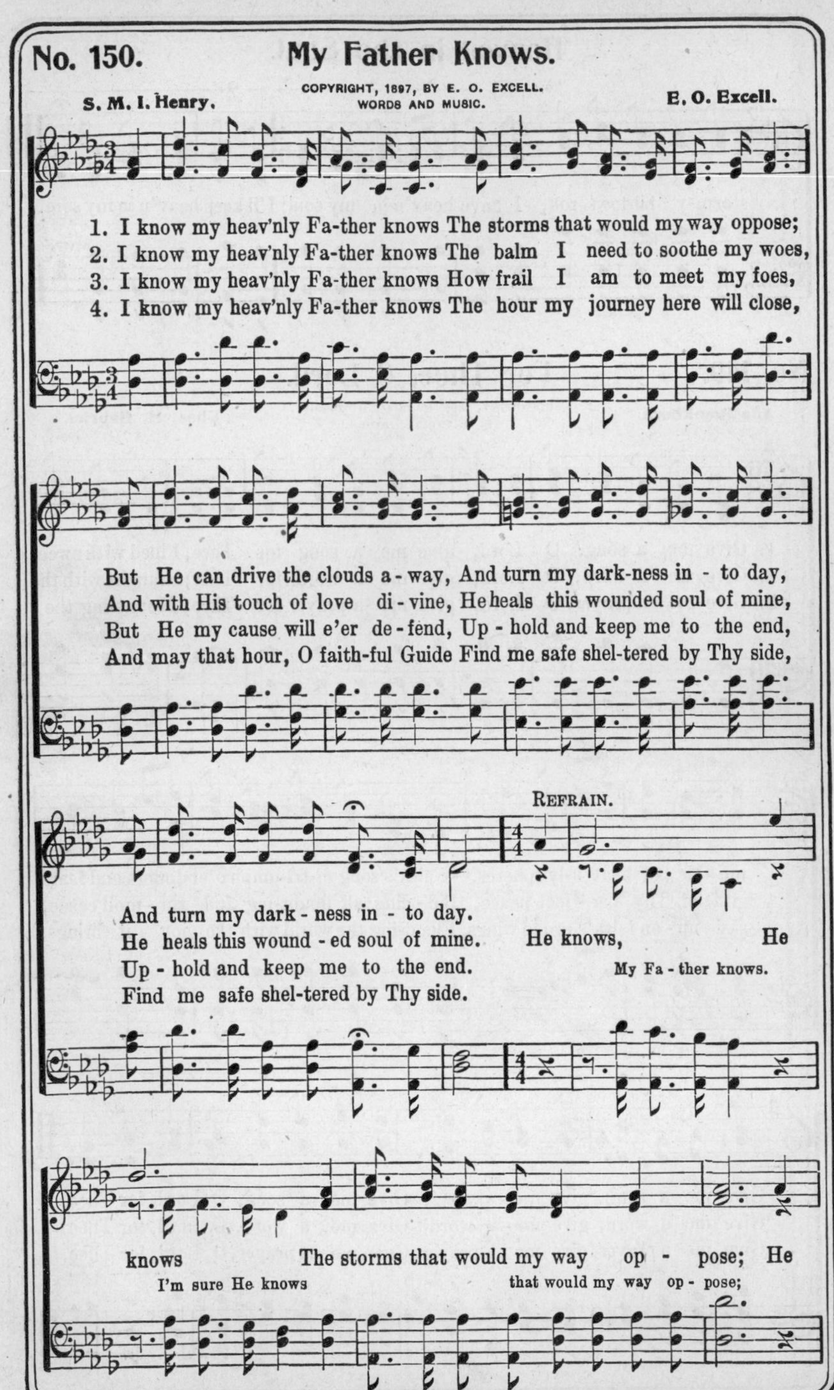
No. 150.
My Father Knows.
COPYRIGHT, 1897, BY E. O. EXCELL.
WORDS AND MUSIC.
S. M. I. Henry.
E. O. Excell.
1. I know my heav'nly Fa-ther knows The storms that would my way oppose;
2. I know my heav'nly Fa-ther knows The balm I need to soothe my woes,
3. I know my heav'nly Fa-ther knows How frail I am to meet my foes,
4. I know my heav'nly Fa-ther knows The hour my journey here will close,
But He can drive the clouds a-way, And turn my dark-ness in - to day,
And with His touch of love di-vine, He heals this wounded soul of mine,
But He my cause will e'er de-fend, Up-hold and keep me to the end,
And may that hour, O faith-ful Guide Find me safe shel-tered by Thy side,
And turn my dark-ness in - to day.
He heals this wound - ed soul of mine.
Up - hold and keep me to the end.
Find me safe shel-tered by Thy side.
REFRAIN.
He knows, He
My Fa - ther knows.
knows The storms that would my way op - pose; He
I'm sure He knows
that would my way op - pose;

My Father Knows.
knows, He knows, And tempers ev'ry wind that blows.
My Fa-ther knows, I'm sure He knows, the wind that blows.
No. 151. The Half Has Never Been Told.
COPYRIGHT, 1883, BY R. E. HUDSON.
USED BY PER.
Frances R. Havergal.
R. E. Hudson.
1. I know I love Thee bet - ter, Lord, Than an - y earth - ly joy,
2. I know that Thou art near - er still, Than an - y earth - ly throng,
3. Thou hast put glad - ness in my heart; Then well may I be glad!
4. O Sav - ior, pre - cious Sav - ior mine! What will Thy pres - ence be,
For Thou hast giv - en me the peace Which noth - ing can de - stroy.
And sweet - er is the tho't of Thee, Than an - y love - ly song.
With - out the se - cret of Thy love, I could not but be sad.
If such a life of love can crown Our walk on earth with Thee?
CHORUS.
The half has nev - er yet been told, Of love so full and free.
The half has nev - er yet been told, The blood—it cleanseth me.
yet been told,

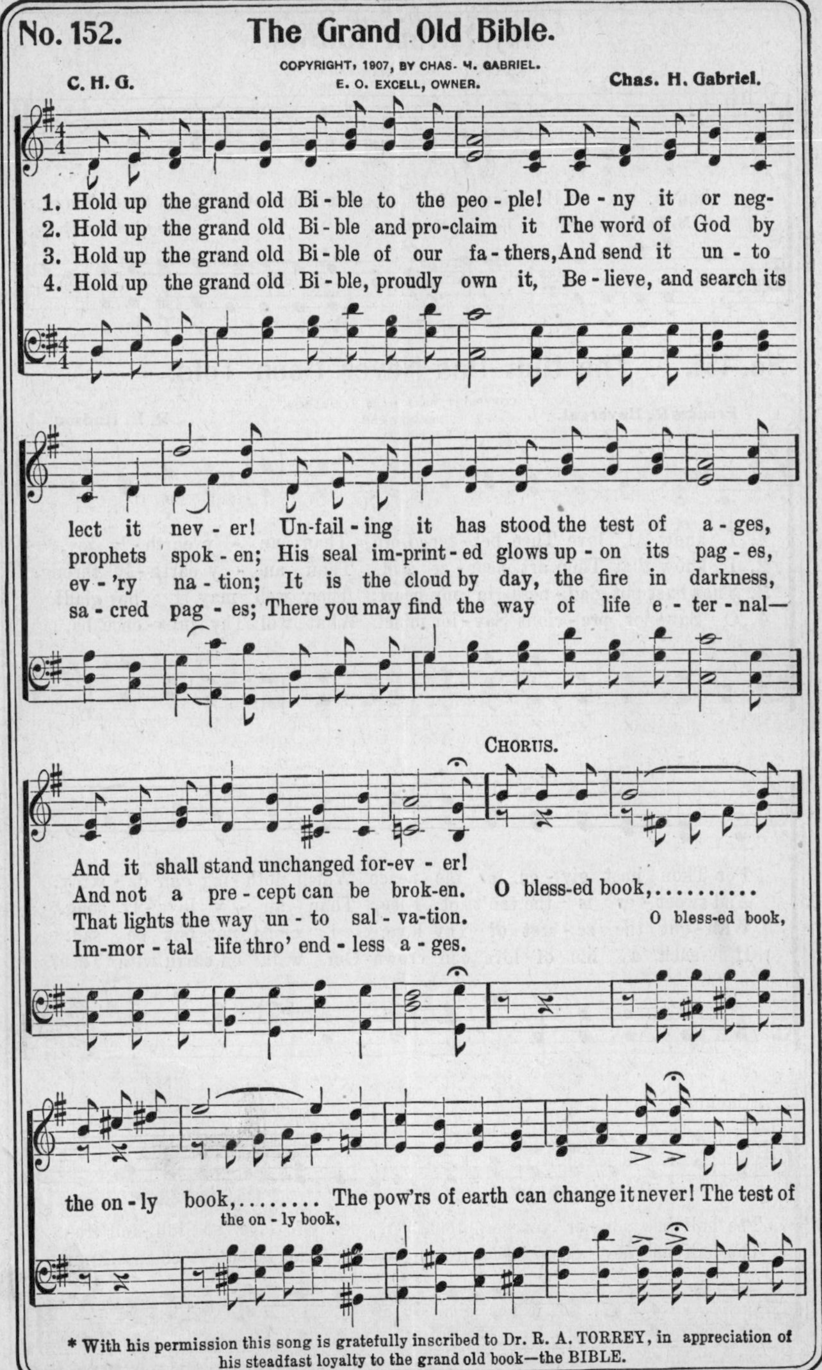
No. 152. The Grand Old Bible.
COPYRIGHT, 1907, BY CHAS. H. GABRIEL.
E. O. EXCELL, OWNER.
C. H. G.
Chas. H. Gabriel.
1. Hold up the grand old Bi-ble to the peo-ple! De-ny it or neg-
2. Hold up the grand old Bi-ble and pro-claim it The word of God by
3. Hold up the grand old Bi-ble of our fa-thers, And send it un-to
4. Hold up the grand old Bi-ble, proudly own it, Be-lieve, and search its
lect it nev-er! Un-fail-ing it has stood the test of a-ges,
prophets spok-en; His seal im-print-ed glows up-on its pag-es,
ev-'ry na-tion; It is the cloud by day, the fire in darkness,
sa-cred pag-es; There you may find the way of life e-ter-nal—
CHORUS.
And it shall stand unchanged for-ev-er!
And not a pre-cept can be brok-en.
That lights the way un-to sal-va-tion.
Im-mor-tal life thro' end-less a-ges.
O bless-ed book,..........
O bless-ed book,
the on-ly book,....... The pow'rs of earth can change it never! The test of
the on-ly book,
* With his permission this song is gratefully inscribed to Dr. R. A. TORREY, in appreciation of his steadfast loyalty to the grand old book—the BIBLE.

The Grand Old Bible.
fire and flood thro' ages it hath stood, And it shall stand unchanged for-ev-er.
No. 153. Beautiful Isle.
Jessie B. Pounds.
COPYRIGHT, 1897, BY E. O. EXCELL.
WORDS AND MUSIC.
J. S. Fearis.
1. Some-where the sun is shin - ing, Some-where the song - birds dwell;
2. Some-where the day is lon - ger, Some-where the task is done;
3. Some-where the load is lift - ed, Close by an o - pen gate;
Hush, then, thy sad re - pin - ing, God lives, and all is well.
Some-where the heart is stron - ger, Some-where the guer - don won.
Some-where the clouds are rift - ed, Some-where the an - gels wait.
CHORUS.
Some - where, Some - where, Beau-ti - ful Isle of Some-where!
Some-where, beau-ti - ful, beau - ti - ful Isle,
Land of the true, where we live a - new,—Beau-ti-ful Isle of Some-where!

No. 154. If There's Sunshine in Your Heart.

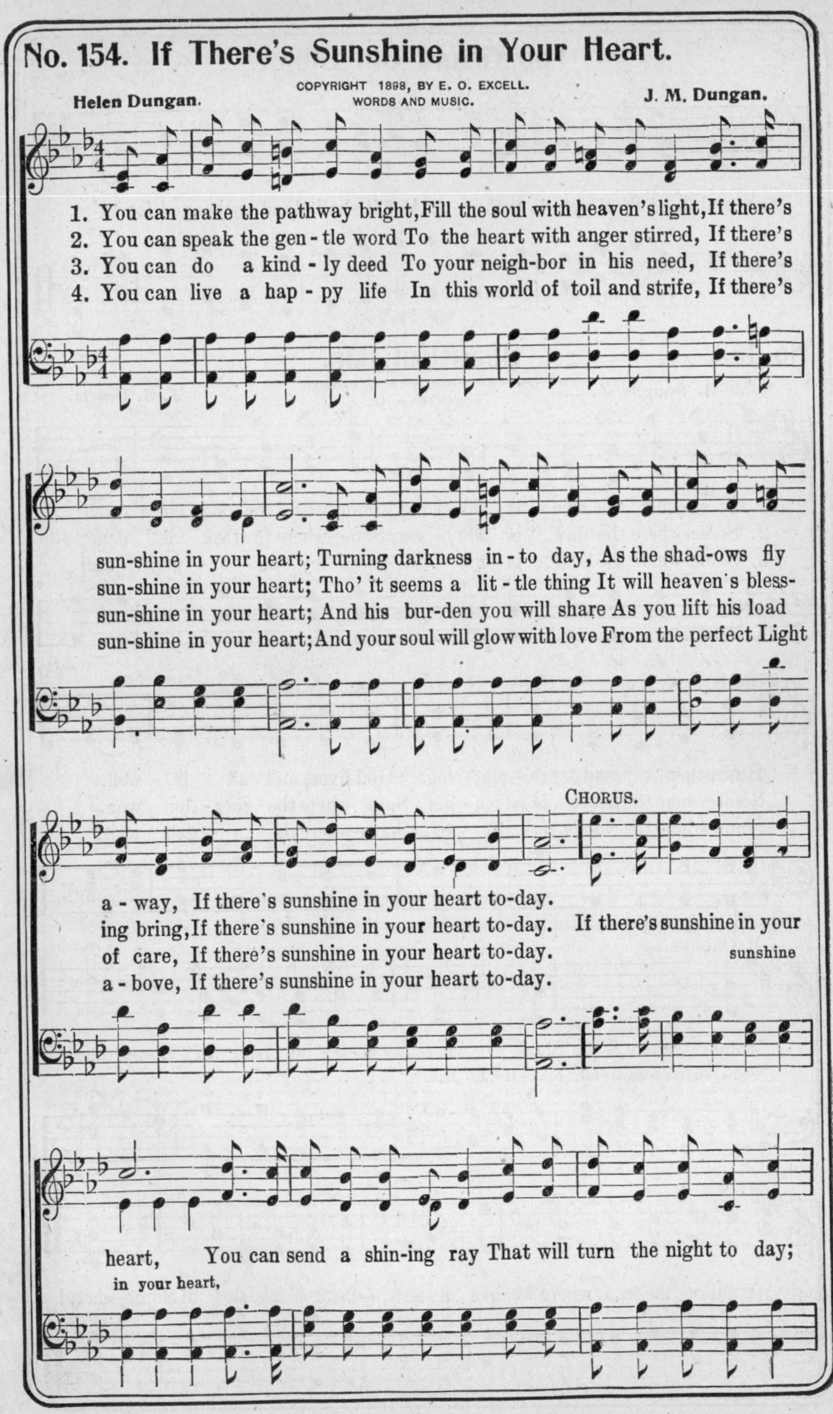

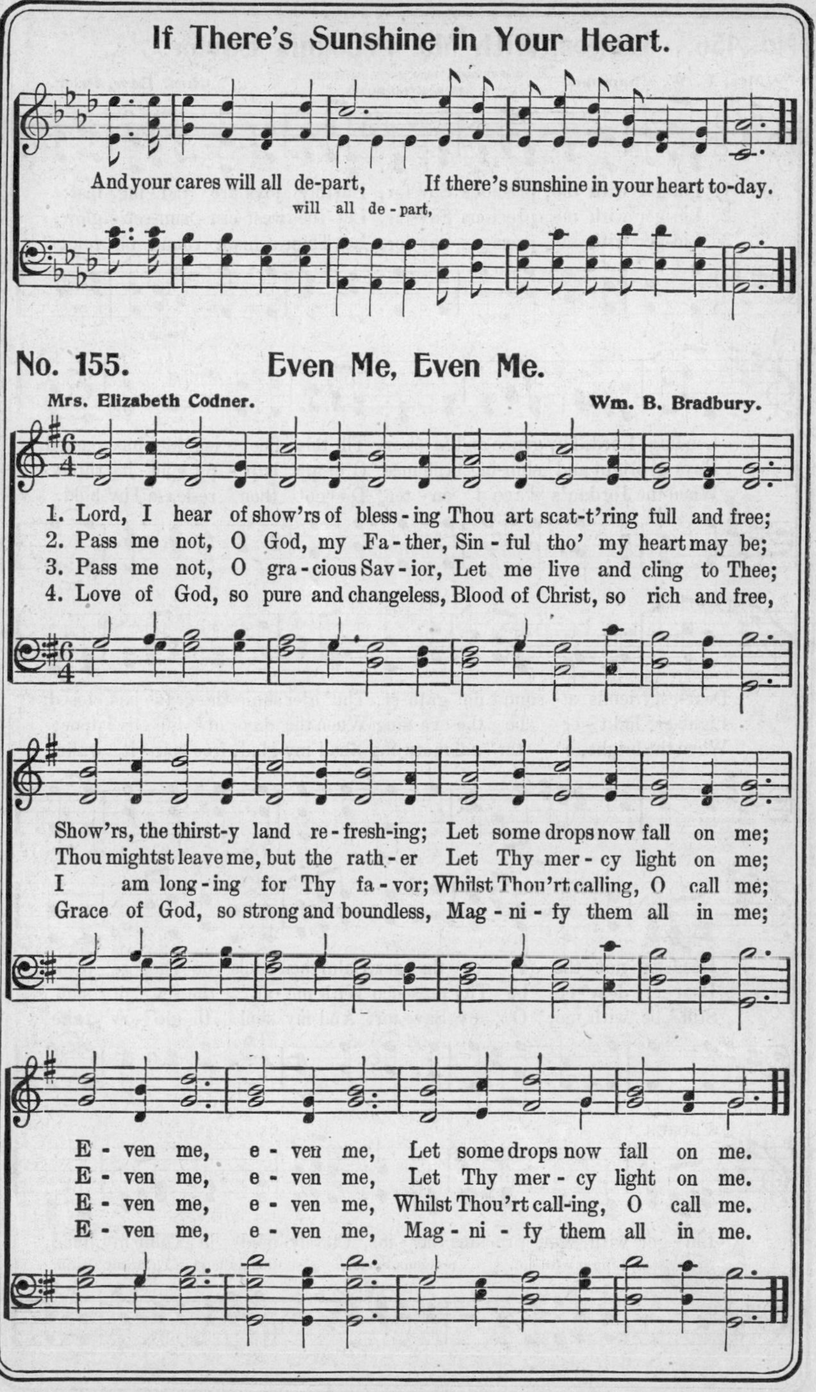
If There's Sunshine in Your Heart.
And your cares will all de-part, If there's sunshine in your heart to-day.
will all de - part,
No. 155. Even Me, Even Me.
Mrs. Elizabeth Codner.
Wm. B. Bradbury.
1. Lord, I hear of show'rs of bless - ing Thou art scat-t'ring full and free;
2. Pass me not, O God, my Fa - ther, Sin - ful tho' my heart may be;
3. Pass me not, O gra - cious Sav - ior, Let me live and cling to Thee;
4. Love of God, so pure and changeless, Blood of Christ, so rich and free,
Show'rs, the thirst-y land re - fresh-ing; Let some drops now fall on me;
Thou mightst leave me, but the rath - er Let Thy mer - cy light on me;
I am long - ing for Thy fa - vor; Whilst Thou'rt calling, O call me;
Grace of God, so strong and boundless, Mag - ni - fy them all in me;
E - ven me, e - ven me, Let some drops now fall on me.
E - ven me, e - ven me, Let Thy mer - cy light on me.
E - ven me, e - ven me, Whilst Thou'rt call-ing, O call me.
E - ven me, e - ven me, Mag - ni - fy them all in me.

No. 156. Linger With Me, Precious Savior.
Mrs. E. W. Chapman.
COPYRIGHT, 1889, BY E. O. EXCELL.
WORDS AND MUSIC.
Chas. Edw. Prior.
1. Lin-ger with me, precious Sav-ior, Earthly joys are fad-ing fast;
2. Lin-ger with me, precious Sav-ior, Let the west-ern sun-set's glow,
3. Lin-ger with me, precious Sav-ior, Let Thine arms a - round me fold;
Lending, Lord, Thy grace and fa - vor Till this fleet - ing life has passed.
Rays of bright and shin-ing brilliance O'er my hap - py spir - it throw.
When the Jordan's wave I en - ter, Do not then re-lease Thy hold.
Dear-est friends a - round me gath-er, Tho' o'er some the grave has closed;
Light-er, light - er be the eve-ning When the day of life is done;
When the bright, e - ter - nal morn-ing Shall my glad, free spir - it wake,
Heed-ing not the i - cy fin - ger, Calm their souls on Thee re - posed.
Dear-er, dear-er be Thy presence With me at the set of sun.
Still be with me, O my Sav - ior, And my soul to glo - ry take.
CHORUS.
Lin - ger with me, precious Sav - ior, Closely hold in Thine my hand;
Linger with me, precious Savior, Closely hold in Thine my hand;

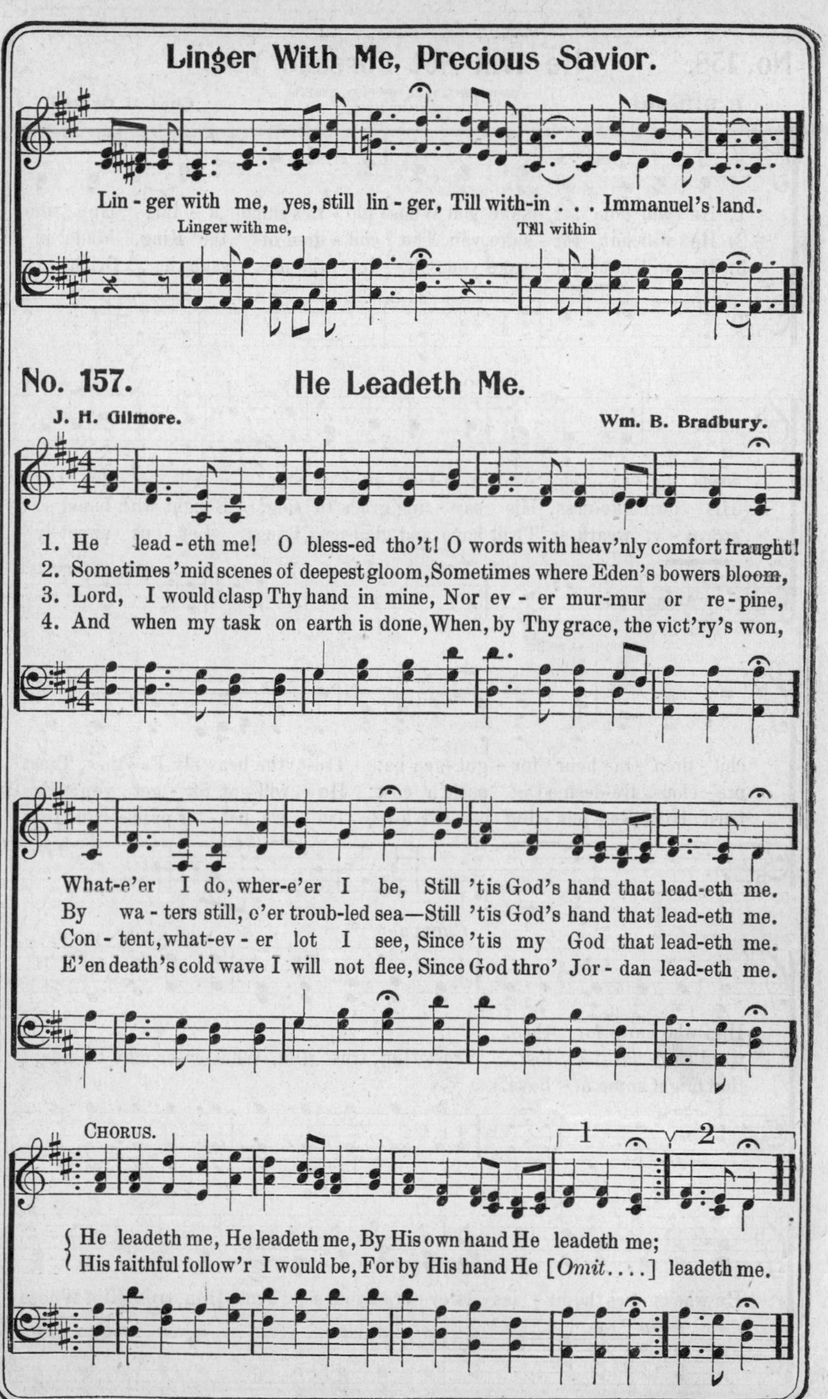
Linger With Me, Precious Savior.
Lin - ger with me, yes, still lin - ger, Till with-in . . . Immanuel's land.
Linger with me,
Till within
No. 157.
He Leadeth Me.
J. H. Gilmore.
Wm. B. Bradbury.
1. He lead - eth me! O bless-ed tho't! O words with heav'nly comfort fraught!
2. Sometimes 'mid scenes of deepest gloom, Sometimes where Eden's bowers bloom,
3. Lord, I would clasp Thy hand in mine, Nor ev - er mur-mur or re - pine,
4. And when my task on earth is done, When, by Thy grace, the vict'ry's won,
What-e'er I do, wher-e'er I be, Still 'tis God's hand that lead-eth me.
By wa - ters still, o'er troub-led sea—Still 'tis God's hand that lead-eth me.
Con - tent, what-ev - er lot I see, Since 'tis my God that lead-eth me.
E'en death's cold wave I will not flee, Since God thro' Jor - dan lead-eth me.
CHORUS.
1
2
He leadeth me, He leadeth me, By His own hand He leadeth me;
His faithful follow'r I would be, For by His hand He [Omit. . . .] leadeth me.

No. 158. He Will Not Forsake You.

E. E. Hewitt.

Chas. H. Gabriel.

He Will Not Forsake You.
glo-ries shine a - far; He will not for-sake you Who numbers ev - 'ry star.
No. 159. 'Tis For You and Me.
E. E. Hewitt.
COPYRIGHT, 1894, BY E. O. EXCELL
E. O. Excell.
1. There's a par - don full and sweet, 'Tis for you, 'tis for me;
2. There's a help for ev - 'ry day, 'Tis for you, 'tis for me;
3. There's a robe of snow - y white 'Tis for you, 'tis for me;
Bless - ed rest at Je - sus' feet, 'Tis for you and me.
Joy and bless - ing by the way, 'Tis for you and me.
There's a home of glo - ry bright, 'Tis for you and me.
CHORUS.
All for you, if you be - lieve, If sal - va - tion you'll re - ceive;
There's a wel - come, warm and true, All for you, all for me.

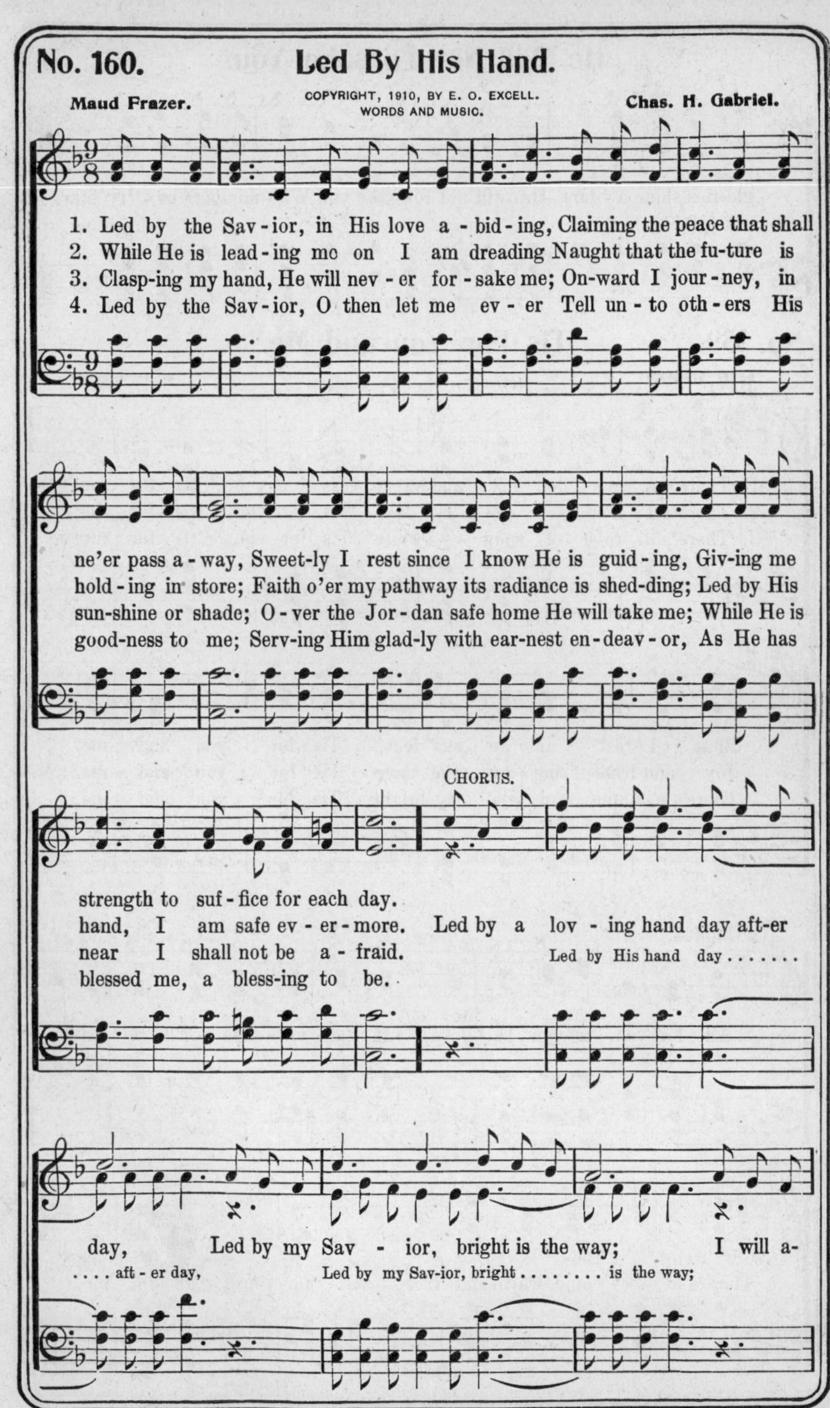
No. 160.
Led By His Hand.
Maud Frazer.
COPYRIGHT, 1910, BY E. O. EXCELL.
WORDS AND MUSIC.
Chas. H. Gabriel.
1. Led by the Sav-ior, in His love a-bid-ing, Claiming the peace that shall
2. While He is lead-ing me on I am dreading Naught that the fu-ture is
3. Clasp-ing my hand, He will nev-er for-sake me; On-ward I jour-ney, in
4. Led by the Sav-ior, O then let me ev-er Tell un-to oth-ers His
ne'er pass a-way, Sweet-ly I rest since I know He is guid-ing, Giv-ing me
hold-ing in store; Faith o'er my pathway its radiance is shed-ding; Led by His
sun-shine or shade; O-ver the Jor-dan safe home He will take me; While He is
good-ness to me; Serv-ing Him glad-ly with ear-nest en-deav-or, As He has
CHORUS.
strength to suf-fice for each day.
hand, I am safe ev-er-more. Led by a lov-ing hand day aft-er
near I shall not be a-fraid. Led by His hand day ....
blessed me, a bless-ing to be.
day, Led by my Sav - ior, bright is the way; I will a-
.... aft-er day, Led by my Sav-ior, bright .... is the way;

Led By His Hand.
bide close to His side, For I am led . . . . . . by His hand.
I will a-bide close to His side, For . . . . I am led by His hand.
No. 161. I Need Thee Every Hour.
Mrs. Annie S. Hawks.
COPYRIGHT, 1900, BY MARY RUNYON LOWRY. RENEWAL, USED BY PER.
Rev. Robert Lowry.
1. I need Thee ev-'ry hour, Most gra - cious Lord; No ten-der voice like Thine Can peace af - ford.
2. I need Thee ev-'ry hour, Stay Thou near by; Temp-ta-tions lose their pow'r When Thou art nigh.
3. I need Thee ev-'ry hour, In joy or pain; Come quick-ly and a-bide, Or life is vain.
4. I need Thee ev-'ry hour, Most Ho - ly One; O make me Thine in-deed, Thou bless - ed Son!
CHORUS.
I need Thee, O I need Thee; Ev-'ry hour I need Thee! O bless me now, my Sav-ior, I come to Thee!

No. 162. Clinging Close to His Hand.
Lizzie DeArmond.
COPYRIGHT, 1910, BY E. O. EXCELL. WORDS AND MUSIC.
Samuel W. Beazley.
1. As I cling to the hand of my Lord each day, What a
2. If I cling to His hand when the way grows dim, What is
3. I will cling to the hand whose nail-prints I see, And will
glad-ness is mine in the heav'nward way! Bless - ed fellowship ours
there I need fear, since I trust in Him? For His love lights the way,
rest in the love that is full and free; Cling - ing ev - er to Him,
all the way a - long, As my glad - ness voi-ces it-self in song.
that my feet must tread, And Faith's day - star brightens the path a-head.
of His grace I sing, Christ, my Sav - ior, my Redeemer, my King.
Chorus.
Cling - ing, cling-ing by faith to my Sav-ior's hand; Cling-ing, cling-ing to
Him who my way hath planned; Cling - ing, cling-ing to Je - sus, my

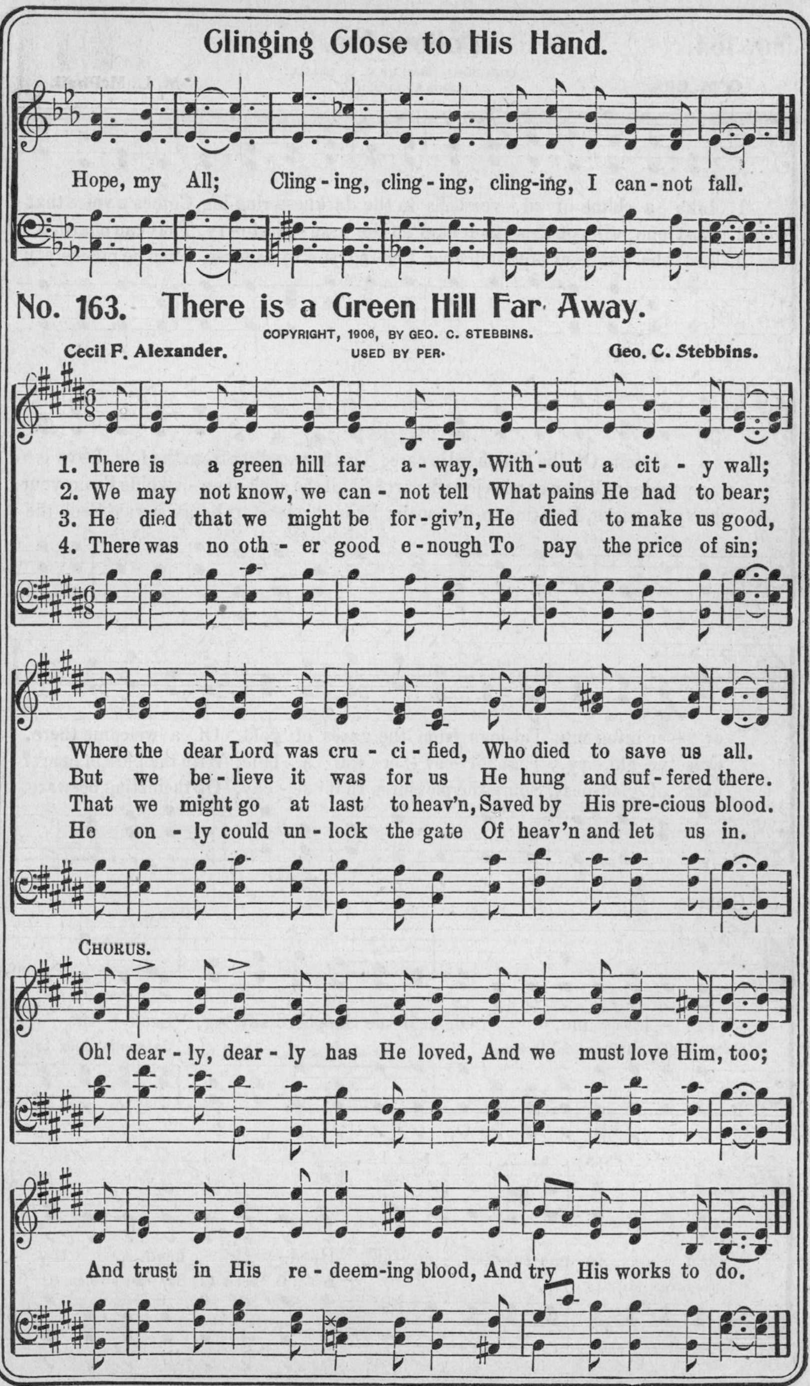
Clinging Close to His Hand.
Hope, my All; Cling-ing, cling-ing, cling-ing, I can-not fall.
No. 163. There is a Green Hill Far Away.
COPYRIGHT, 1906, BY GEO. C. STEBBINS.
USED BY PER.
Cecil F. Alexander.
Geo. C. Stebbins.
1. There is a green hill far a-way, With-out a cit-y wall;
2. We may not know, we can-not tell What pains He had to bear;
3. He died that we might be for-giv'n, He died to make us good,
4. There was no oth-er good e-nough To pay the price of sin;
Where the dear Lord was cru-ci-fied, Who died to save us all.
But we be-lieve it was for us He hung and suf-fered there.
That we might go at last to heav'n, Saved by His pre-cious blood.
He on-ly could un-lock the gate Of heav'n and let us in.
CHORUS.
Oh! dear-ly, dear-ly has He loved, And we must love Him, too;
And trust in His re-deem-ing blood, And try His works to do.

No. 164. Follow Me.
G. M. Bills.
COPYRIGHT, 1899, BY E. O. EXCELL.
WORDS AND MUSIC.
M. L. McPhail.
1. Like a chime of sil - ver bells In the darkness ring-ing, Comes a voice that
2. Lost one, will you close your ears To the mag - ic sto - ry, That can charm a
3. Lo! the tempt-er doth de-ceive, Lur-ing you to sadness, Then he mocks you
ev - er tells Of the Shepherd's care; To the wand'rer from the fold, Love is
way your fears When earth's joys depart? Shall the spell of e - vil hide From your
while you grieve, Pointing to de - spair; From his fet-ters break a-way, Seek the
ev - er bring-ing, Tid-ings from the gates of gold, Of a welcome there.
eyes the glo - ry, That for - ev - er will a - bide, With the pure in heart?
path of glad-ness, Spurn the pleasures that de - cay, Of their sting be-ware.
CHORUS.
"Fol - low me," Oh hear the Shepherd say-ing, "Seek the
"Fol-low, fol - low, fol-low me,"
"Seek the door to
door to pas-tures ev - er fair," Heed, O heed thy
pas-tures fair, to
Heed, O heed thy Sav - ior's voice, O

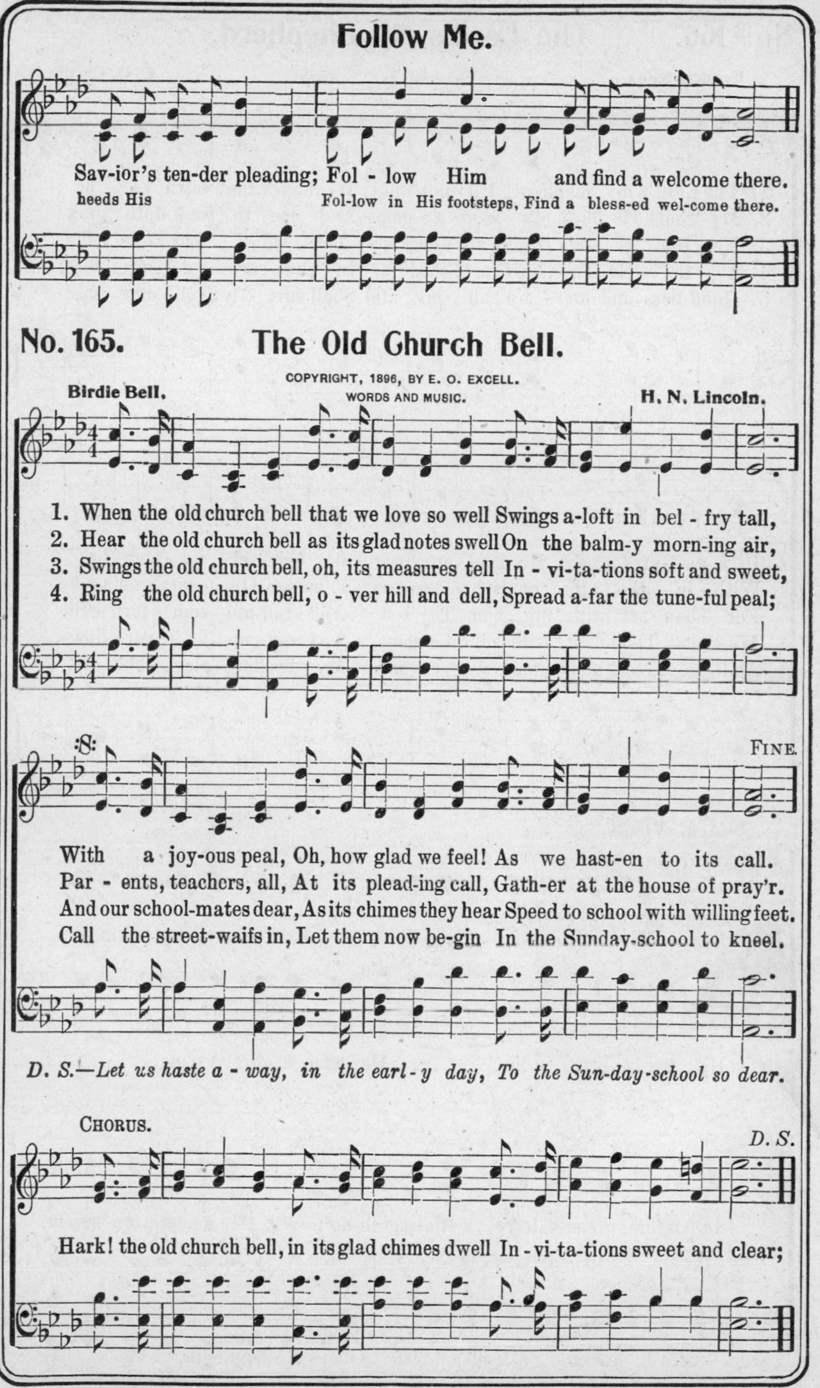
Follow Me.
Sav-ior's ten-der pleading; Fol - low Him and find a welcome there.
heeds His Fol-low in His footsteps, Find a bless-ed wel-come there.
No. 165. The Old Church Bell.
COPYRIGHT, 1896, BY E. O. EXCELL.
WORDS AND MUSIC.
Birdie Bell.
H. N. Lincoln.
1. When the old church bell that we love so well Swings a-loft in bel - fry tall,
2. Hear the old church bell as its glad notes swell On the balm-y morn-ing air,
3. Swings the old church bell, oh, its measures tell In - vi-ta-tions soft and sweet,
4. Ring the old church bell, o - ver hill and dell, Spread a-far the tune-ful peal;
FINE.
With a joy-ous peal, Oh, how glad we feel! As we hast-en to its call.
Par - ents, teachers, all, At its plead-ing call, Gath-er at the house of pray'r.
And our school-mates dear, As its chimes they hear Speed to school with willing feet.
Call the street-waifs in, Let them now be-gin In the Sunday-school to kneel.
D. S.—Let us haste a - way, in the earl - y day, To the Sun-day-school so dear.
CHORUS.
D. S.
Hark! the old church bell, in its glad chimes dwell In - vi-ta-tions sweet and clear;

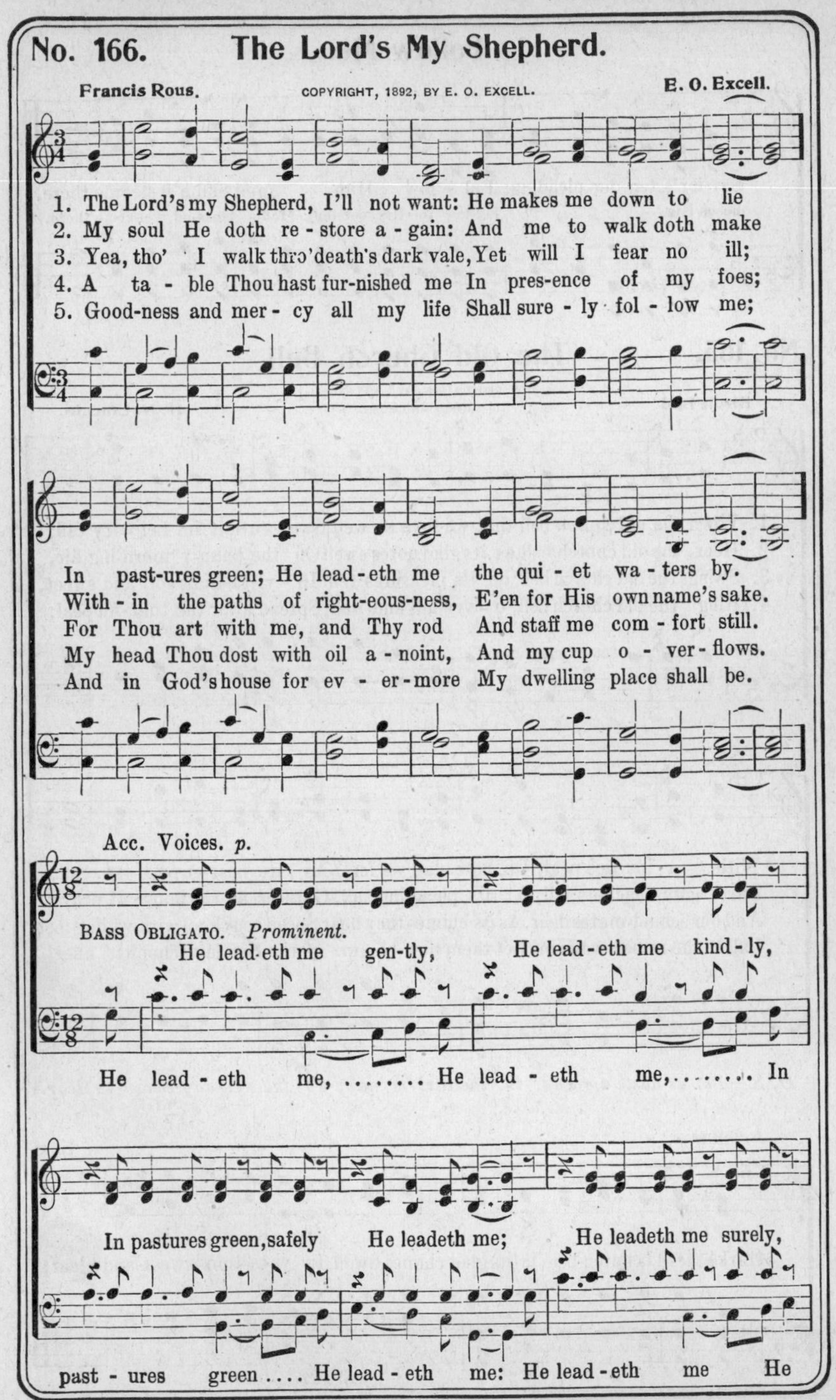
No. 166. The Lord's My Shepherd.
Francis Rous.
COPYRIGHT, 1892, BY E. O. EXCELL.
E. O. Excell.
1. The Lord's my Shepherd, I'll not want: He makes me down to lie
2. My soul He doth re - store a - gain: And me to walk doth make
3. Yea, tho' I walk thro' death's dark vale, Yet will I fear no ill;
4. A ta - ble Thou hast fur-nished me In pres-ence of my foes;
5. Good-ness and mer - cy all my life Shall sure - ly fol - low me;
In past-ures green; He lead-eth me the qui - et wa - ters by.
With - in the paths of right-eous-ness, E'en for His own name's sake.
For Thou art with me, and Thy rod And staff me com - fort still.
My head Thou dost with oil a - noint, And my cup o - ver - flows.
And in God's house for ev - er-more My dwelling place shall be.
Acc. Voices. p.
BASS OBLIGATO. Prominent.
He lead-eth me gen-tly, He lead-eth me kind-ly,
He lead - eth me, ... He lead - eth me,........ In
In pastures green, safely He leadeth me; He leadeth me surely,
past - ures green .... He lead - eth me: He lead - eth me He

The Lord's My Shepherd,
He leadeth me gen-tly, By His own hand, kindly He leadeth me.
lead-eth me, By His own hand He lead-eth me.
No. 167. Never Lose Sight of Jesus.
COPYRIGHT, 1895, BY E. O. EXCELL. WORDS AND MUSIC.
Rev. J. Oatman, Jr.
E. O. Excell.
1. Oh, Pil-grim bound for the heav'n-ly land, Nev-er lose sight of Je-sus;
2. When-e'er you're tempted to go a-stray, Nev-er lose sight of Je-sus;
3. Tho' dark the path-way may seem a-head, Nev-er lose sight of Je-sus;
4. When death is knock-ing out-side the door, Nev-er lose sight of Je-sus;
FINE.
He'll lead you gen-tly with lov-ing hand, Nev-er lose sight of Je-sus.
Press on-ward, up-ward, the nar-row way, Nev-er lose sight of Je-sus.
"I will be with you," His word hath said, Nev-er lose sight of Je-sus.
Till safe-ly land-ed on Canaan's shore, Nev-er lose sight of Je-sus.
D. S.—Day and night He will lead you right, Nev-er lose sight of Je-sus.
CHORUS.
D. S.
Nev-er lose sight of Je-sus, Nev-er lose sight of Je-sus;

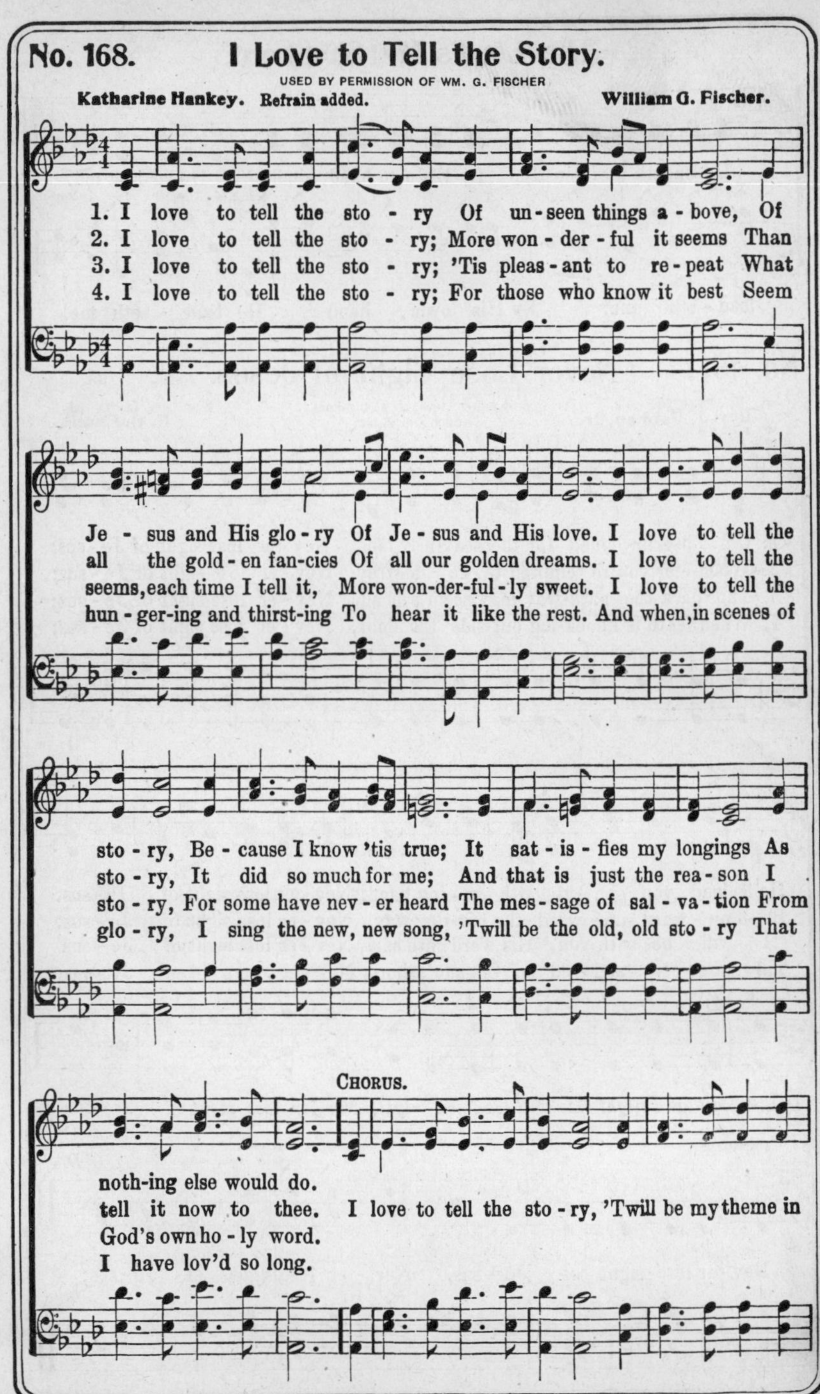
No. 168. I Love to Tell the Story.
USED BY PERMISSION OF WM. G. FISCHER
Katharine Hankey. Refrain added.
William G. Fischer.
1. I love to tell the sto - ry Of un-seen things a - bove, Of
2. I love to tell the sto - ry; More won - der - ful it seems Than
3. I love to tell the sto - ry; 'Tis pleas - ant to re - peat What
4. I love to tell the sto - ry; For those who know it best Seem
Je - sus and His glo - ry Of Je - sus and His love. I love to tell the
all the gold - en fan-cies Of all our golden dreams. I love to tell the
seems, each time I tell it, More won-der-ful - ly sweet. I love to tell the
hun - ger-ing and thirst-ing To hear it like the rest. And when, in scenes of
sto - ry, Be - cause I know 'tis true; It sat - is - fies my longings As
sto - ry, It did so much for me; And that is just the rea - son I
sto - ry, For some have nev - er heard The mes - sage of sal - va - tion From
glo - ry, I sing the new, new song, 'Twill be the old, old sto - ry That
CHORUS.
noth-ing else would do.
tell it now to thee. I love to tell the sto - ry, 'Twill be my theme in
God's own ho - ly word.
I have lov'd so long.

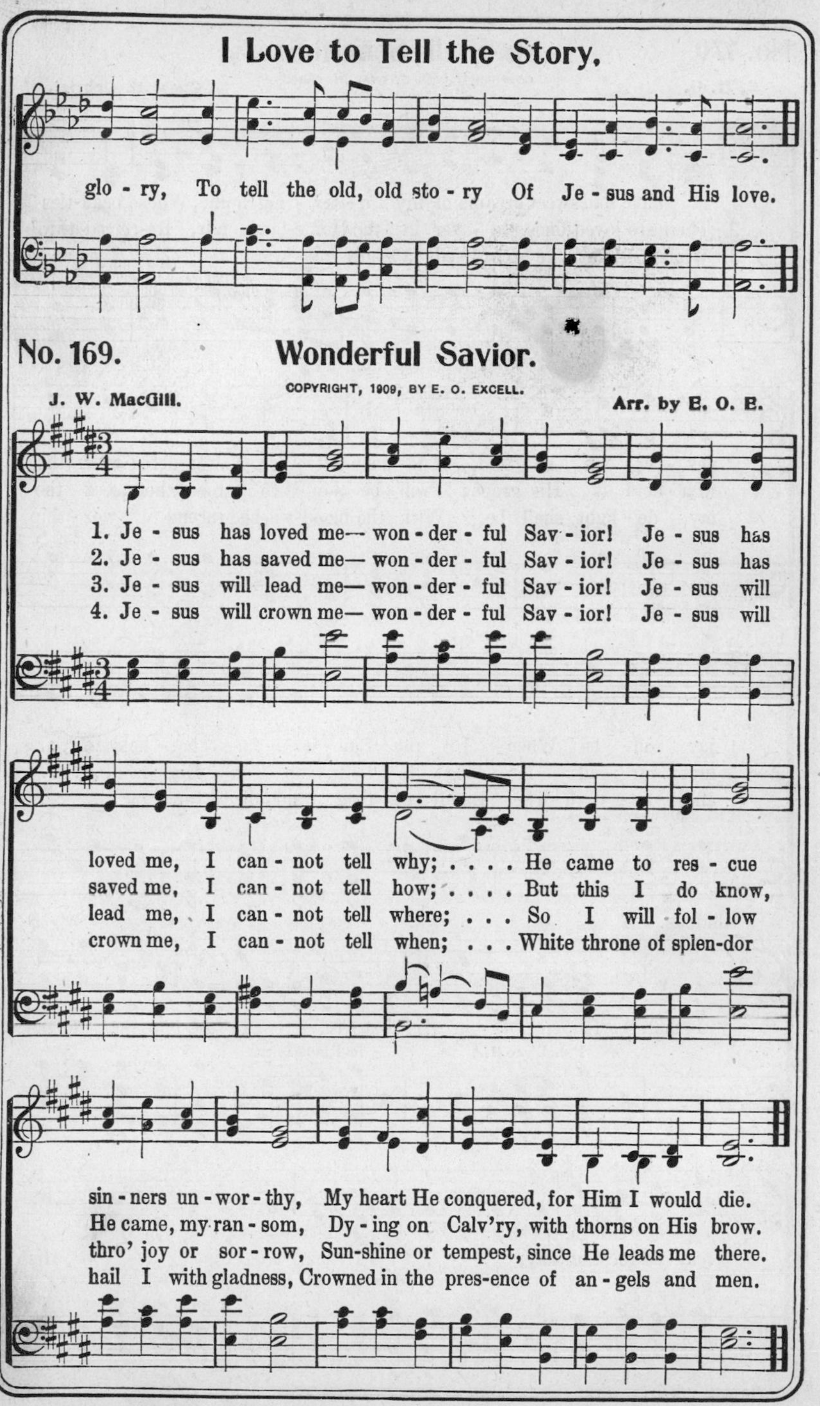
I Love to Tell the Story.
glo - ry, To tell the old, old sto - ry Of Je - sus and His love.
No. 169. Wonderful Savior.
COPYRIGHT, 1909, BY E. O. EXCELL.
J. W. MacGill.
Arr. by E. O. E.
1. Je - sus has loved me— won - der - ful Sav - ior! Je - sus has
2. Je - sus has saved me— won - der - ful Sav - ior! Je - sus has
3. Je - sus will lead me— won - der - ful Sav - ior! Je - sus will
4. Je - sus will crown me— won - der - ful Sav - ior! Je - sus will
loved me, I can - not tell why; . . . . He came to res - cue
saved me, I can - not tell how; . . . . But this I do know,
lead me, I can - not tell where; . . . So I will fol - low
crown me, I can - not tell when; . . . White throne of splen-dor
sin - ners un - wor - thy, My heart He conquered, for Him I would die.
He came, my ran - som, Dy - ing on Calv'ry, with thorns on His brow.
thro' joy or sor - row, Sun-shine or tempest, since He leads me there.
hail I with gladness, Crowned in the pres-ence of an - gels and men.

No. 170. I Shall See Him.
C. H. G.
COPYRIGHT, 1902, BY CHAS. H. GABRIEL.
E. O. EXCELL, OWNER.
Chas. H. Gabriel.
1. I have had sweet dreams of my e - ter - nal home, Whose beau-ties
2. There are loved ones o - ver in the Home-land fair, Re-ceived thro'
3. While the un - re - cord - ed a - ges on - ward roll, My joy and
nev - er can be told, And have oft - en won-dered what the
won - ders of His grace; 'Twill be joy to meet them, but the
my de - light shall be, With the blood-washed throng to wor - ship
joy will be When I my Sav - ior's face be - hold.......
first of all I long to look up - on His face.......
and a - dore The Lamb of God who died for me........
CHORUS.
I shall see Him in His beau - ty, In the morning of the
I shall see Him
in His beau-ty.
res - ur-rec-tion day; I shall see Him in His
I shall see Him;
I shall see Him

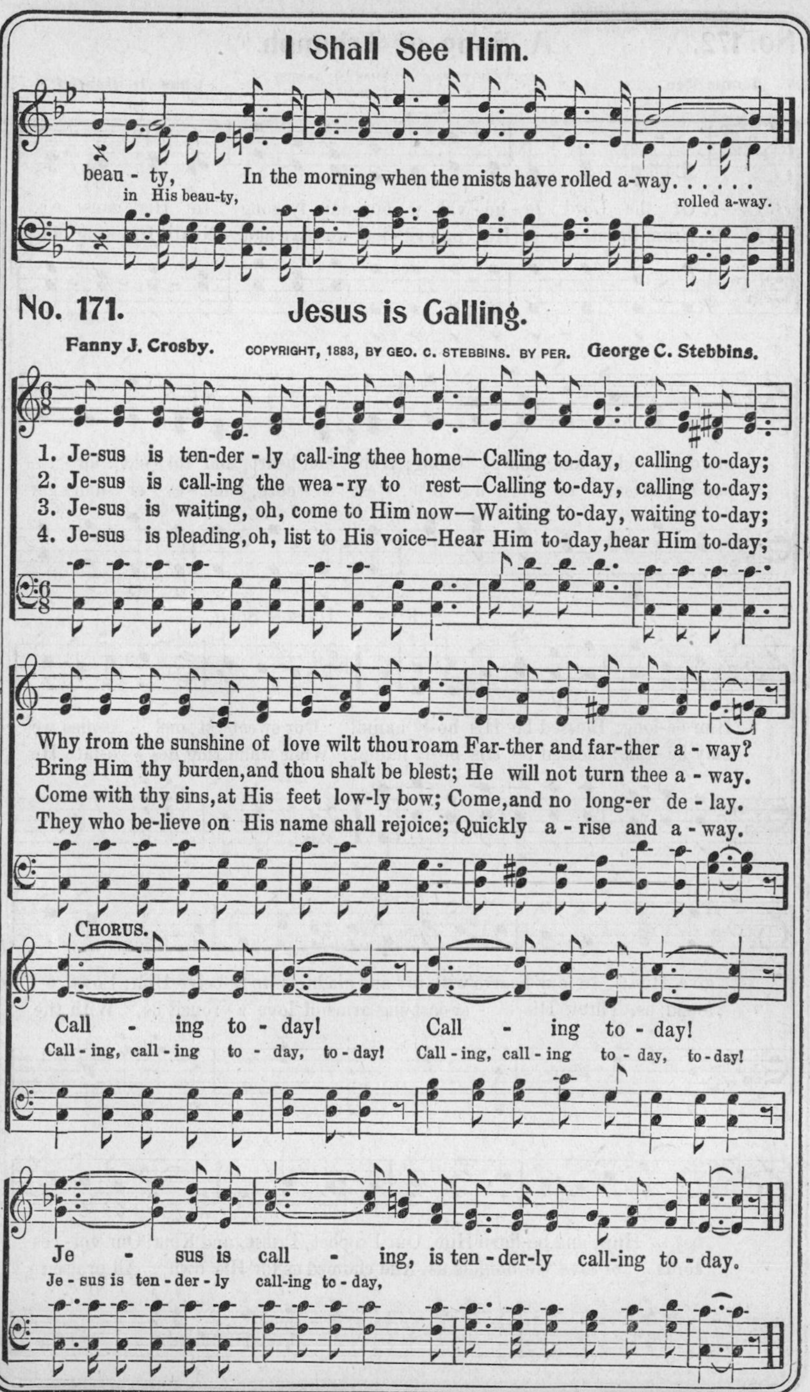
I Shall See Him.
beau - ty, In the morning when the mists have rolled a-way. . . . . .
in His beau-ty,
rolled a-way.
No. 171.
Jesus is Calling.
Fanny J. Crosby.
COPYRIGHT, 1883, BY GEO. C. STEBBINS. BY PER.
George C. Stebbins.
1. Je-sus is ten-der - ly call-ing thee home—Calling to-day, calling to-day;
2. Je-sus is call-ing the wea - ry to rest—Calling to-day, calling to-day;
3. Je-sus is waiting, oh, come to Him now—Waiting to-day, waiting to-day;
4. Je-sus is pleading, oh, list to His voice-Hear Him to-day, hear Him to-day;
Why from the sunshine of love wilt thou roam Far-ther and far-ther a - way?
Bring Him thy burden, and thou shalt be blest; He will not turn thee a - way.
Come with thy sins, at His feet low-ly bow; Come, and no long-er de - lay.
They who be-lieve on His name shall rejoice; Quickly a - rise and a - way.
CHORUS.
Call - ing to - day! Call - ing to - day!
Call - ing, call - ing to - day, to - day! Call - ing, call - ing to - day, to - day!
Je - sus is call - ing, is ten - der-ly call-ing to - day.
Je - sus is ten - der - ly call-ing to - day,

No. 172. A Song of Triumph.
Jennie Ree.
COPYRIGHT, 1902, BY CHAS. H. GABRIEL.
E. O. EXCELL, OWNER.
Chas. H. Gabriel.
D. C.—1. Of the Lord Je-ho-vah is our dai-ly song! In His cause we march, a glad and hap-py throng; Hand, and heart, and tal-ent un-to Him be-long; Blessed be His ho-ly name!
D. C.—2. From the storm in His pa-vil-ion we may hide, 'Neath His wing in peace and safe-ty may a-bide, Rest se-cure, what-ev-er dan-ger may be-tide; Blessed be His ho-ly name!
FINE.
UNISON SOLO.
Our sweet-est mel-o-dies we give Him; In our hearts with joy and gladness we re-ceive Him; Love, o-bey Him, and be-lieve Him, Our Prophet, Priest, and King! Our voi-ces
While wand'ring des-o-late He found us, Threw His ev-er-last-ing arms of love a-round us, With the cords of love He bounds us, And claimed us for His own; All praise to

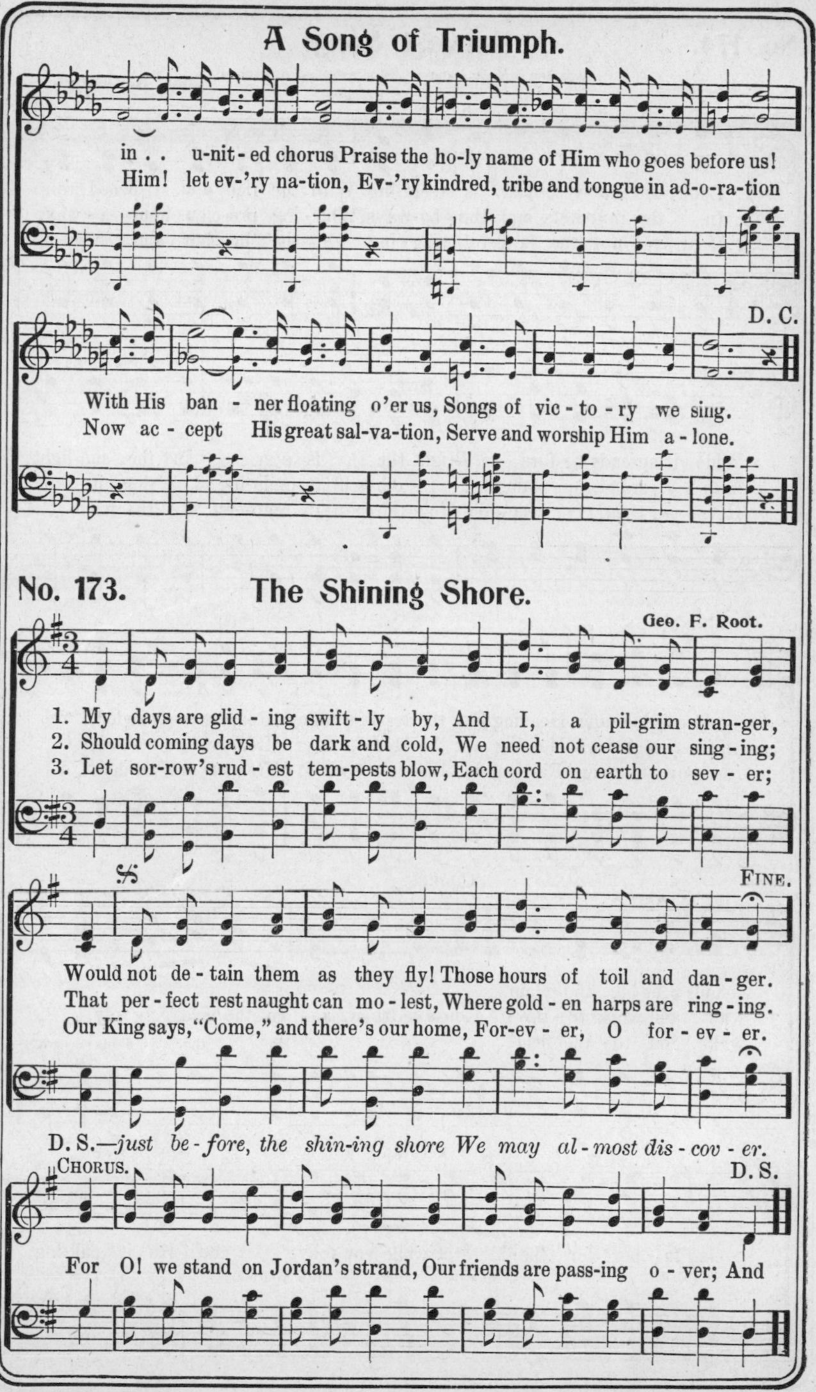
A Song of Triumph.
in . . u-nit - ed chorus Praise the ho-ly name of Him who goes before us!
Him! let ev-'ry na-tion, Ev-'ry kindred, tribe and tongue in ad-o-ra-tion
D. C.
With His ban - ner floating o'er us, Songs of vic - to - ry we sing.
Now ac - cept His great sal-va-tion, Serve and worship Him a - lone.
No. 173. The Shining Shore.
Geo. F. Root.
1. My days are glid - ing swift - ly by, And I, a pil-grim stran-ger,
2. Should coming days be dark and cold, We need not cease our sing - ing;
3. Let sor-row's rud - est tem-pests blow, Each cord on earth to sev - er;
FINE.
Would not de - tain them as they fly! Those hours of toil and dan - ger.
That per - fect rest naught can mo - lest, Where gold - en harps are ring - ing.
Our King says, "Come," and there's our home, For-ev - er, O for - ev - er.
D. S.—just be - fore, the shin-ing shore We may al - most dis - cov - er.
CHORUS.
D. S.
For O! we stand on Jordan's strand, Our friends are pass-ing o - ver; And

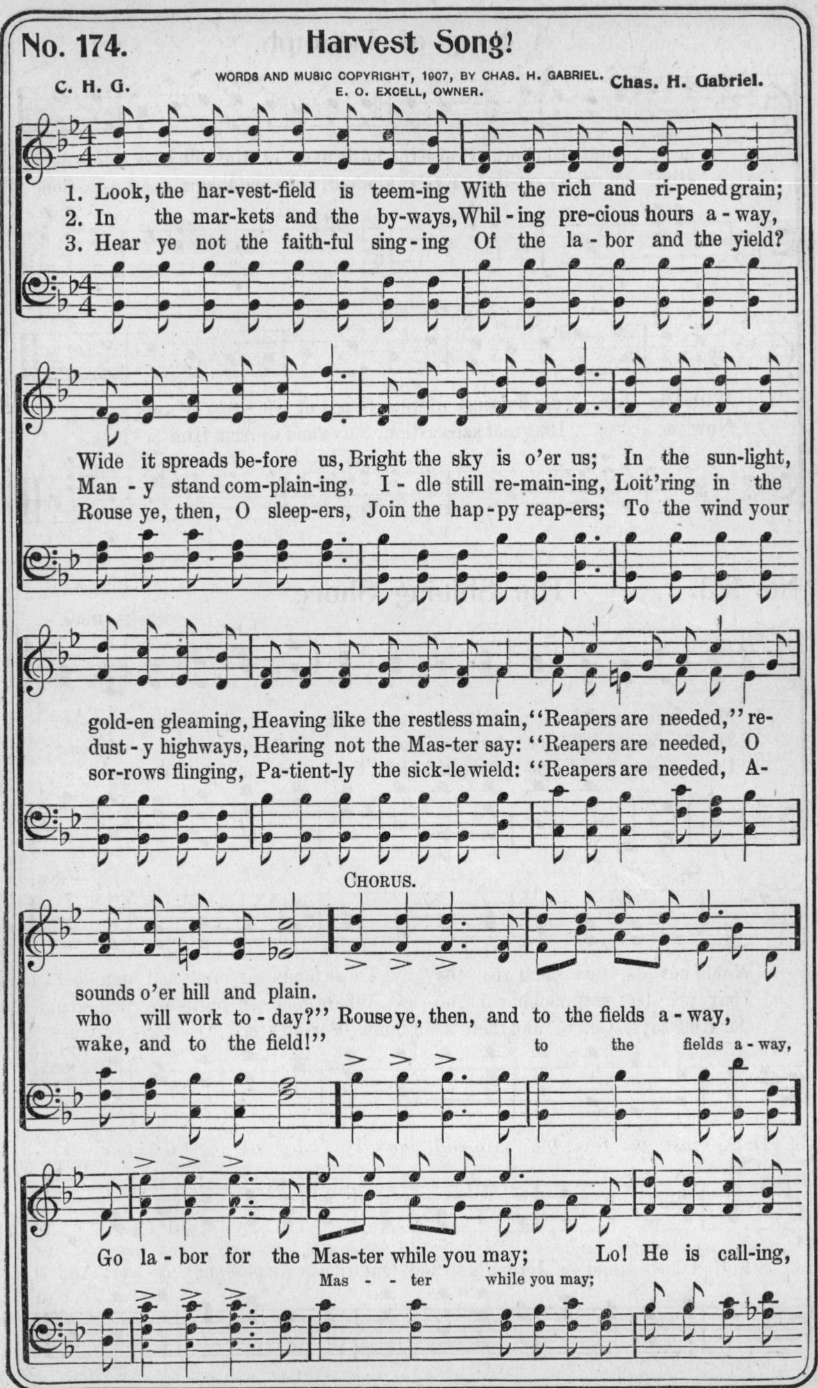
No. 174. Harvest Song!
C. H. G.
WORDS AND MUSIC COPYRIGHT, 1907, BY CHAS. H. GABRIEL.
E. O. EXCELL, OWNER.
Chas. H. Gabriel.
1. Look, the har-vest-field is teem-ing With the rich and ri-pened grain;
2. In the mar-kets and the by-ways, Whil-ing pre-cious hours a-way,
3. Hear ye not the faith-ful sing-ing Of the la-bor and the yield?
Wide it spreads be-fore us, Bright the sky is o'er us; In the sun-light,
Man-y stand com-plain-ing, I-dle still re-main-ing, Loit'ring in the
Rouse ye, then, O sleep-ers, Join the hap-py reap-ers; To the wind your
gold-en gleaming, Heaving like the restless main, "Reapers are needed," re-
dust-y highways, Hearing not the Mas-ter say: "Reapers are needed, O
sor-rows flinging, Pa-tient-ly the sick-le wield: "Reapers are needed, A-
CHORUS.
sounds o'er hill and plain.
who will work to-day?" Rouse ye, then, and to the fields a-way,
wake, and to the field!"
to the fields a-way,
Go la-bor for the Mas-ter while you may; Lo! He is call-ing,
Mas-ter while you may;

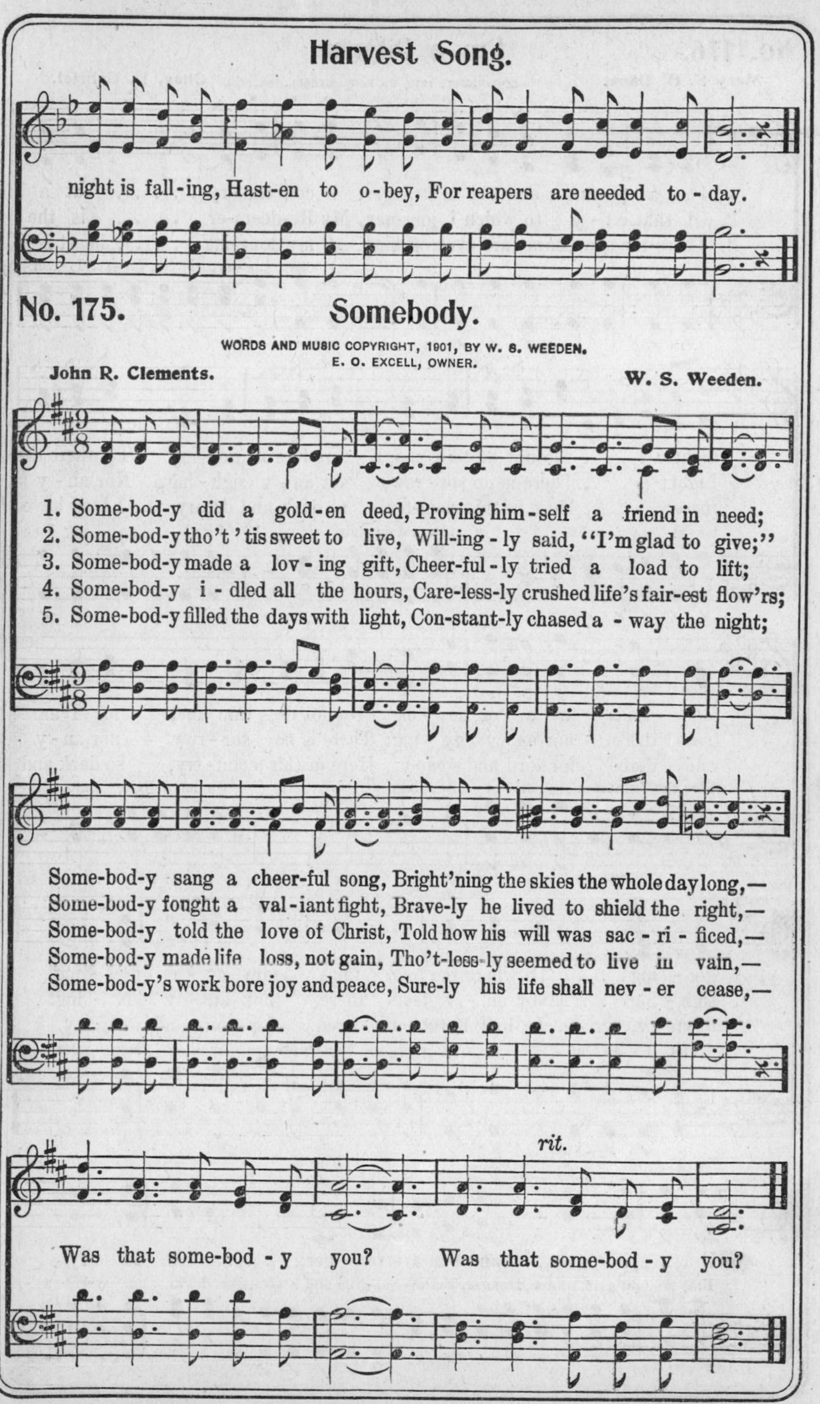
Harvest Song.
night is fall-ing, Hast-en to o-bey, For reapers are needed to-day.
No. 175.
Somebody.
WORDS AND MUSIC COPYRIGHT, 1901, BY W. S. WEEDEN.
E. O. EXCELL, OWNER.
John R. Clements.
W. S. Weeden.
1. Some-bod-y did a gold-en deed, Proving him-self a friend in need;
2. Some-bod-y tho't 'tis sweet to live, Will-ing-ly said, "I'm glad to give;"
3. Some-bod-y made a lov-ing gift, Cheer-ful-ly tried a load to lift;
4. Some-bod-y i-dled all the hours, Care-less-ly crushed life's fair-est flow'rs;
5. Some-bod-y filled the days with light, Con-stant-ly chased a-way the night;
Some-bod-y sang a cheer-ful song, Bright'ning the skies the whole day long,—
Some-bod-y fought a val-iant fight, Brave-ly he lived to shield the right,—
Some-bod-y told the love of Christ, Told how his will was sac-ri-ficed,—
Some-bod-y made life loss, not gain, Tho't-less-ly seemed to live in vain,—
Some-bod-y's work bore joy and peace, Sure-ly his life shall nev-er cease,—
rit.
Was that some-bod-y you? Was that some-bod-y you?

No. 176. I'm a Pilgrim.
Mary S. B. Dana.
COPYRIGHT, 1910. BY E. O. EXCELL.
Chas. H. Gabriel.
1. I'm a pil-grim, and I'm a stranger; I can tar-ry . . . . . but a
2. Of that cit-y to which I jour-ney, My Re-deem-er . . . . . is the
3. There the sun-beams are ev-er shining,—O my long-ing . . . . . heart is
I can tar-ry, I can tar-ry, I can
night!. . . . . Do not de-tain me, for I am go-ing To where the
Light; . . . . There is no sor-row, nor an-y sigh-ing, Nor an-y
there;. . . . . Here in this coun-try, so dark and dreary, I long have
tar-ry but a night! Do not de-tain me, for I am go-ing To
foun-tains are ev-er flow-ing; Do not de-tain me, for I am
tears there, nor an-y dy-ing; There is no sor-row, nor an-y
wan-dered, for-lorn and wear-y; Here in this coun-try, so dark and
where the fountains are ev-er flow-ing; Do not de-tain me,
go-ing. . . . To where the foun-tains are ev-er flow-ing.
sigh-ing, . . . Nor an-y tears there, nor an-y dy-ing.
drear-y, ... I long have wan-dered, for-lorn and wear-y.
for I am go-ing To where the foun-tains are ev-er flow-ing.
CHORUS.
I'm a pil-grim, and I'm a stran-ger; . . . . I can tar-ry
I'm a pil-grim and a stranger, I'm a pil-grim and a stranger; I can tar-ry but a

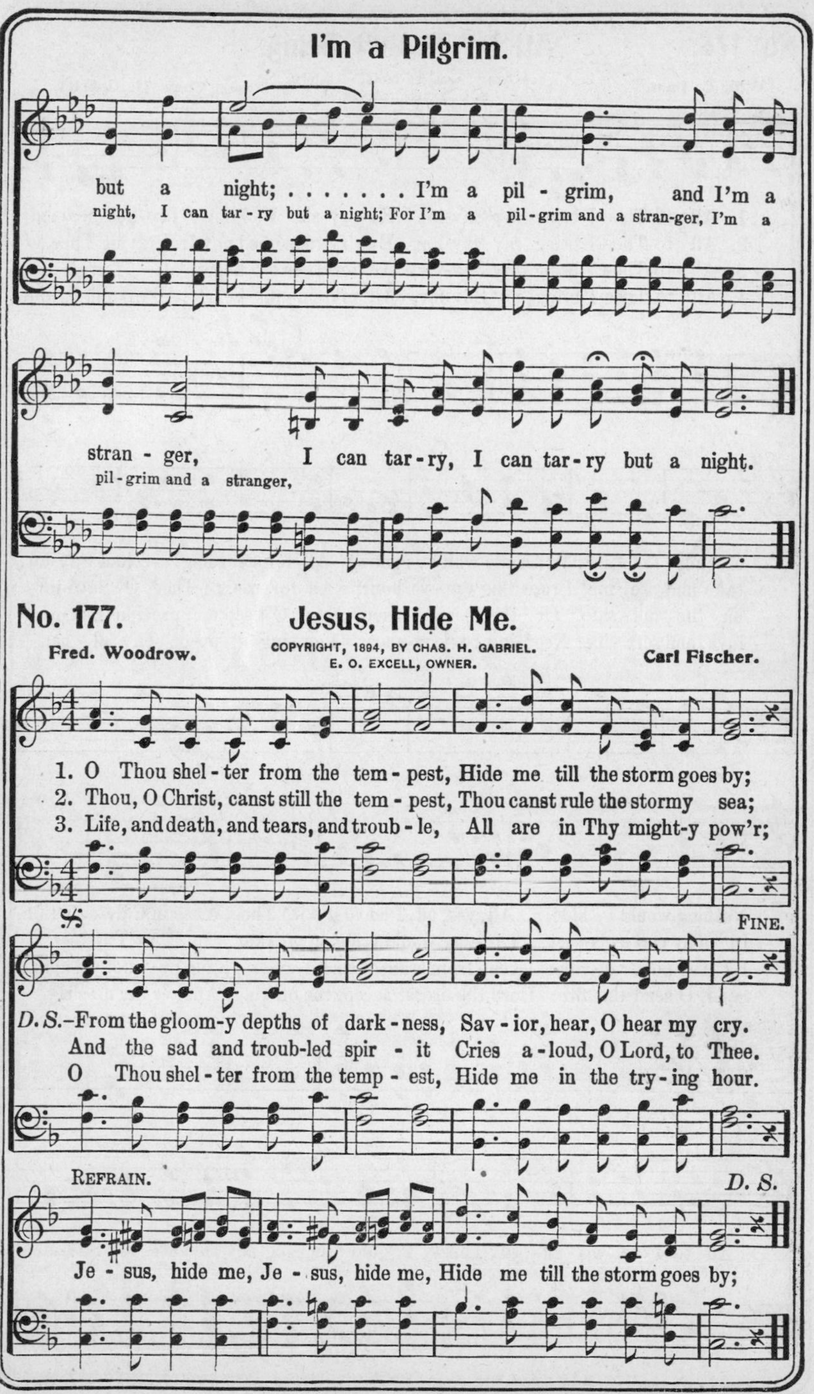
I'm a Pilgrim.
but a night; . . . . I'm a pil - grim, and I'm a
night, I can tar - ry but a night; For I'm a pil - grim and a stran - ger, I'm a
stran - ger, I can tar - ry, I can tar - ry but a night.
pil - grim and a stranger,
No. 177.
Jesus, Hide Me.
Fred. Woodrow.
COPYRIGHT, 1894, BY CHAS. H. GABRIEL.
E. O. EXCELL, OWNER.
Carl Fischer.
1. O Thou shel - ter from the tem - pest, Hide me till the storm goes by;
2. Thou, O Christ, canst still the tem - pest, Thou canst rule the stormy sea;
3. Life, and death, and tears, and troub - le, All are in Thy might - y pow'r;
FINE.
D. S.–From the gloom - y depths of dark - ness, Sav - ior, hear, O hear my cry.
And the sad and troub - led spir - it Cries a - loud, O Lord, to Thee.
O Thou shel - ter from the temp - est, Hide me in the try - ing hour.
REFRAIN.
D. S.
Je - sus, hide me, Je - sus, hide me, Hide me till the storm goes by;

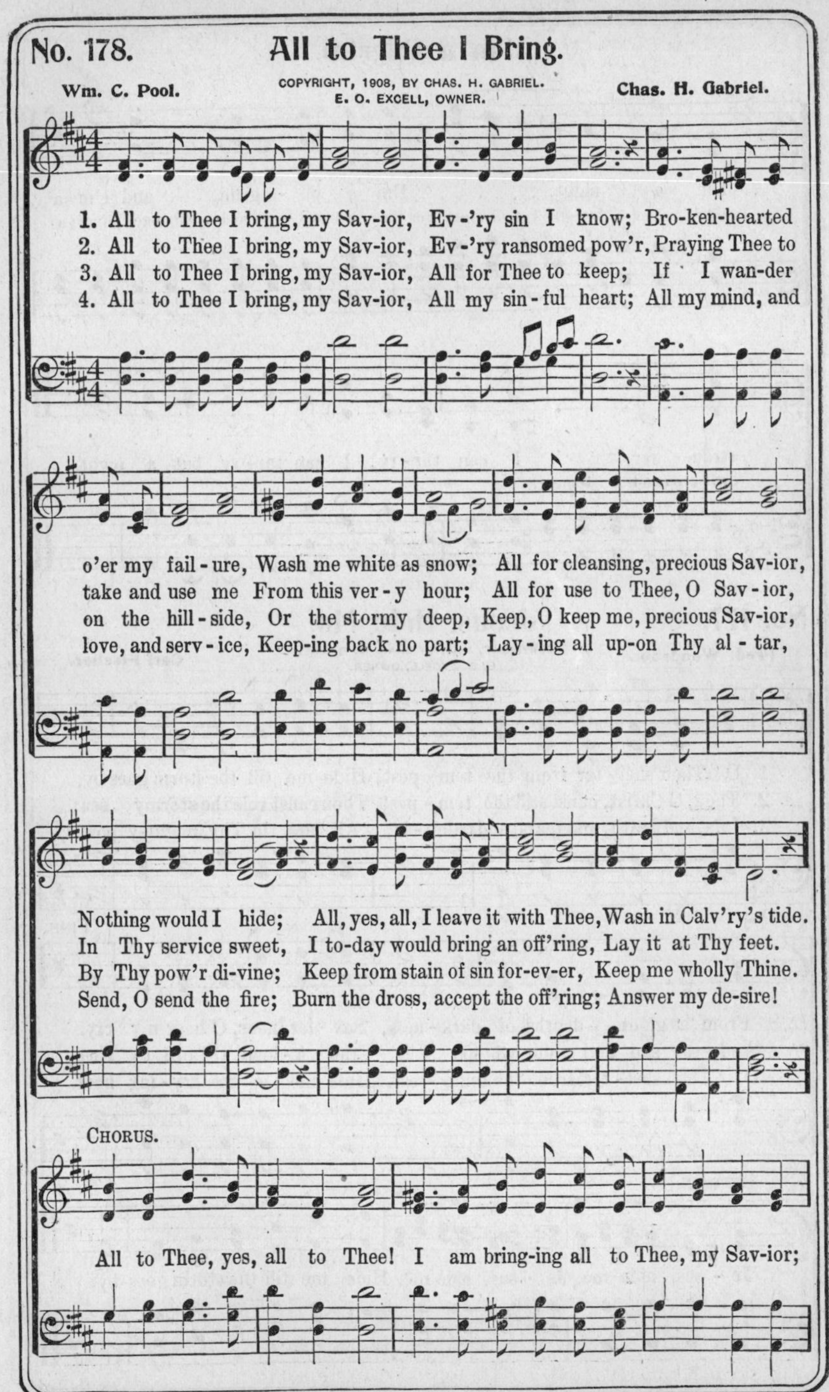
No. 178. All to Thee I Bring.
Wm. C. Pool.
COPYRIGHT, 1908, BY CHAS. H. GABRIEL.
E. O. EXCELL, OWNER.
Chas. H. Gabriel.
1. All to Thee I bring, my Sav-ior, Ev-'ry sin I know; Bro-ken-hearted
2. All to Thee I bring, my Sav-ior, Ev-'ry ransomed pow'r, Praying Thee to
3. All to Thee I bring, my Sav-ior, All for Thee to keep; If I wan-der
4. All to Thee I bring, my Sav-ior, All my sin-ful heart; All my mind, and
o'er my fail-ure, Wash me white as snow; All for cleansing, precious Sav-ior,
take and use me From this ver-y hour; All for use to Thee, O Sav-ior,
on the hill-side, Or the stormy deep, Keep, O keep me, precious Sav-ior,
love, and serv-ice, Keep-ing back no part; Lay-ing all up-on Thy al-tar,
Nothing would I hide; All, yes, all, I leave it with Thee, Wash in Calv'ry's tide.
In Thy service sweet, I to-day would bring an off'ring, Lay it at Thy feet.
By Thy pow'r di-vine; Keep from stain of sin for-ev-er, Keep me wholly Thine.
Send, O send the fire; Burn the dross, accept the off'ring; Answer my de-sire!
CHORUS.
All to Thee, yes, all to Thee! I am bring-ing all to Thee, my Sav-ior;

All to Thee I Bring.
All to Thee, yes, all to Thee, Sav-ior, I am bring-ing all to Thee.
No. 179.
Forgiven.
C. H. G.
COPYRIGHT, 1906, BY CHAS. H. GABRIEL.
E. O. EXCELL, OWNER.
Chas. H. Gabriel.
1. A song is ring-ing in my soul, "For-giv-en! for-giv-en!"
2. When first to me the message came, "For-giv-en! for-giv-en!"
3. I'm sing-ing on my way to heav'n, "For-giv-en! for-giv-en!"
4. I'll sing while He shall lend me breath, "For-giv-en! for-giv-en!"
Thro' grace I'm ev-'ry whit made whole, My sins are washed a-way.
I shout-ed glo-ry to His name, My sins are washed a-way.
For blest as-sur-ance He has giv'n, My sins are washed a-way.
And praise Him in the hour of death, My sins are washed a-way.
CHORUS.
For-giv-en! for-giv-en! My heart is sing-ing all the time!
For-giv-en! for-giv-en! My sins are washed (Omit ....) a-way!

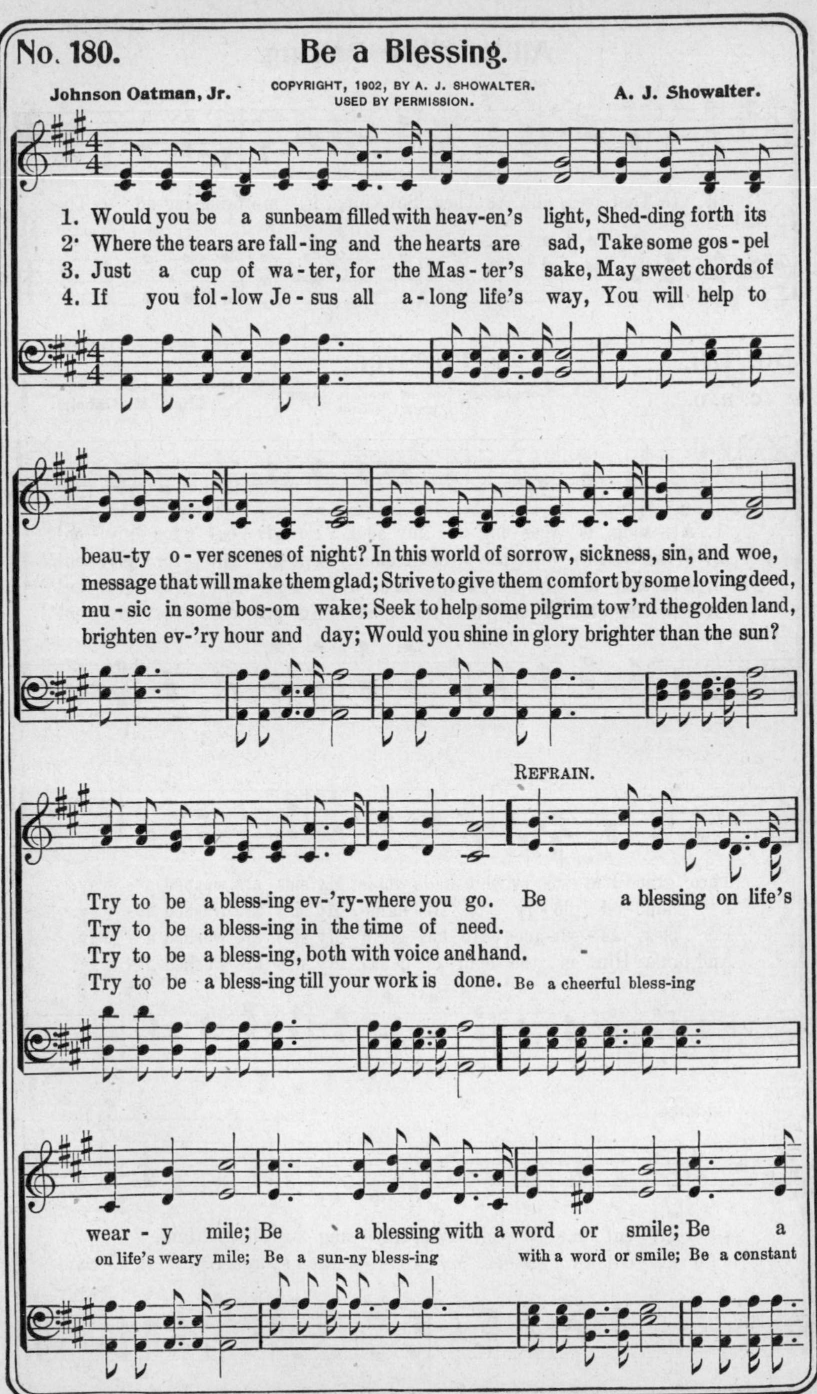
No. 180.
Be a Blessing.
Johnson Oatman, Jr.
COPYRIGHT, 1902, BY A. J. SHOWALTER.
USED BY PERMISSION.
A. J. Showalter.
1. Would you be a sunbeam filled with heav-en's light, Shed-ding forth its
2. Where the tears are fall-ing and the hearts are sad, Take some gos-pel
3. Just a cup of wa-ter, for the Mas-ter's sake, May sweet chords of
4. If you fol-low Je-sus all a-long life's way, You will help to
beau-ty o-ver scenes of night? In this world of sorrow, sickness, sin, and woe,
message that will make them glad; Strive to give them comfort by some loving deed,
mu-sic in some bos-om wake; Seek to help some pilgrim tow'rd the golden land,
brighten ev-'ry hour and day; Would you shine in glory brighter than the sun?
Try to be a bless-ing ev-'ry-where you go.
Try to be a bless-ing in the time of need.
Try to be a bless-ing, both with voice and hand.
Try to be a bless-ing till your work is done.
REFRAIN.
Be a blessing on life's
Be a cheerful bless-ing
wear-y mile; Be a blessing with a word or smile; Be a
on life's weary mile; Be a sun-ny bless-ing with a word or smile; Be a constant

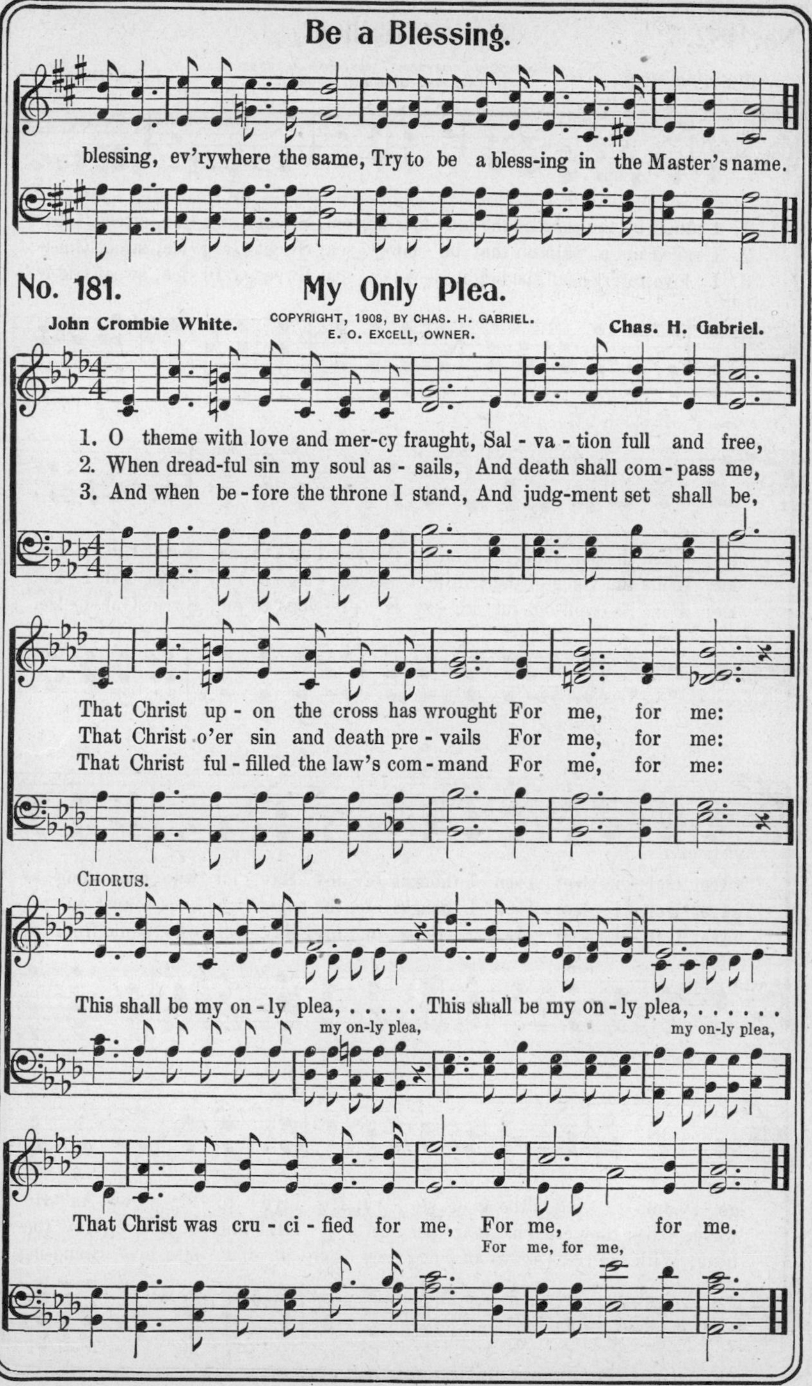
Be a Blessing.
blessing, ev'rywhere the same, Try to be a bless-ing in the Master's name.
No. 181.
My Only Plea.
John Crombie White.
COPYRIGHT, 1908, BY CHAS. H. GABRIEL.
E. O. EXCELL, OWNER.
Chas. H. Gabriel.
1. O theme with love and mer-cy fraught, Sal - va - tion full and free,
2. When dread-ful sin my soul as - sails, And death shall com - pass me,
3. And when be - fore the throne I stand, And judg-ment set shall be,
That Christ up - on the cross has wrought For me, for me:
That Christ o'er sin and death pre - vails For me, for me:
That Christ ful - filled the law's com - mand For me, for me:
Chorus.
This shall be my on - ly plea, ... This shall be my on - ly plea, ...
my on-ly plea,
my on-ly plea,
That Christ was cru - ci - fied for me, For me, for me.
For me, for me,

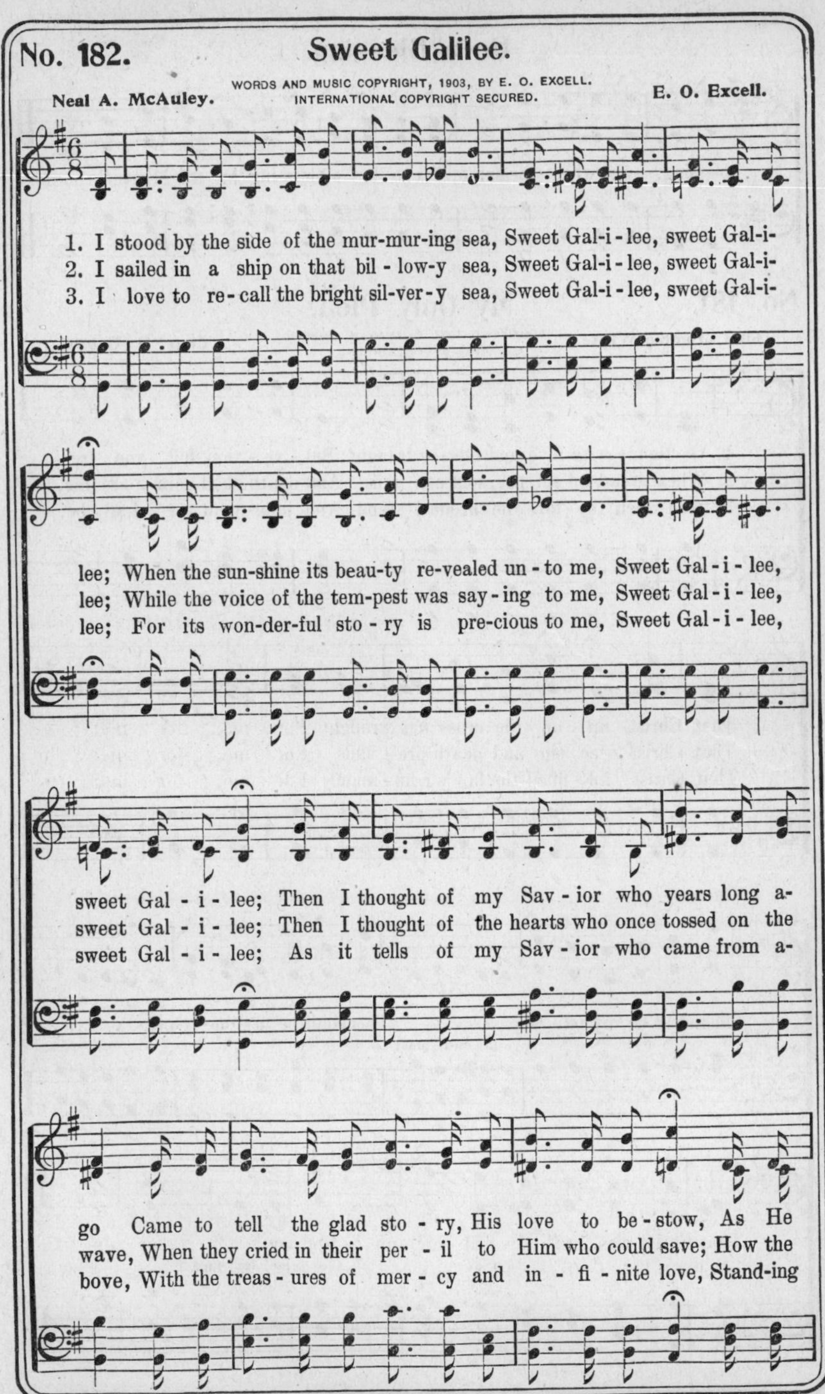
No. 182. Sweet Galilee.
WORDS AND MUSIC COPYRIGHT, 1903, BY E. O. EXCELL.
INTERNATIONAL COPYRIGHT SECURED.
Neal A. McAuley.
E. O. Excell.
1. I stood by the side of the mur-mur-ing sea, Sweet Gal-i-lee, sweet Gal-i-
2. I sailed in a ship on that bil - low-y sea, Sweet Gal-i - lee, sweet Gal-i-
3. I love to re-call the bright sil-ver-y sea, Sweet Gal-i - lee, sweet Gal-i-
lee; When the sun-shine its beau-ty re-vealed un - to me, Sweet Gal - i - lee,
lee; While the voice of the tem-pest was say-ing to me, Sweet Gal - i - lee,
lee; For its won-der-ful sto - ry is pre-cious to me, Sweet Gal - i - lee,
sweet Gal - i - lee; Then I thought of my Sav - ior who years long a-
sweet Gal - i - lee; Then I thought of the hearts who once tossed on the
sweet Gal - i - lee; As it tells of my Sav - ior who came from a-
go Came to tell the glad sto - ry, His love to be - stow, As He
wave, When they cried in their per - il to Him who could save; How the
bove, With the treas - ures of mer - cy and in - fi - nite love, Stand-ing

Sweet Galilee.
stood by the side of that murmuring sea, Sweet Gal-i-lee, sweet Gal-i-lee.
Master spoke peace to that bil-low-y sea, Sweet Gal-i-lee, sweet Gal-i-lee.
there by the side of that sil-ver-y sea, Sweet Gal-i-lee, sweet Gal-i-lee.
No. 183. Our Loving Redeemer.
Ella M. Smedley.
COPYRIGHT, 1910, BY E. O. EXCELL. WORDS AND MUSIC.
Jno. R. Sweney.
1. The eyes of the Lord are up-on us, He lead-eth wher-ev-er He will;
2. The eyes of the Lord are up-on us, Di-rect-ing the path that we tread,
3. The eyes of the Lord are up-on us; When troubled and sorrow-oppressed,
4. The eyes of the Lord are up-on us, Then fol-low our Sav-ior and Guide;
FINE.
But send-eth the light of His Spir-it, Our souls with His blessing to fill.
While soft-ly and gen-tly a-round us The dews of His mer-cy are shed.
We hear, like the voice of a shep-herd, "Come hither, ye wear-y, and rest!"
Hold fast to His life-giv-ing prom-ise, And trust-ful-ly walk by His side.
D. S.—prayer that we of-fer in se-cret Our lov-ing Re-deem-er will hear.
CHORUS.
D. S.
The eyes of the Lord are up-on us, Our gracious Pro-tect-or is near; The

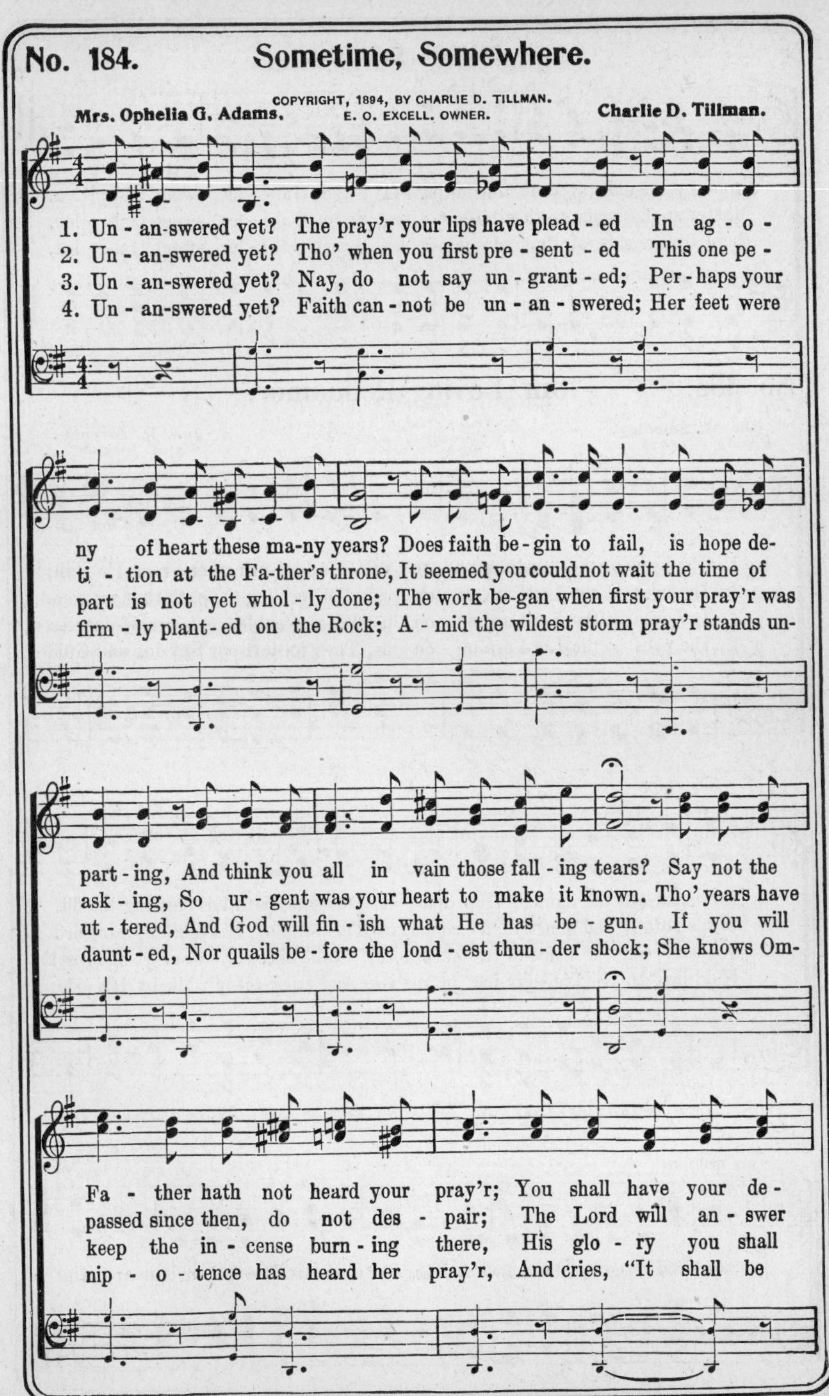

No. 184.
Sometime, Somewhere.
COPYRIGHT, 1894, BY CHARLIE D. TILLMAN.
E. O. EXCELL, OWNER.
Mrs. Ophelia G. Adams.
Charlie D. Tillman.
1. Un - an-swered yet? The pray'r your lips have plead - ed In ag - o - ny of heart these ma-ny years? Does faith be-gin to fail, is hope de- part - ing, And think you all in vain those fall - ing tears? Say not the Fa - ther hath not heard your pray'r; You shall have your de -
2. Un - an-swered yet? Tho' when you first pre - sent - ed This one pe - ti - tion at the Fa-ther's throne, It seemed you could not wait the time of ask - ing, So ur - gent was your heart to make it known. Tho' years have passed since then, do not des - pair; The Lord will an - swer
3. Un - an-swered yet? Nay, do not say un - grant - ed; Per - haps your part is not yet whol - ly done; The work be-gan when first your pray'r was ut - tered, And God will fin - ish what He has be - gun. If you will keep the in - cense burn - ing there, His glo - ry you shall
4. Un - an-swered yet? Faith can - not be un - an - swered; Her feet were firm - ly plant - ed on the Rock; A - mid the wildest storm pray'r stands un- daunt - ed, Nor quails be - fore the lond - est thun - der shock; She knows Om- nip - o - tence has heard her pray'r, And cries, "It shall be

Sometime, Somewhere.
rit.
ad lib.
sire, sometime, somewhere, You shall have your desire, sometime,somewhere.
you, sometime, somewhere, The Lord will an-swer you, sometime,somewhere.
see, sometime, somewhere, His glo - ry you shall see, sometime,somewhere.
done,sometime, somewhere,"And cries "It shall be done, sometime,somewhere."
No. 185.
Peace to My Soul.
COPYRIGHT, 1908, BY E. O. EXCELL. WORDS AND MUSIC
Fanny J. Crosby.
Jno. R. Sweney.
1. O Jes - us, my Sav - ior, All glo - ry to Thee; Sweet peace in be-
2. What heights of en - joy - ment, What rapture is mine; While faith-ful - ly
3. Should sor-row o'er-take me, Thy word is my stay; Should tri - als be-
4. O lov - ing Re - deem - er, What-ev - er Thy will; In tempests or
CHORUS.
liev - ing Thou giv - est to me.
trust-ing Thy promise di - vine. Peace, peace to my soul Flows like a
fall me Thou guidest my way.
sun-shine, I'll fol-low Thee still.
beau-ti-ful riv - er; Peace, hallow'd and pure, Constant a-bid-ing for-ev - er.

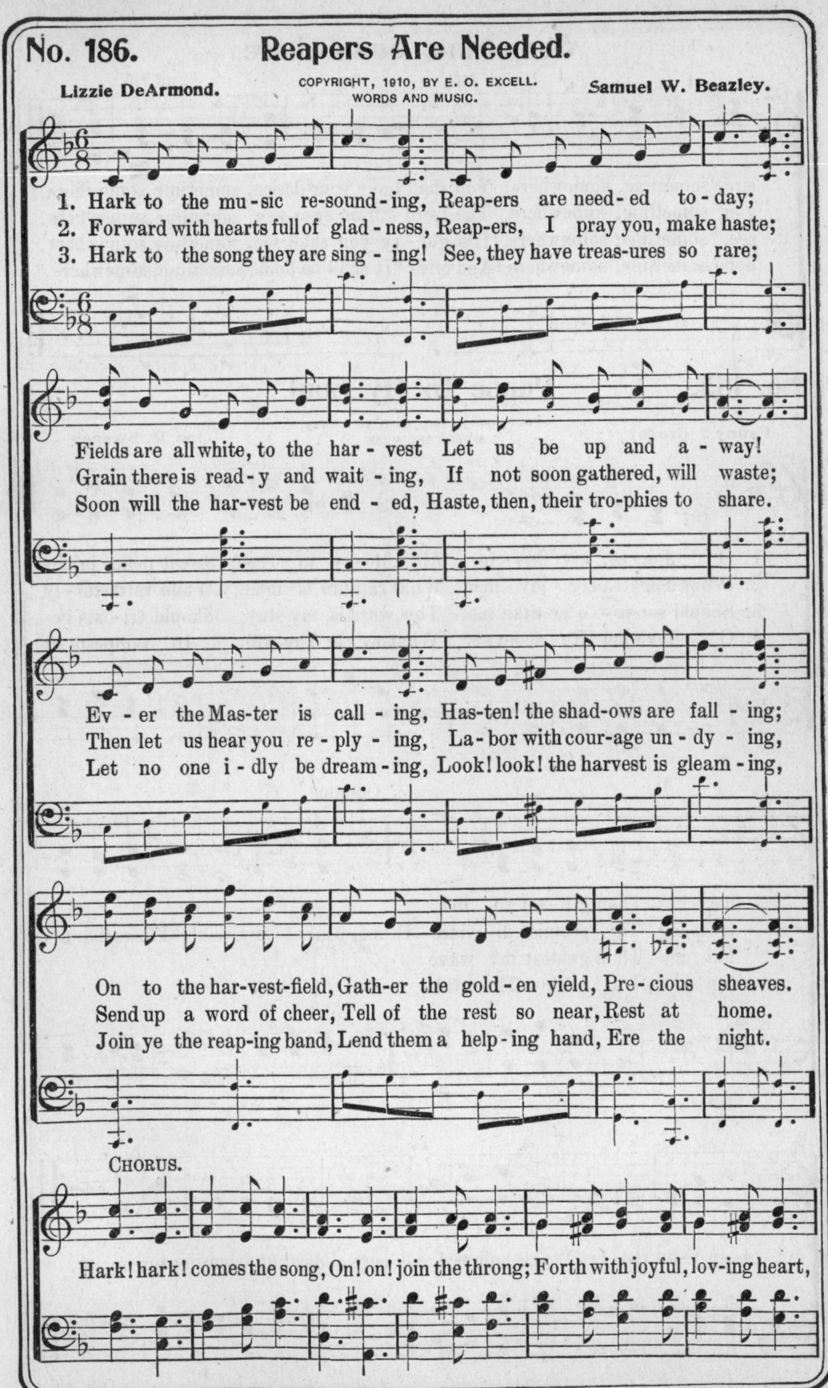
No. 186. Reapers Are Needed.
Lizzie DeArmond.
COPYRIGHT, 1910, BY E. O. EXCELL.
WORDS AND MUSIC.
Samuel W. Beazley.
1. Hark to the mu-sic re-sound-ing, Reap-ers are need-ed to-day;
2. Forward with hearts full of glad-ness, Reap-ers, I pray you, make haste;
3. Hark to the song they are sing-ing! See, they have treas-ures so rare;
Fields are all white, to the har-vest Let us be up and a-way!
Grain there is read-y and wait-ing, If not soon gathered, will waste;
Soon will the har-vest be end-ed, Haste, then, their tro-phies to share.
Ev-er the Mas-ter is call-ing, Has-ten! the shad-ows are fall-ing;
Then let us hear you re-ply-ing, La-bor with cour-age un-dy-ing,
Let no one i-dly be dream-ing, Look! look! the harvest is gleam-ing,
On to the har-vest-field, Gath-er the gold-en yield, Pre-cious sheaves.
Send up a word of cheer, Tell of the rest so near, Rest at home.
Join ye the reap-ing band, Lend them a help-ing hand, Ere the night.
CHORUS.
Hark! hark! comes the song, On! on! join the throng; Forth with joyful, lov-ing heart,

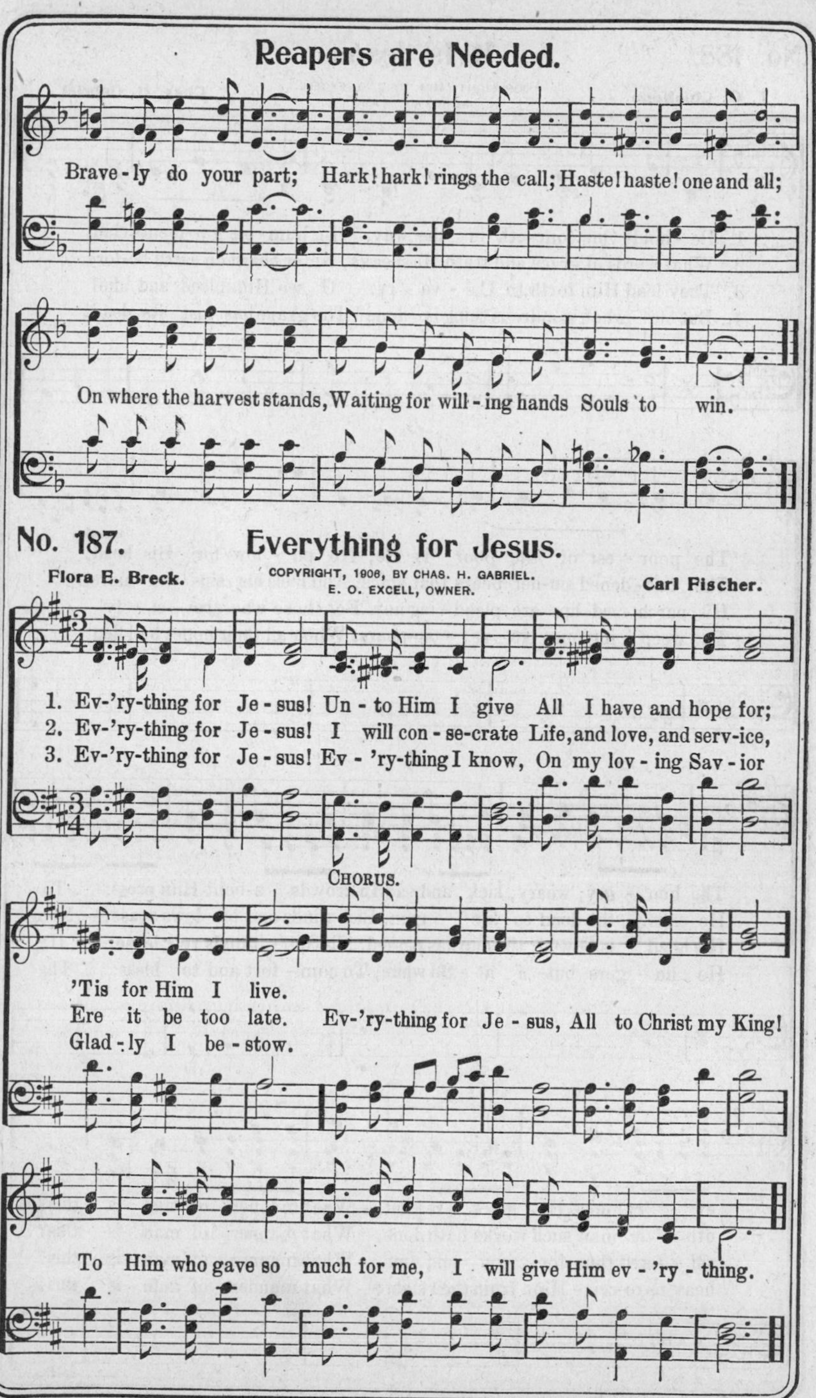

Reapers are Needed.
Brave-ly do your part; Hark! hark! rings the call; Haste! haste! one and all;
On where the harvest stands, Waiting for will-ing hands Souls to win.
No. 187. Everything for Jesus.
Flora E. Breck.
COPYRIGHT, 1906, BY CHAS. H. GABRIEL.
E. O. EXCELL, OWNER.
Carl Fischer.
1. Ev-'ry-thing for Je-sus! Un-to Him I give All I have and hope for; 'Tis for Him I live.
2. Ev-'ry-thing for Je-sus! I will con-se-crate Life, and love, and serv-ice, Ere it be too late.
3. Ev-'ry-thing for Je-sus! Ev-'ry-thing I know, On my lov-ing Sav-ior Glad-ly I be-stow.
CHORUS.
Ev-'ry-thing for Je-sus, All to Christ my King!
To Him who gave so much for me, I will give Him ev-'ry-thing.

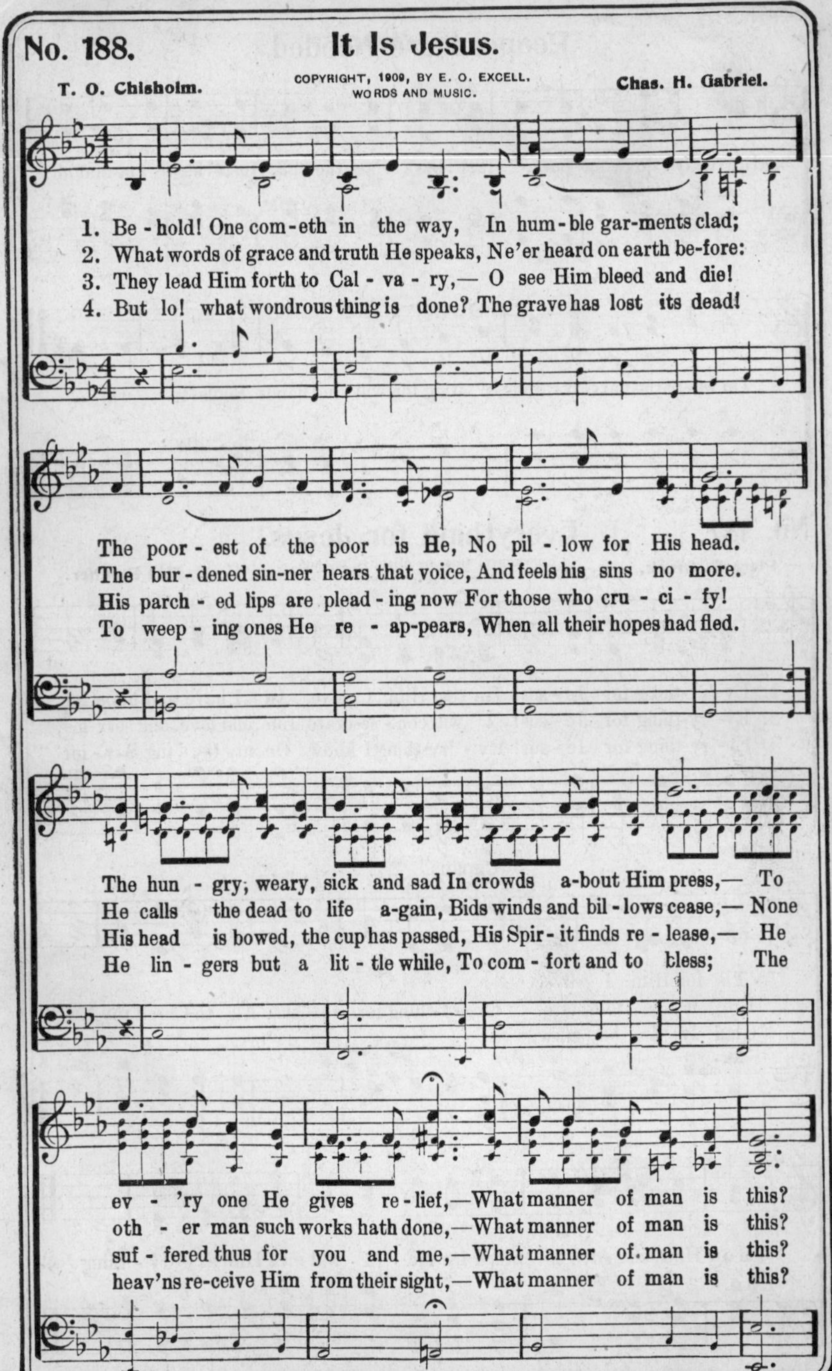
No. 188.
It Is Jesus.
T. O. Chisholm.
COPYRIGHT, 1909, BY E. O. EXCELL. WORDS AND MUSIC.
Chas. H. Gabriel.
1. Be - hold! One com - eth in the way, In hum - ble gar - ments clad;
2. What words of grace and truth He speaks, Ne'er heard on earth be - fore:
3. They lead Him forth to Cal - va - ry,— O see Him bleed and die!
4. But lo! what wondrous thing is done? The grave has lost its dead!
The poor - est of the poor is He, No pil - low for His head.
The bur - dened sin - ner hears that voice, And feels his sins no more.
His parch - ed lips are plead - ing now For those who cru - ci - fy!
To weep - ing ones He re - ap - pears, When all their hopes had fled.
The hun - gry, weary, sick and sad In crowds a - bout Him press,— To
He calls the dead to life a - gain, Bids winds and bil - lows cease,— None
His head is bowed, the cup has passed, His Spir - it finds re - lease,— He
He lin - gers but a lit - tle while, To com - fort and to bless; The
ev - 'ry one He gives re - lief,—What manner of man is this?
oth - er man such works hath done,—What manner of man is this?
suf - fered thus for you and me,—What manner of. man is this?
heav'ns re - ceive Him from their sight,—What manner of man is this?

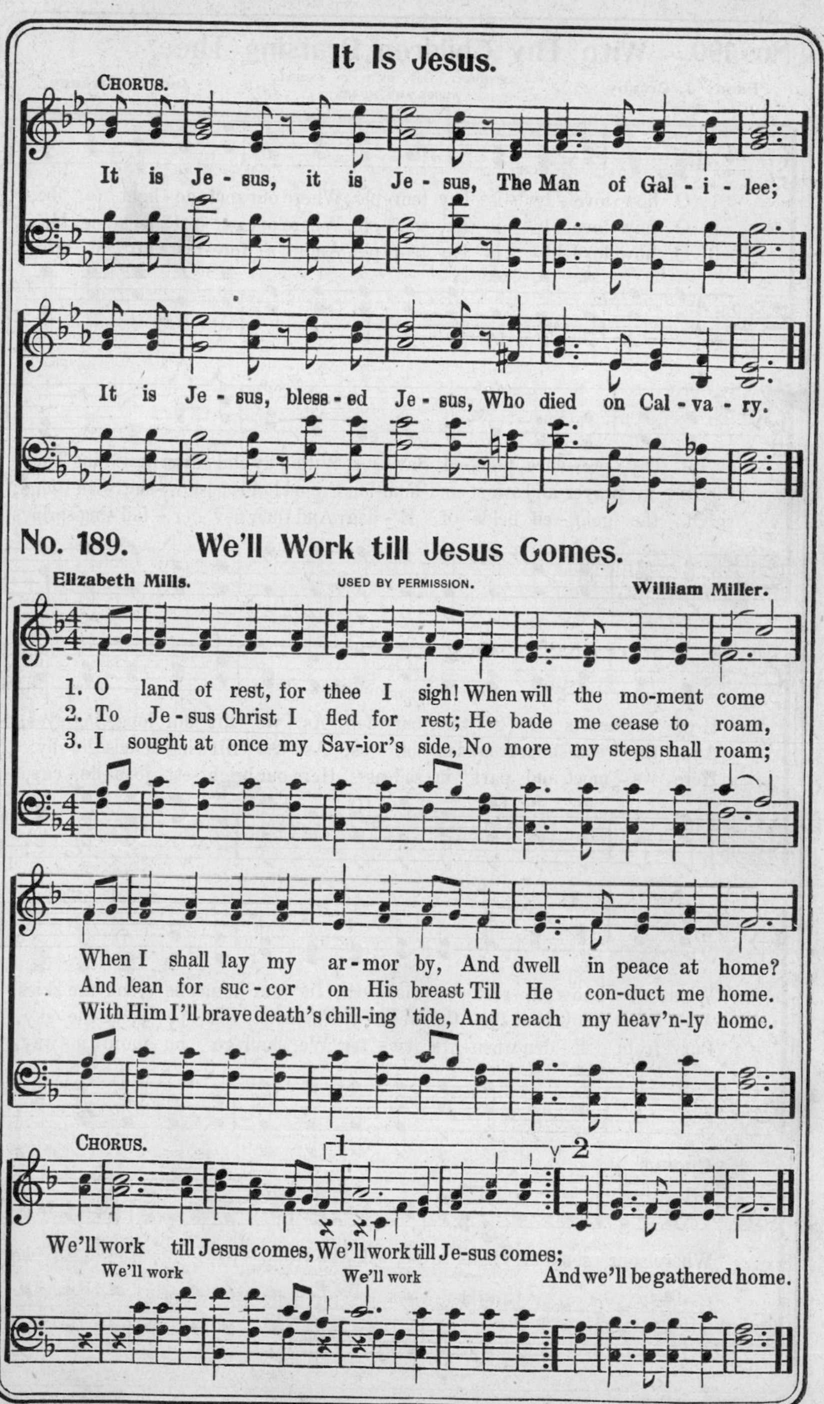
It Is Jesus.
Chorus.
It is Je - sus, it is Je - sus, The Man of Gal - i - lee;
It is Je - sus, bless - ed Je - sus, Who died on Cal - va - ry.
No. 189. We'll Work till Jesus Comes.
Elizabeth Mills.
USED BY PERMISSION.
William Miller.
1. O land of rest, for thee I sigh! When will the mo-ment come
2. To Je - sus Christ I fled for rest; He bade me cease to roam,
3. I sought at once my Sav-ior's side, No more my steps shall roam;
When I shall lay my ar - mor by, And dwell in peace at home?
And lean for suc - cor on His breast Till He con-duct me home.
With Him I'll brave death's chill-ing tide, And reach my heav'n-ly home.
Chorus.
We'll work till Jesus comes, We'll work till Je-sus comes;
We'll work
We'll work
And we'll be gathered home.

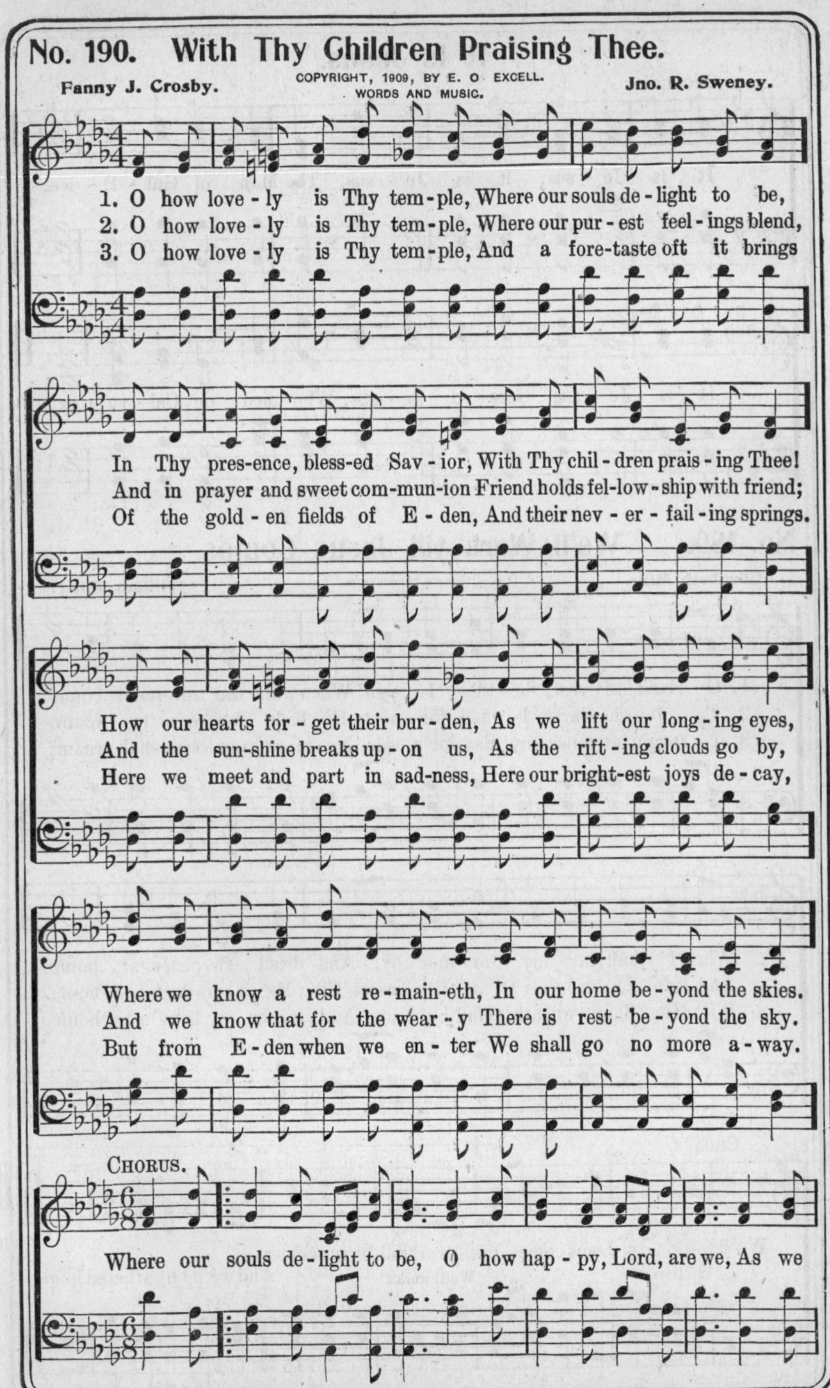
No. 190. With Thy Children Praising Thee.
Fanny J. Crosby.
COPYRIGHT, 1909, BY E. O EXCELL.
WORDS AND MUSIC.
Jno. R. Sweney.
1. O how love - ly is Thy tem - ple, Where our souls de - light to be,
2. O how love - ly is Thy tem - ple, Where our pur - est feel - ings blend,
3. O how love - ly is Thy tem - ple, And a fore-taste oft it brings
In Thy pres-ence, bless-ed Sav - ior, With Thy chil - dren prais - ing Thee!
And in prayer and sweet com-mun-ion Friend holds fel-low - ship with friend;
Of the gold - en fields of E - den, And their nev - er - fail - ing springs.
How our hearts for - get their bur - den, As we lift our long - ing eyes,
And the sun-shine breaks up - on us, As the rift - ing clouds go by,
Here we meet and part in sad-ness, Here our bright-est joys de - cay,
Where we know a rest re - main-eth, In our home be - yond the skies.
And we know that for the wear - y There is rest be - yond the sky.
But from E - den when we en - ter We shall go no more a - way.
CHORUS.
Where our souls de - light to be, O how hap - py, Lord, are we, As we

With Thy Children Praising Thee.
1
gath-er in Thy tem-ple With Thy chil-dren prais-ing Thee; Where our
2
gath-er in Thy tem-ple With Thy chil-dren prais-ing Thee.
No. 191. Thy Way is Best.
Dr. Victor M. Staley.
COPYRIGHT, 1902, BY CHAS. H. GABRIEL. E. O. EXCELL, OWNER.
Chas. H. Gabriel.
1. Teach me, O God, to yield my all To Thy de-cree;
2. Tho' storms may for a time rage wild, And buf-fet me,
3. If Thou, O Fa-ther, be my Guide In weal or woe,
What-e'er in life shall me be-fall, Make me to see
Thou wilt not e'er for-sake Thy child, And I shall see
I will not fear, what-e'er be-tide, For I shall know
REFRAIN.
Thy way is best, is ev-er best, And lead-eth un-to rest. . .
Thy way is best, is ev-er best, And lead-eth un-to sweetest rest.

No. 192.
He Will Hide Me.
James Rowe.
WORDS AND MUSIC COPYRIGHT, 1908, BY E. O. EXCELL.
INTERNATIONAL COPYRIGHT SECURED.
E. O. Excell.
1. When by storm my bark is driv - en Wild - ly o'er the troub - led tide; Christ, whose heart by me was riv - en, Will my soul in safe - ty hide.
2. When by sin's dark clouds sur - round-ed, And I seem to all but fail; He, whose hands and feet I wound-ed, He will hide me from the gale.
3. When my soul longs for the mor - row, When I try, but can - not sing; He, whose head I bowed in sor - row, He will hide me 'neath His wing.
CHORUS. (Small notes for 1st Sopranos.)
He will hide me, safe - ly hide me, Till my
He will hide me, safe-ly hide me, He will hide me, safe-ly hide me, Till my tri - als,

He Will Hide Me.
tri - als all are o'er; He will hide me,
till my tri - als all are o'er, all are o'er; He will hide me, safe - ly hide me,
safe - ly hide me In His love for - ev - - er-more.
He will hide me, safely hide me In His love for-ev-er-more, for-ev-er-more, for - ev - er - more.
No. 193. Take My Life, and Let it Be.
F. R. Havergal.
Wm. B. Bradbury.
1. Take my life, and let it be Con - se - crat - ed, Lord, to Thee;
2. Take my feet, and let them be Swift and beau - ti - ful for Thee;
3. Take my sil - ver and my gold, Not a mite would I with-hold;
4. Take my will, and make it Thine, It shall be no lon - ger mine;
Cho.—Lord, I give my life to Thee, Thine for - ev - er - more to be;
D. C. for Chorus.
Take my hands, and let them move At the im - pulse of Thy love.
Take my voice, and let me sing Al-ways, on - ly, for my King.
Take my mo - ments and my days, Let them flow in cease-less praise.
Take my heart, it is Thine own, It shall be Thy roy - al throne.
Lord, I give my life to Thee, Thine for - ev - er-more to be.

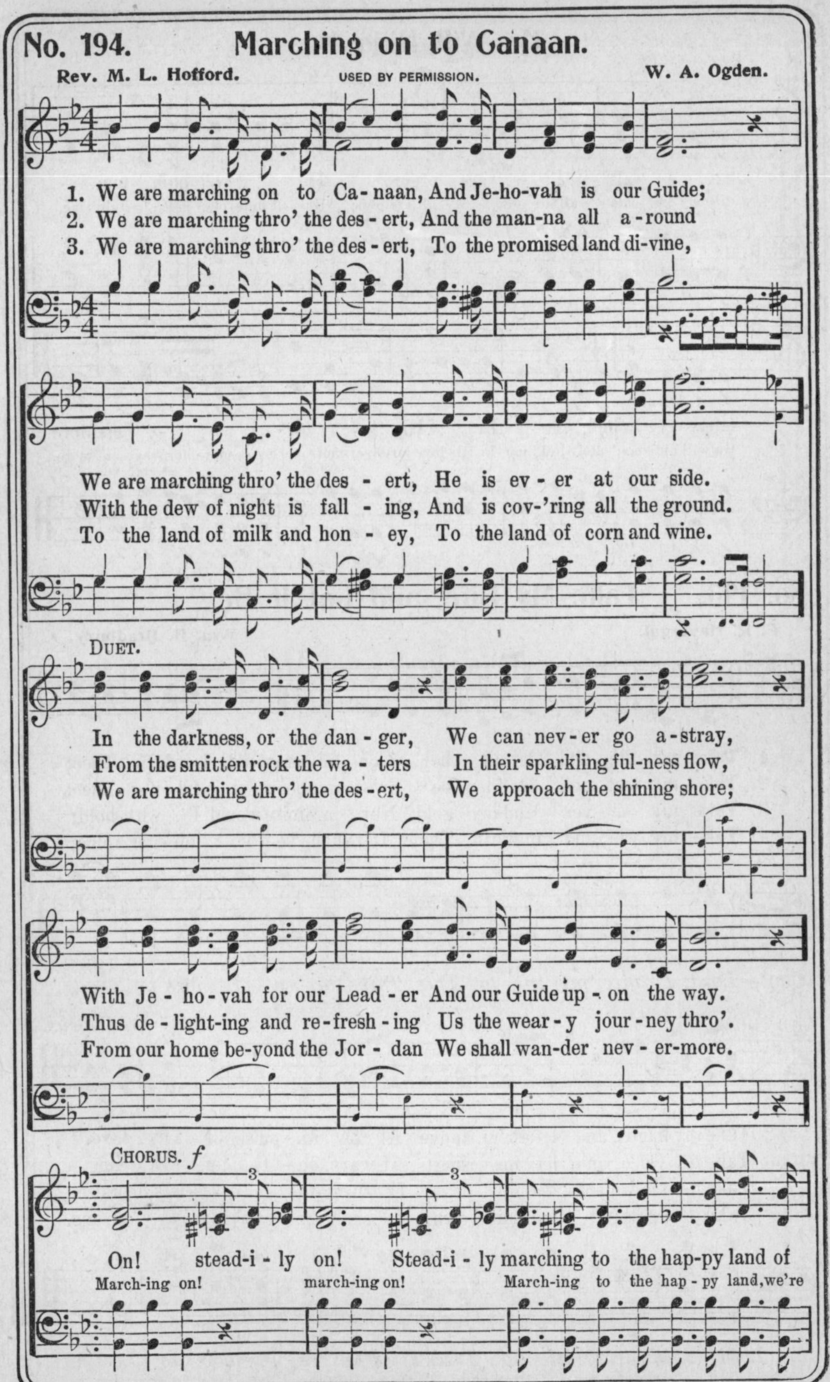
No. 194. Marching on to Canaan.
Rev. M. L. Hofford.
USED BY PERMISSION.
W. A. Ogden.
1. We are marching on to Ca-naan, And Je-ho-vah is our Guide;
2. We are marching thro' the des-ert, And the man-na all a-round
3. We are marching thro' the des-ert, To the promised land di-vine,
We are marching thro' the des-ert, He is ev-er at our side.
With the dew of night is fall-ing, And is cov-'ring all the ground.
To the land of milk and hon-ey, To the land of corn and wine.
DUET.
In the darkness, or the dan-ger, We can nev-er go a-stray,
From the smitten rock the wa-ters In their sparkling ful-ness flow,
We are marching thro' the des-ert, We approach the shining shore;
With Je-ho-vah for our Lead-er And our Guide up-on the way.
Thus de-light-ing and re-fresh-ing Us the wear-y jour-ney thro'.
From our home be-yond the Jor-dan We shall wan-der nev-er-more.
CHORUS. f
On! stead-i-ly on! Stead-i-ly marching to the hap-py land of
March-ing on! march-ing on! March-ing to the hap-py land, we're

Marching on to Canaan.
Ca-naan; On! stead-i-ly on! Ver-i-ly guid-ed by Je-ho-vah's hand are
marching on; Marching on! marching on! Guid-ed by Je - ho-vah's hand are
After last stanza repeat pp
we. Stead-i-ly marching to the hap-py land we go.
we, guid-ed are we. March-ing to the hap-py land we go, marching home.
No. 195. I am Trusting, Lord, in Thee.
Wm. McDonald.
USED BY PERMISSION.
W. G. Fischer.
1. I am com-ing to the cross; I am poor, and weak, and blind;
2. Long my heart has sighed for Thee, Long has e - vil reigned with-in;
3. Here I give my all to Thee, Friends, and time, and earth - ly store;
Cho.—I am trust-ing, Lord, in Thee; Blest Lamb of Cal - va - ry;
D. C. for Chorus.
I am count - ing all but dross, I shall full sal - va - tion find.
Je - sus sweet - ly speaks to me,— "I will cleanse you from all sin."
Soul and bod - y Thine to be, Whol - ly Thine for - ev - er - more.
Hum-bly at Thy cross I bow, Save me, Je - sus, save me now.

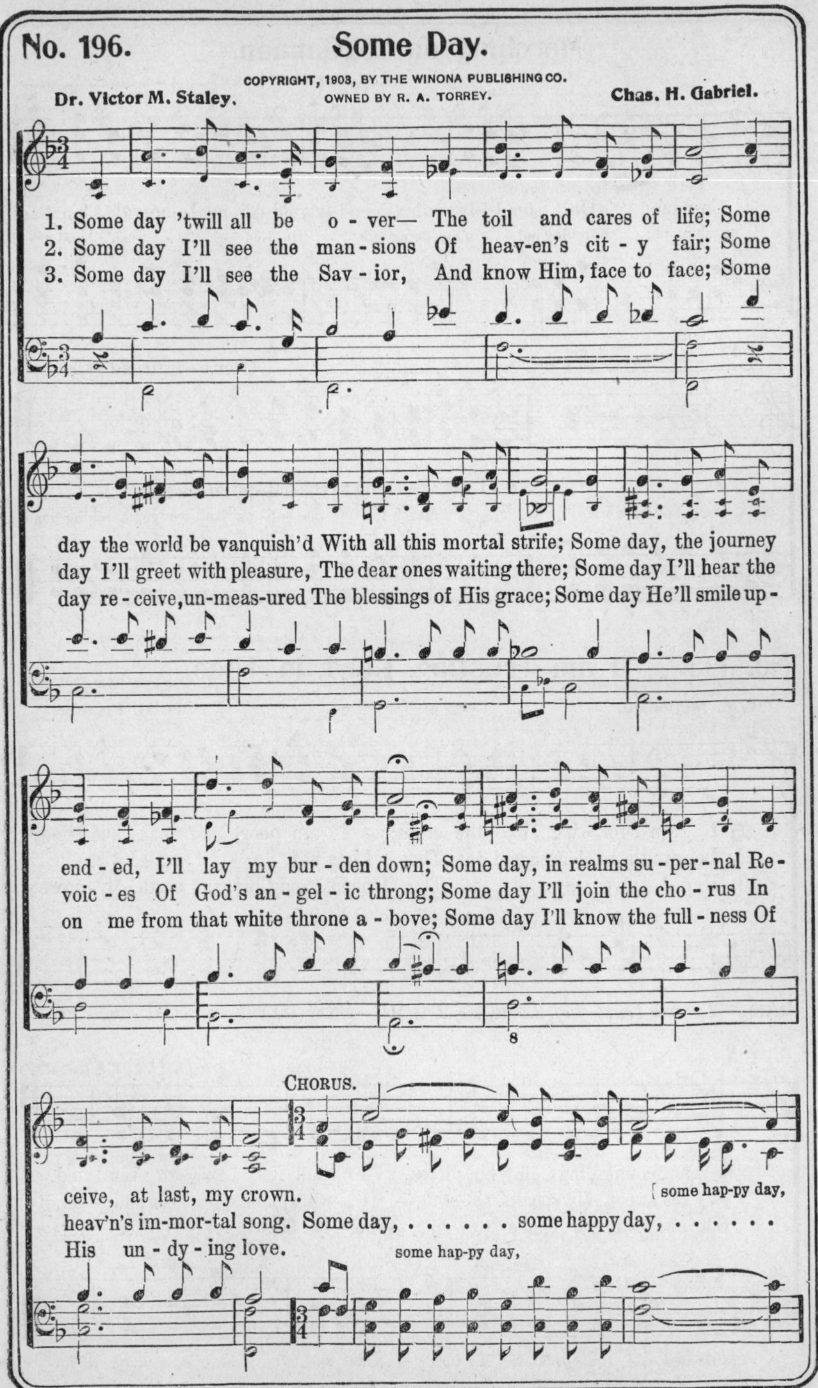
No. 196. Some Day.
COPYRIGHT, 1903, BY THE WINONA PUBLISHING CO.
OWNED BY R. A. TORREY.
Dr. Victor M. Staley.
Chas. H. Gabriel.
1. Some day 'twill all be o - ver— The toil and cares of life; Some
2. Some day I'll see the man - sions Of heav-en's cit - y fair; Some
3. Some day I'll see the Sav - ior, And know Him, face to face; Some
day the world be vanquish'd With all this mortal strife; Some day, the journey
day I'll greet with pleasure, The dear ones waiting there; Some day I'll hear the
day re - ceive, un-meas-ured The blessings of His grace; Some day He'll smile up -
end - ed, I'll lay my bur - den down; Some day, in realms su - per - nal Re -
voic - es Of God's an - gel - ic throng; Some day I'll join the cho - rus In
on me from that white throne a - bove; Some day I'll know the full - ness Of
ceive, at last, my crown.
heav'n's im-mor-tal song.
His un - dy - ing love.
CHORUS.
Some day, ... some happy day, ...
some hap-py day,
some hap-py day,

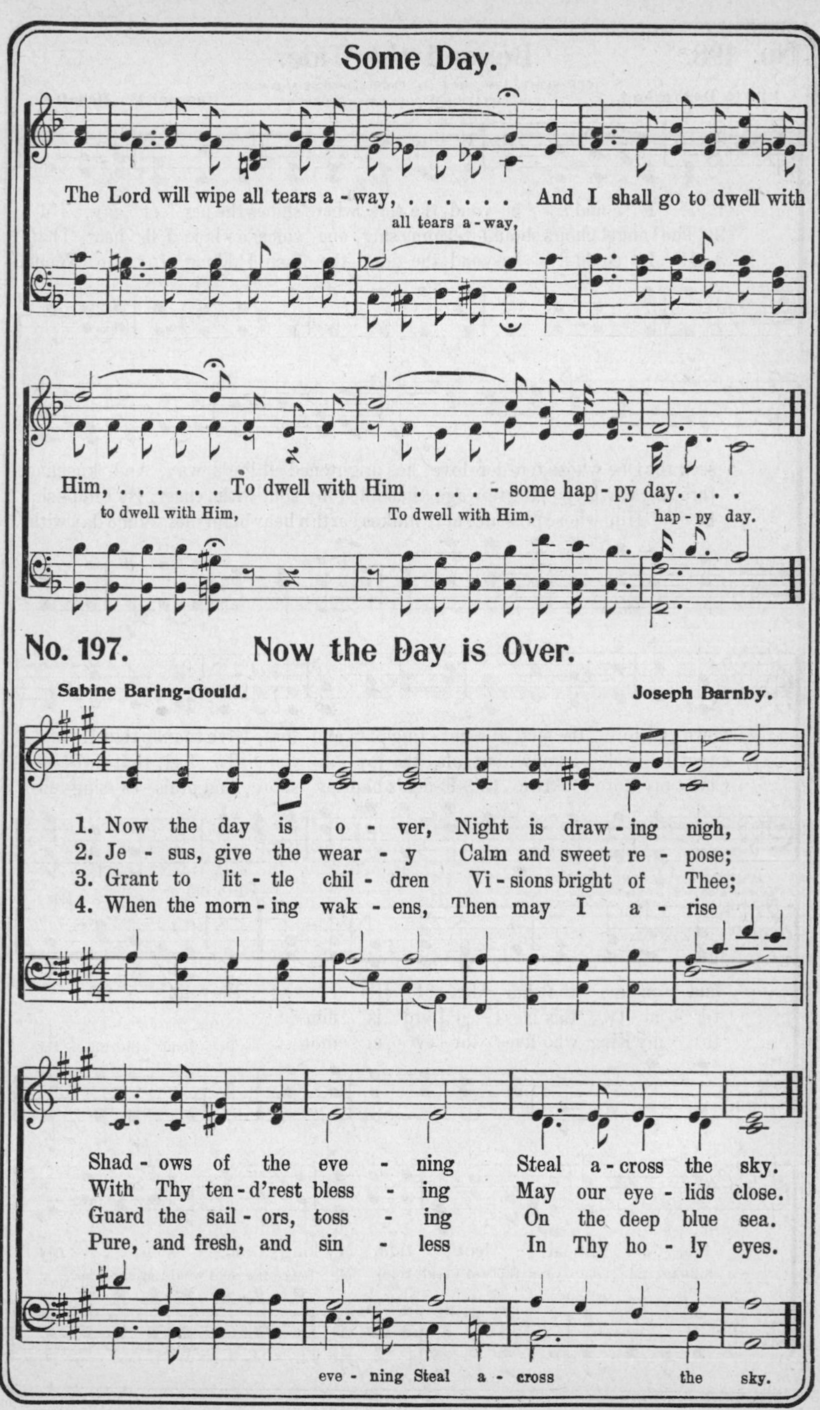
Some Day.
The Lord will wipe all tears a-way, ... And I shall go to dwell with
all tears a-way,
Him, ... To dwell with Him . . . . . - some hap-py day. . . .
to dwell with Him,
To dwell with Him,
hap-py day.
No. 197.
Now the Day is Over.
Sabine Baring-Gould.
Joseph Barnby.
1. Now the day is o-ver, Night is draw-ing nigh,
2. Je-sus, give the wear-y Calm and sweet re-pose;
3. Grant to lit-tle chil-dren Vi-sions bright of Thee;
4. When the morn-ing wak-ens, Then may I a-rise
Shad-ows of the eve-ning Steal a-cross the sky.
With Thy ten-d'rest bless-ing May our eye-lids close.
Guard the sail-ors, toss-ing On the deep blue sea.
Pure, and fresh, and sin-less In Thy ho-ly eyes.
eve-ning Steal a-cross the sky.

No. 198.
Beyond the Tide.
Lizzie DeArmond.
COPYRIGHT, 1904, BY E. O. EXCELL, WORDS AND MUSIC.
INTERNATIONAL COPYRIGHT SECURED.
Samuel W. Beazley.
1. If I could fly be-yond the tide, where shines the per-fect day, I'd
2. Tho' angel choirs should welcome sing, one voice a-lone I'll hear, That
3. If I could fly be-yond the tide, the face I'd long to see Would
seek the One whose ten-der love has brightened all life's way, And, kneeling
thro' my earth-ly pil-grim-age has filled my soul with cheer; Its mu-sic
be of Him whose presence here makes earth a heav'n for me; Some day with
down be-fore His feet, for-get-ting pain and loss, Give thanks that He had
sweet full well I know, but oh, the joy di-vine, To feel, that thro' e-
Christ my Lord I'll rise to E-den's hap-py shore, And prais-es sing un-
laid on me the bur-den of His cross.
ter-ni-ty, this bless-ed Lord is mine!
to my King who lives for-ev-er-more.
CHORUS.
Be-yond the
Be-yond the tide, the
tide, . . . the si-lent tide, My long-ing soul, . . . my
roll-ing tide, be-yond the si-lent tide, My long-ing soul would ev-er be,

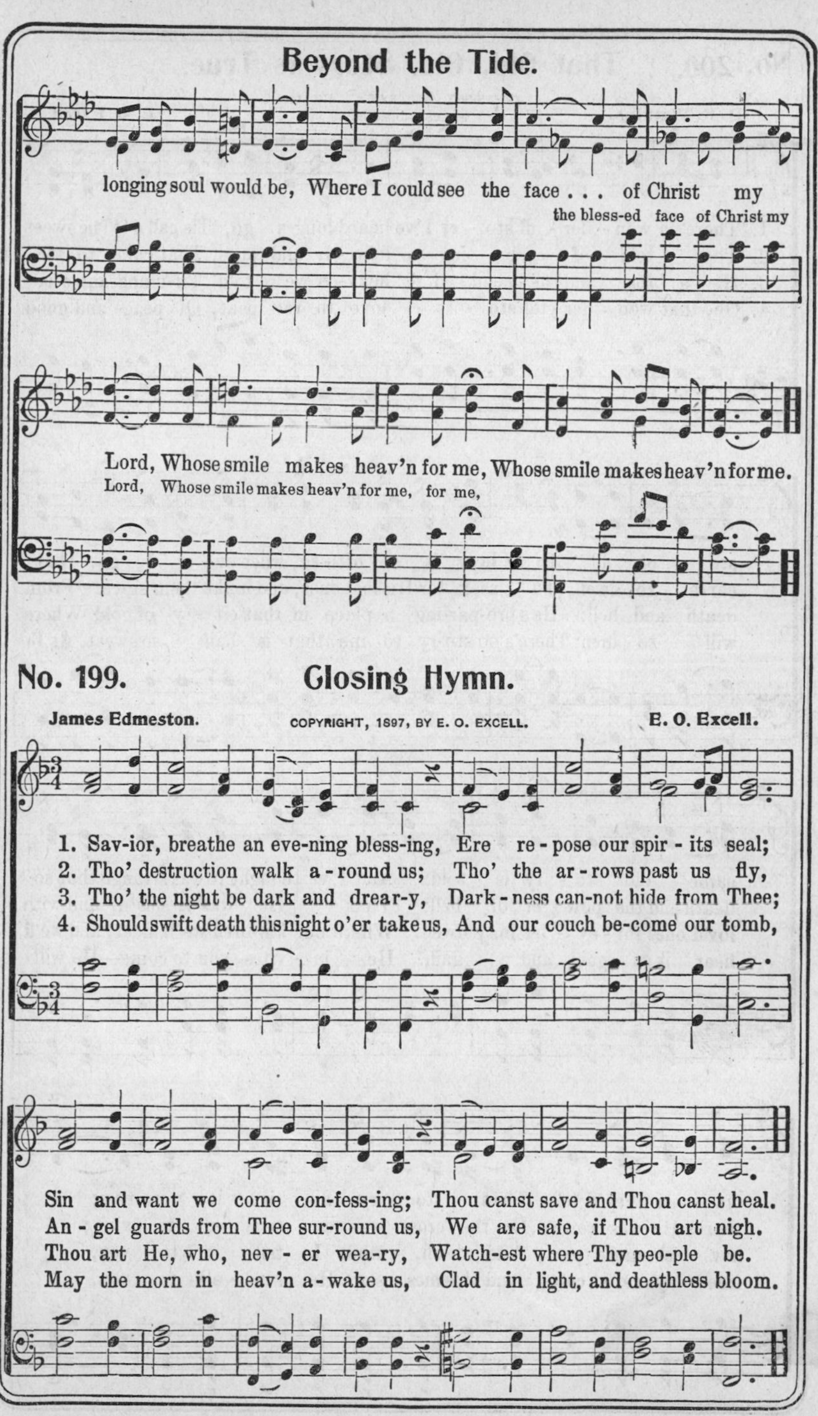
Beyond the Tide.
longing soul would be, Where I could see the face . . . of Christ my
the bless-ed face of Christ my
Lord, Whose smile makes heav'n for me, Whose smile makes heav'n for me.
Lord, Whose smile makes heav'n for me, for me,
No. 199. Closing Hymn.
James Edmeston.
COPYRIGHT, 1897, BY E. O. EXCELL.
E. O. Excell.
1. Sav-ior, breathe an eve-ning bless-ing, Ere re-pose our spir-its seal;
2. Tho' destruction walk a-round us; Tho' the ar-rows past us fly,
3. Tho' the night be dark and drear-y, Dark-ness can-not hide from Thee;
4. Should swift death this night o'er take us, And our couch be-come our tomb,
Sin and want we come con-fess-ing; Thou canst save and Thou canst heal.
An-gel guards from Thee sur-round us, We are safe, if Thou art nigh.
Thou art He, who, nev-er wea-ry, Watch-est where Thy peo-ple be.
May the morn in heav'n a-wake us, Clad in light, and deathless bloom.

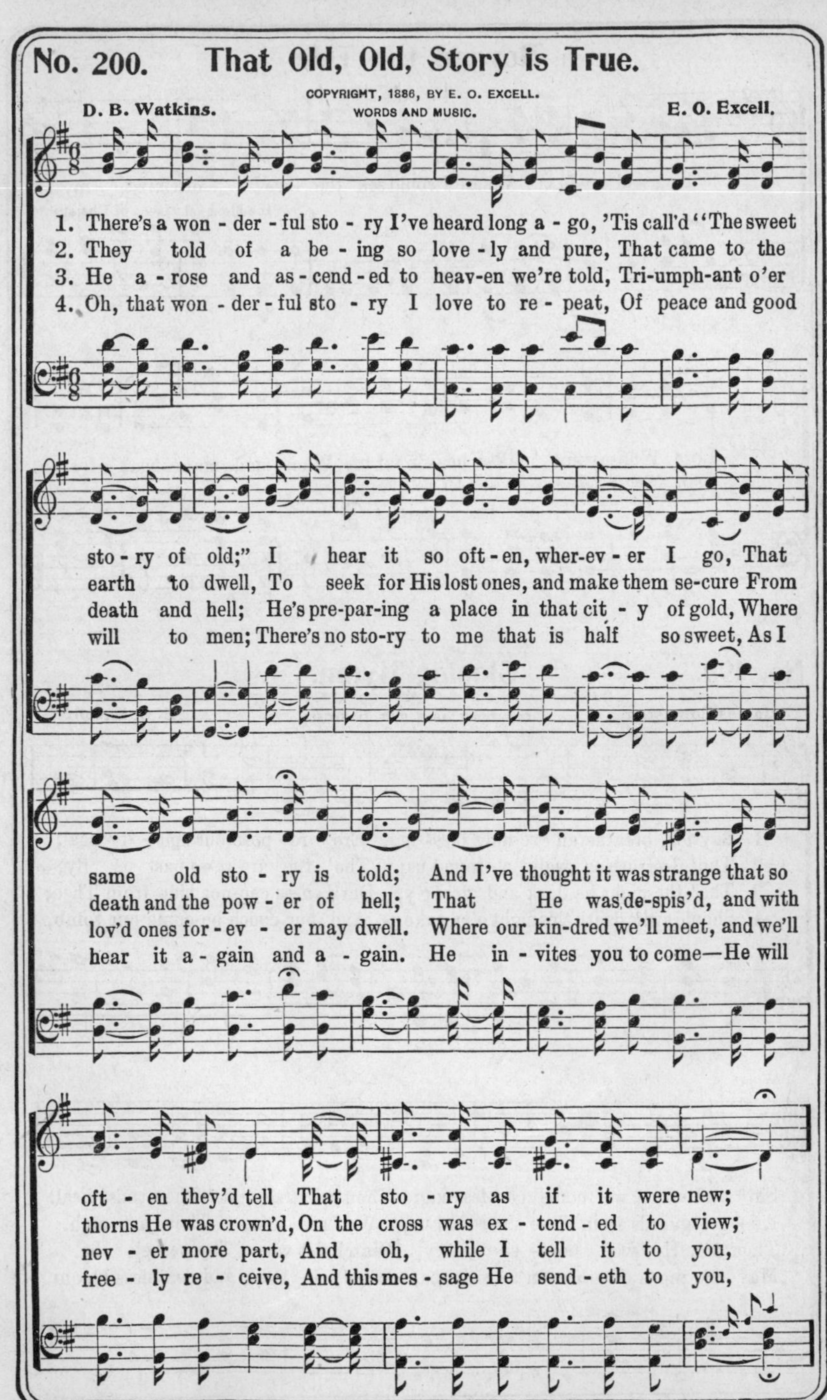

No. 200. That Old, Old, Story is True.
COPYRIGHT, 1886, BY E. O. EXCELL.
D. B. Watkins.
WORDS AND MUSIC.
E. O. Excell.
1. There's a won - der - ful sto - ry I've heard long a - go, 'Tis call'd "The sweet
2. They told of a be - ing so love - ly and pure, That came to the
3. He a - rose and as - cend - ed to heav-en we're told, Tri-umph-ant o'er
4. Oh, that won - der - ful sto - ry I love to re - peat, Of peace and good
sto - ry of old;" I hear it so oft - en, wher-ev - er I go, That
earth to dwell, To seek for His lost ones, and make them se-cure From
death and hell; He's pre-par-ing a place in that cit - y of gold, Where
will to men; There's no sto-ry to me that is half so sweet, As I
same old sto - ry is told; And I've thought it was strange that so
death and the pow - er of hell; That He was de-spis'd, and with
lov'd ones for - ev - er may dwell. Where our kin-dred we'll meet, and we'll
hear it a - gain and a - gain. He in - vites you to come—He will
oft - en they'd tell That sto - ry as if it were new;
thorns He was crown'd, On the cross was ex - tend - ed to view;
nev - er more part, And oh, while I tell it to you,
free - ly re - ceive, And this mes - sage He send - eth to you,

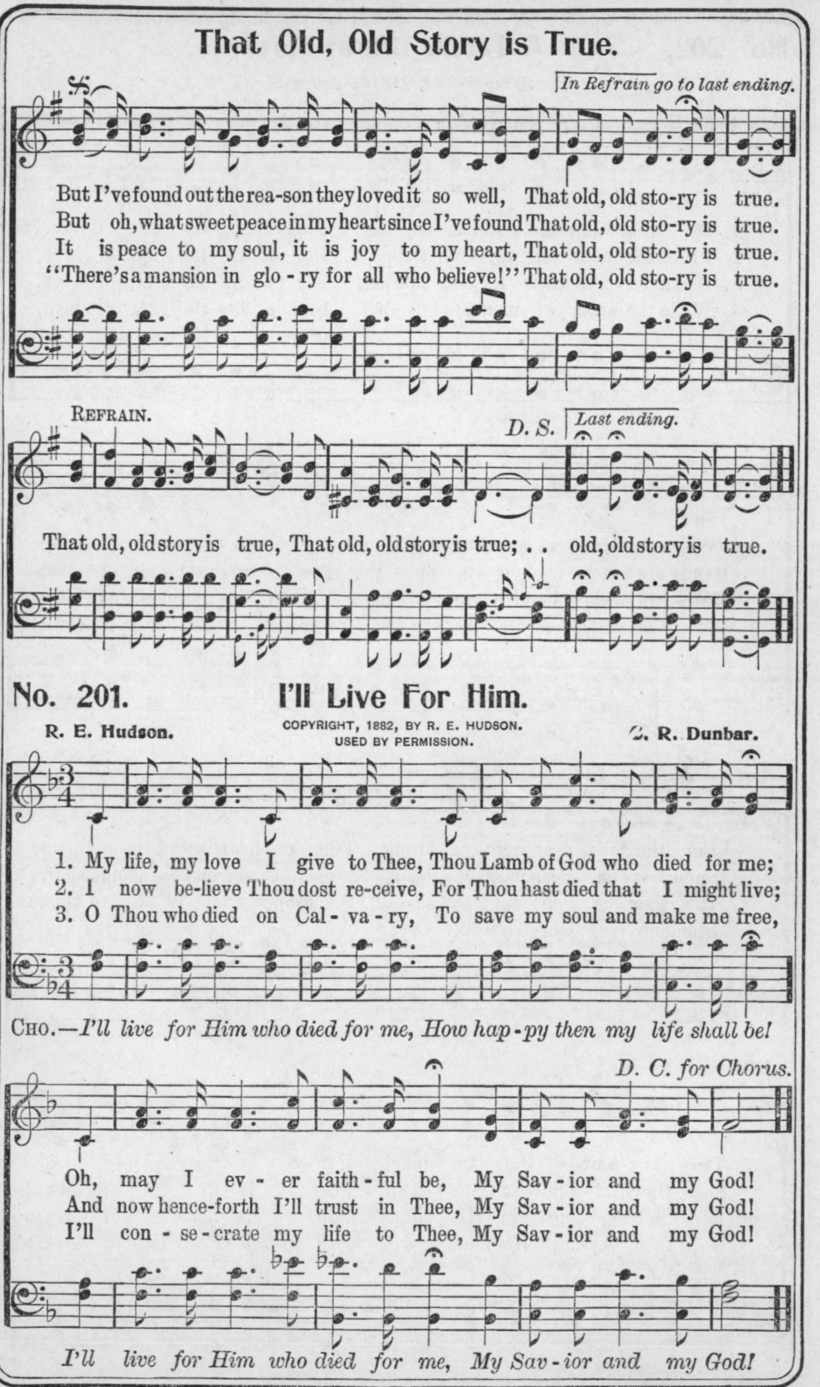
That Old, Old Story is True.
In Refrain go to last ending.
But I've found out the rea-son they loved it so well, That old, old sto-ry is true.
But oh, what sweet peace in my heart since I've found That old, old sto-ry is true.
It is peace to my soul, it is joy to my heart, That old, old sto-ry is true.
"There's a mansion in glo - ry for all who believe!" That old, old sto-ry is true.
REFRAIN.
D. S.
Last ending.
That old, old story is true, That old, old story is true; . . old, old story is true.
No. 201.
I'll Live For Him.
R. E. Hudson.
COPYRIGHT, 1882, BY R. E. HUDSON.
USED BY PERMISSION.
C. R. Dunbar.
1. My life, my love I give to Thee, Thou Lamb of God who died for me;
2. I now be-lieve Thou dost re-ceive, For Thou hast died that I might live;
3. O Thou who died on Cal - va - ry, To save my soul and make me free,
CHO.—I'll live for Him who died for me, How hap - py then my life shall be!
D. C. for Chorus.
Oh, may I ev - er faith - ful be, My Sav - ior and my God!
And now hence-forth I'll trust in Thee, My Sav - ior and my God!
I'll con - se - crate my life to Thee, My Sav - ior and my God!
I'll live for Him who died for me, My Sav - ior and my God!

No. 202. A Little Bit of Love.
To my Friend, Marion Lawrance.
E. O. E.
COPYRIGHT, 1904, BY E. O. EXCELL. WORDS AND MUSIC.
INTERNATIONAL COPYRIGHT SECURED.
E. O. Excell.
1. Do you know the world is dy-ing For a lit-tle bit of love?
2. From the poor of ev-'ry cit-y, For a lit-tle bit of love,
3. Down be-fore their i-dols fall-ing, For a lit-tle bit of love,
4. While the souls of men are dy-ing For a lit-tle bit of love,
Ev-'ry-where we hear the sigh-ing For a lit-tle bit of love;
Hands are reach-ing out in pit-y For a lit-tle bit of love;
Ma-ny souls in vain are call-ing For a lit-tle bit of love;
While the chil-dren too are cry-ing For a lit-tle bit of love;
For the love that rights a wrong, Fills the heart with hope and song;
Some have bur-dens hard to bear, Some have sorrows we should share;
If they die in sin and shame, Some-one sure-ly is to blame
Stand no long-er i-dly by, You can help them if you try;
They have wait-ed, oh, so long, For a lit-tle bit of love.
Shall they fal-ter and de-spair For a lit-tle bit of love.
For not go-ing in His name, With a lit-tle bit of love.
Go, then, say-ing, "Here am I," With a lit-tle bit of love.

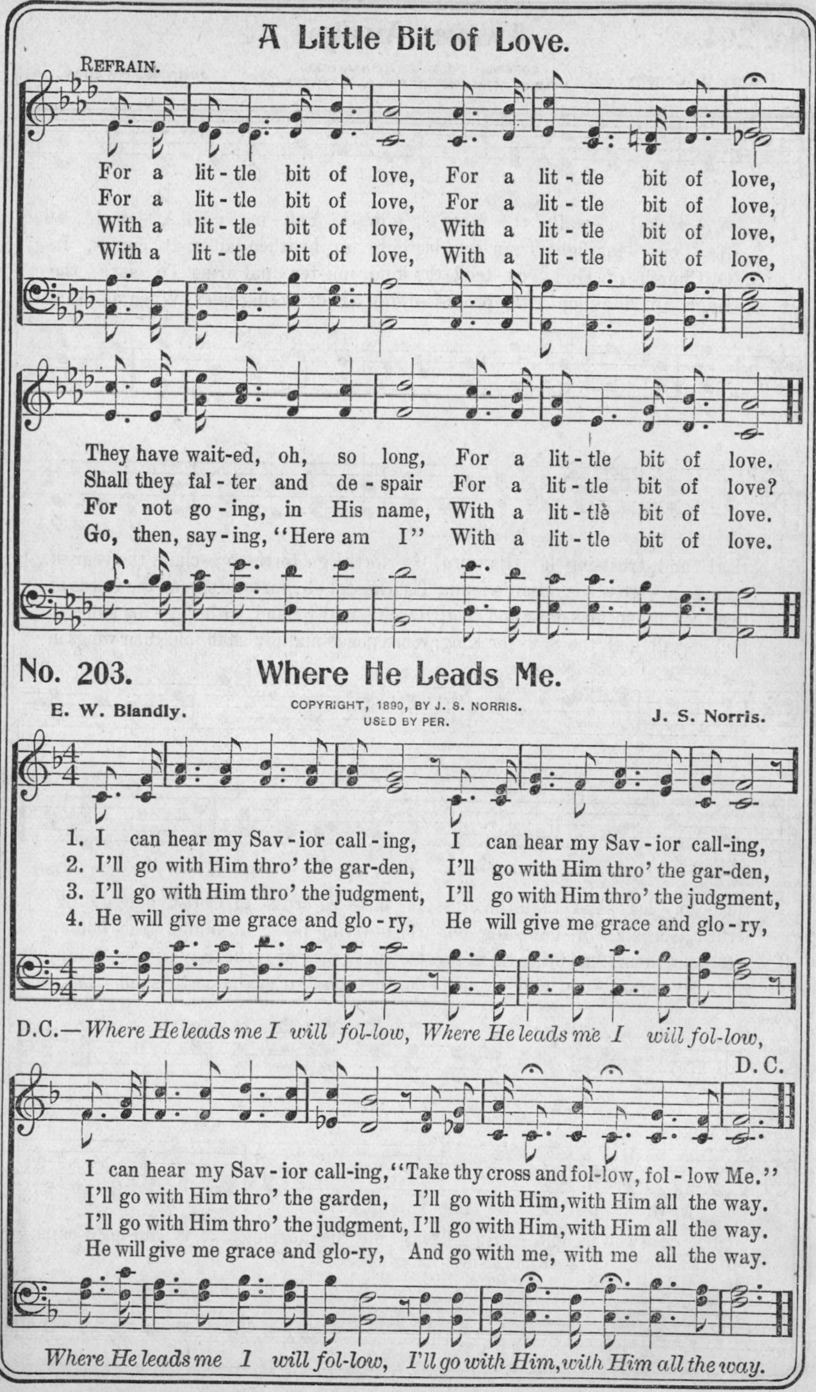
A Little Bit of Love.
Refrain.
For a lit - tle bit of love, For a lit - tle bit of love,
For a lit - tle bit of love, For a lit - tle bit of love,
With a lit - tle bit of love, With a lit - tle bit of love,
With a lit - tle bit of love, With a lit - tle bit of love,
They have wait-ed, oh, so long, For a lit - tle bit of love.
Shall they fal - ter and de - spair For a lit - tle bit of love?
For not go - ing, in His name, With a lit - tle bit of love.
Go, then, say - ing, "Here am I" With a lit - tle bit of love.
No. 203. Where He Leads Me.
E. W. Blandly.
COPYRIGHT, 1890, BY J. S. NORRIS.
USED BY PER.
J. S. Norris.
1. I can hear my Sav - ior call - ing, I can hear my Sav - ior call-ing,
2. I'll go with Him thro' the gar-den, I'll go with Him thro' the gar-den,
3. I'll go with Him thro' the judgment, I'll go with Him thro' the judgment,
4. He will give me grace and glo - ry, He will give me grace and glo - ry,
D.C.—Where He leads me I will fol-low, Where He leads me I will fol-low,
D. C.
I can hear my Sav - ior call-ing, "Take thy cross and fol-low, fol - low Me."
I'll go with Him thro' the garden, I'll go with Him, with Him all the way.
I'll go with Him thro' the judgment, I'll go with Him, with Him all the way.
He will give me grace and glo-ry, And go with me, with me all the way.
Where He leads me I will fol-low, I'll go with Him, with Him all the way.

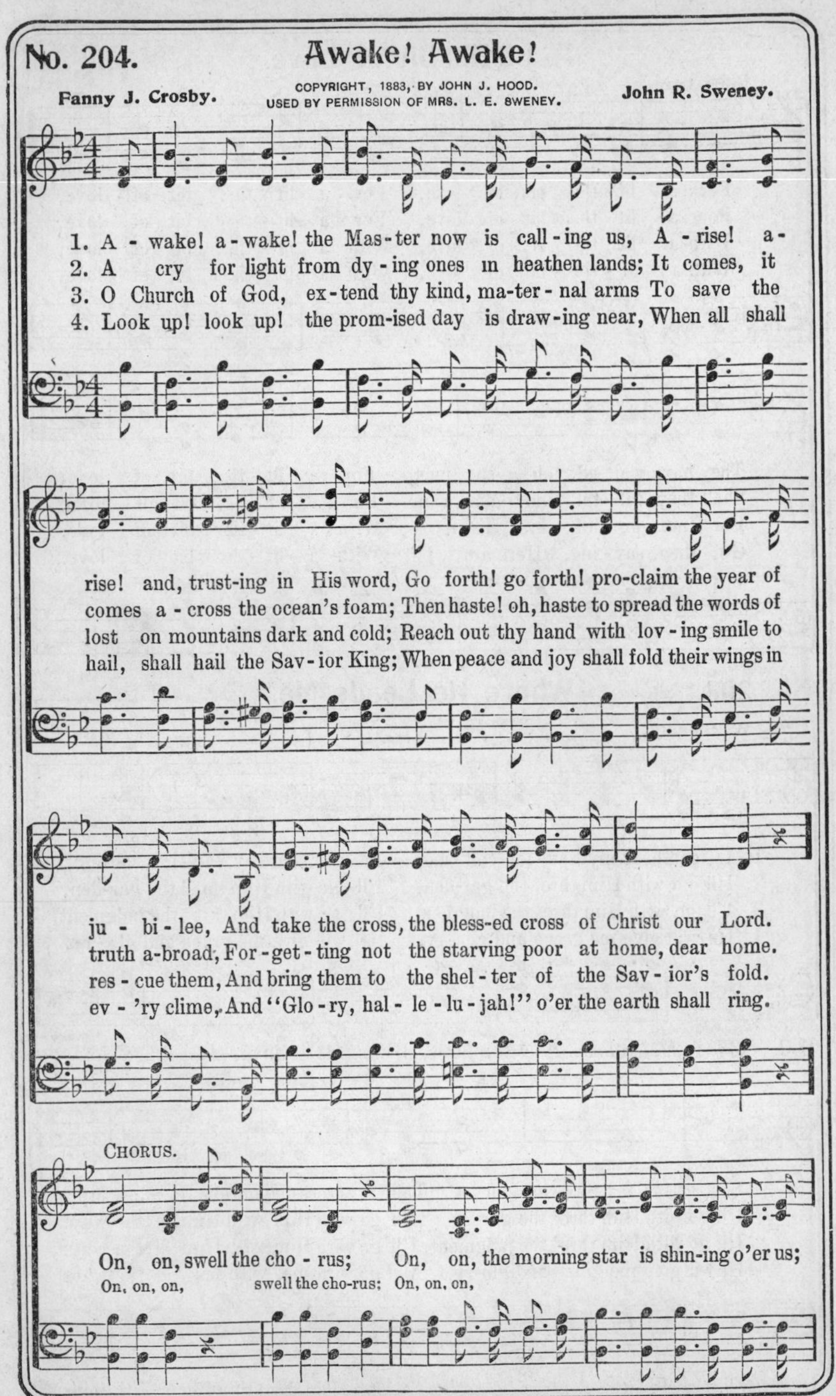
No. 204.
Awake! Awake!
Fanny J. Crosby.
COPYRIGHT, 1883, BY JOHN J. HOOD.
USED BY PERMISSION OF MRS. L. E. SWENEY.
John R. Sweney.
1. A - wake! a - wake! the Mas - ter now is call - ing us, A - rise! a -
2. A cry for light from dy - ing ones in heathen lands; It comes, it
3. O Church of God, ex - tend thy kind, ma - ter - nal arms To save the
4. Look up! look up! the prom - ised day is draw - ing near, When all shall
rise! and, trust - ing in His word, Go forth! go forth! pro - claim the year of
comes a - cross the ocean's foam; Then haste! oh, haste to spread the words of
lost on mountains dark and cold; Reach out thy hand with lov - ing smile to
hail, shall hail the Sav - ior King; When peace and joy shall fold their wings in
ju - bi - lee, And take the cross, the bless - ed cross of Christ our Lord.
truth a - broad, For - get - ting not the starving poor at home, dear home.
res - cue them, And bring them to the shel - ter of the Sav - ior's fold.
ev - 'ry clime, And "Glo - ry, hal - le - lu - jah!" o'er the earth shall ring.
CHORUS.
On, on, swell the cho - rus; On, on, the morning star is shin - ing o'er us;
On, on, on, swell the cho - rus; On, on, on,

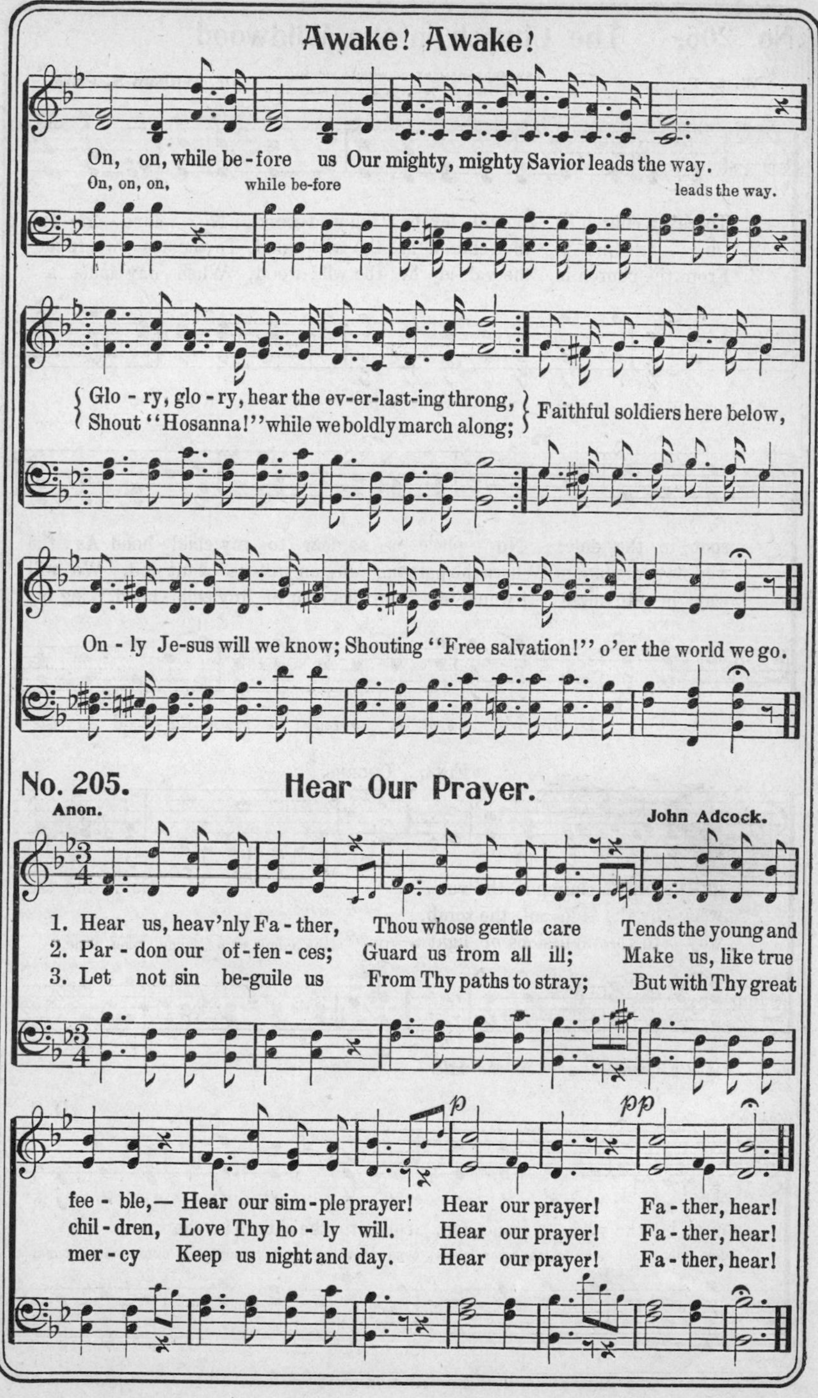
Awake! Awake!
On, on, while be-fore us Our mighty, mighty Savior leads the way.
On, on, on, while be-fore leads the way.
Glo - ry, glo - ry, hear the ev-er-last-ing throng,
Shout "Hosanna!" while we boldly march along;
Faithful soldiers here below,
On - ly Je-sus will we know; Shouting "Free salvation!" o'er the world we go.
No. 205.
Hear Our Prayer.
Anon.
John Adcock.
1. Hear us, heav'nly Fa - ther, Thou whose gentle care Tends the young and
2. Par - don our of-fen - ces; Guard us from all ill; Make us, like true
3. Let not sin be-guile us From Thy paths to stray; But with Thy great
fee - ble,— Hear our sim-ple prayer! Hear our prayer! Fa - ther, hear!
chil - dren, Love Thy ho - ly will. Hear our prayer! Fa - ther, hear!
mer - cy Keep us night and day. Hear our prayer! Fa - ther, hear!

No. 206. The Church in the Wildwood.

W. S. P. NEW ARRANGEMENT OF WORDS AND MUSIC Dr. William S. Pitts.

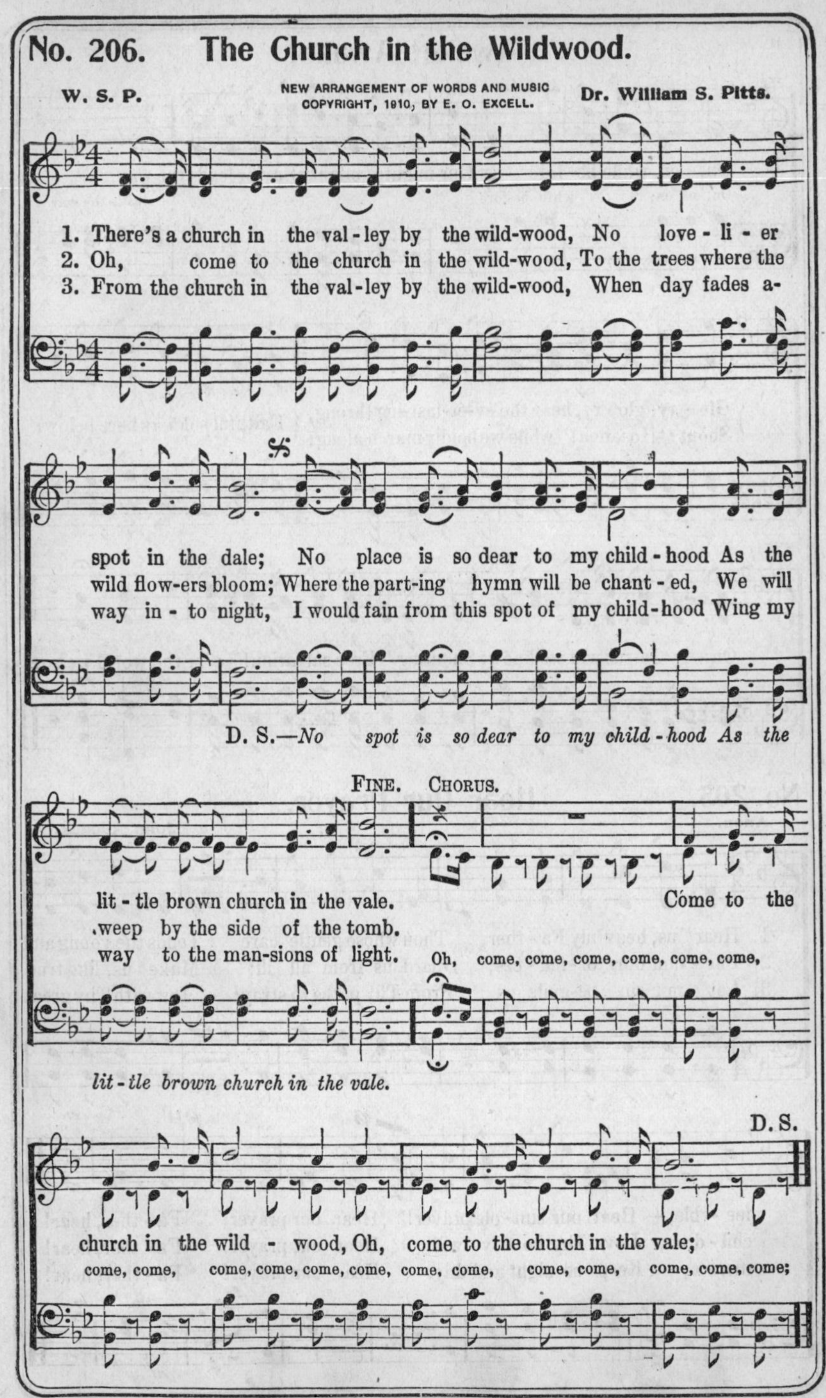

Childrens Songs

No. 207. I'll Be a Sunbeam.

To my grandson, Edwin O. Excell, Jr.

Nellie Talbot. | COPYRIGHT, 1900, BY E. O. EXCELL. WORDS AND MUSIC. | E. O. Excell.

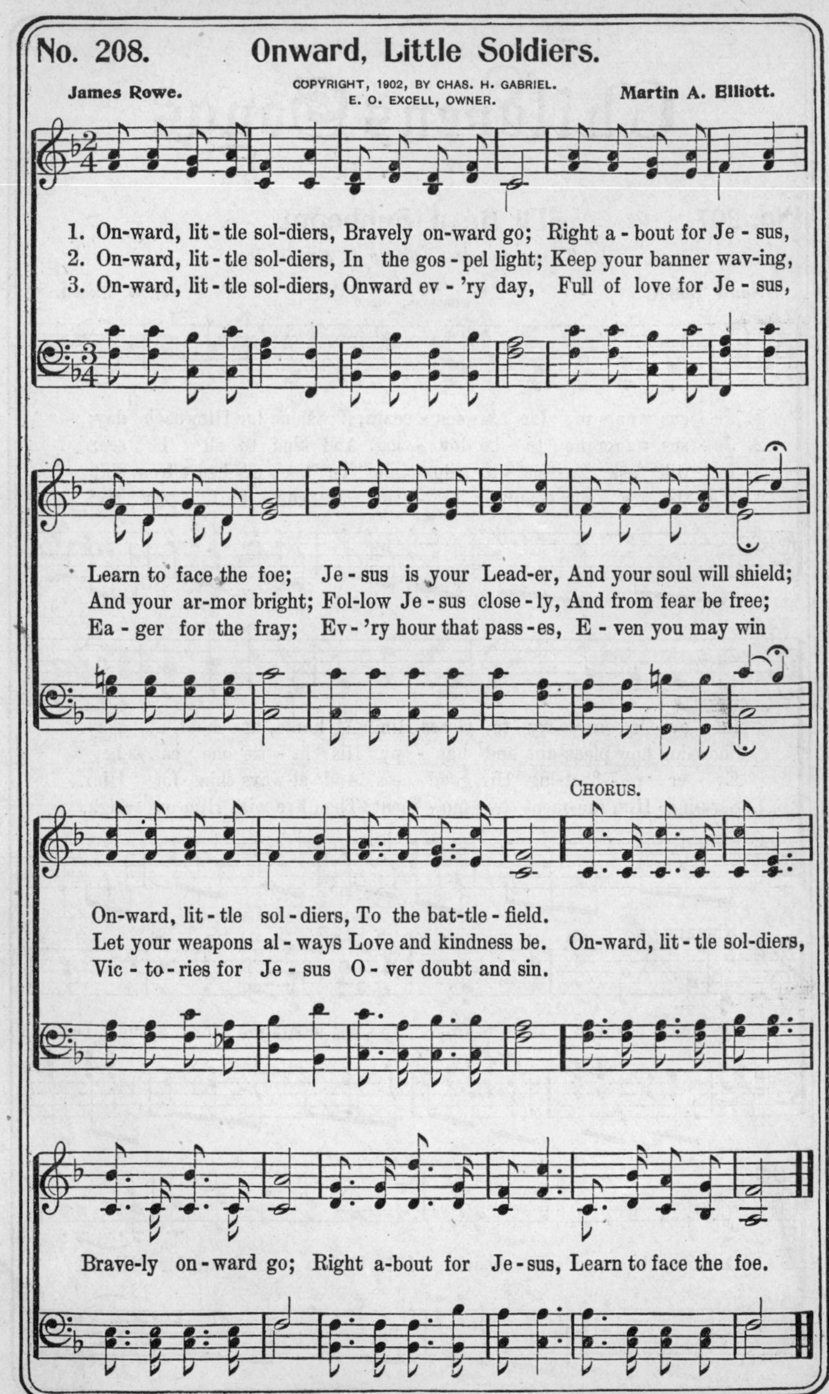
No. 208. Onward, Little Soldiers.
James Rowe.
COPYRIGHT, 1902, BY CHAS. H. GABRIEL.
E. O. EXCELL, OWNER.
Martin A. Elliott.
1. On-ward, lit - tle sol-diers, Bravely on-ward go; Right a - bout for Je - sus,
2. On-ward, lit - tle sol-diers, In the gos - pel light; Keep your banner wav-ing,
3. On-ward, lit - tle sol-diers, Onward ev - 'ry day, Full of love for Je - sus,
Learn to face the foe; Je - sus is your Lead-er, And your soul will shield;
And your ar-mor bright; Fol-low Je - sus close - ly, And from fear be free;
Ea - ger for the fray; Ev - 'ry hour that pass - es, E - ven you may win
CHORUS.
On-ward, lit - tle sol - diers, To the bat-tle - field.
Let your weapons al - ways Love and kindness be. On-ward, lit - tle sol-diers,
Vic - to - ries for Je - sus O - ver doubt and sin.
Brave-ly on - ward go; Right a-bout for Je - sus, Learn to face the foe.

No. 209. Little Soldiers.
COPYRIGHT, 1906, BY CHAS. H. GABRIEL.
E. O. EXCELL, OWNER.
Lena Thompson.
Chas. H. Gabriel.
1. We are sol-diers, lit-tle sol-diers, Fighting for our King and Lord;
2. We are sol-diers, lit-tle sol-diers, Bravely fight-ing ev-'ry sin;
3. When at last the fight is o-ver, And we've reach'd the heav'nly shore,
Ev-'ry time we win a bat-tle, He has promised a re-ward;
With our Sav-ior for our Cap-tain We shall all our bat-tles win;
We shall hear our Sav-ior say-ing, "Rest, my sol-diers, ev-er-more;
He has promised ev-'ry sol-dier, If they dare the right to do,
He has promised, if we ask Him, He will help us day by day;
You have bravely fought my battles, Bravely fought and no-bly won,
FINE.
Promised them a crown of glo-ry, If they fight the bat-tle through.
So we'll brave-ly march to bat-tle, Pray-ing, sing-ing all the way.
En-ter in-to joys e-ter-nal—Sol-diers of the Lord, well done!"
D. S.—ban-ner bright, For God and right, We're sure to win the day.
CHORUS.
So we march, march a-way, Not a mo-ment's de-lay, 'Neath our

No. 210. Sunbeams Bright.
Lizzie DeArmond.
COPYRIGHT, 1906, BY CHAS. H. GABRIEL. E. O. EXCELL, OWNER.
Chas. H. Gabriel.
1. Just a lit - tle sun-beam bright, Swift-ly 1earth-ward wing - ing,
2. Just a lit - tle sun-beam bright, Down from 3heav-en shin - ing,
3. Just a lit - tle sun-beam bright, Do - ing well its du - ty,
2Wa - king up the sleep - ing flow'rs, Joy and glad-ness bring - ing.
Giv - ing clouds that look so drear, Each a sil - ver 4lin - ing.
Tell - ing of the 3Fa-ther's love, 5Fill - ing earth with beau - ty.
CHORUS.
Shin - ing bright-ly ev - 'ry day, 6Driv-ing gloom-y clouds a - way,
Lit - tle sun-beams we would be, 7Point-ing ev - er, Lord, to Thee.
MOTIONS:—1. Raise right hand high, then bring it swiftly downward. 2. Stoop lightly, make motions as if lifting up flowers. 3. Point up. 4. Raise right hand and describe a semi-circle with it. 5. Hold arms out wide and bring them slowly together, till palms of hands touch. 6. Move right hand and arm with sweeping motion from left to right, 7. Pointing right hand slowly upwards.

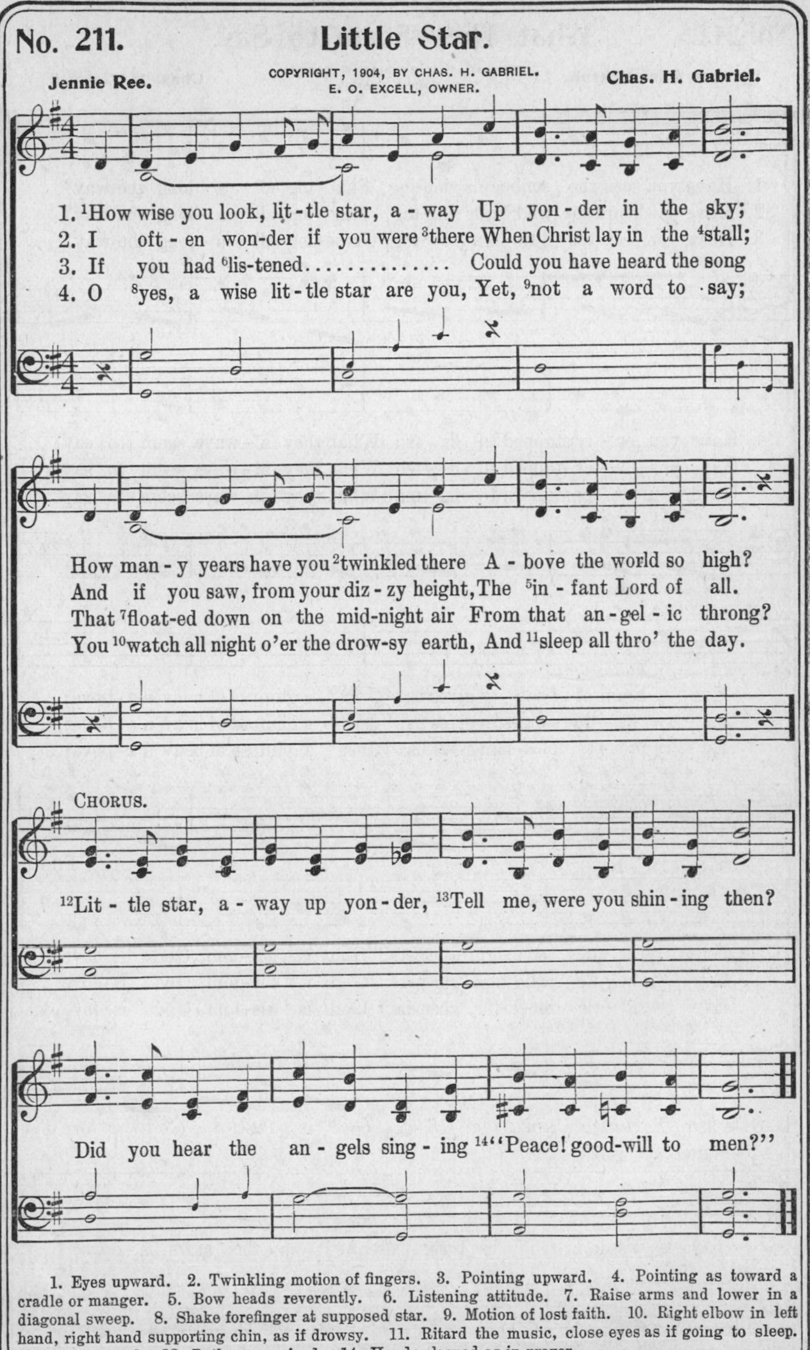
No. 211. Little Star.
Jennie Ree.
COPYRIGHT, 1904, BY CHAS. H. GABRIEL. E. O. EXCELL, OWNER.
Chas. H. Gabriel.
1. [1]How wise you look, lit-tle star, a-way Up yon-der in the sky; How man-y years have you [2]twinkled there A-bove the world so high?
2. I oft-en won-der if you were [3]there When Christ lay in the [4]stall; And if you saw, from your diz-zy height, The [5]in-fant Lord of all.
3. If you had [6]lis-tened............. Could you have heard the song That [7]float-ed down on the mid-night air From that an-gel-ic throng?
4. O [8]yes, a wise lit-tle star are you, Yet, [9]not a word to say; You [10]watch all night o'er the drow-sy earth, And [11]sleep all thro' the day.
CHORUS.
[12]Lit-tle star, a-way up yon-der, [13]Tell me, were you shin-ing then? Did you hear the an-gels sing-ing [14]"Peace! good-will to men?"
1. Eyes upward. 2. Twinkling motion of fingers. 3. Pointing upward. 4. Pointing as toward a cradle or manger. 5. Bow heads reverently. 6. Listening attitude. 7. Raise arms and lower in a diagonal sweep. 8. Shake forefinger at supposed star. 9. Motion of lost faith. 10. Right elbow in left hand, right hand supporting chin, as if drowsy. 11. Ritard the music, close eyes as if going to sleep. 12. Eyes upward. 13. Both arms raised. 14. Hands clasped as in prayer.

No. 212. What They Seem to Say.
Eleanor Allen Schroll.
COPYRIGHT, 1908, BY CHAS. H. GABRIEL.
E. O. EXCELL, OWNER.
Chas. H. Gabriel.
1. Have you seen the sunbeams shin-ing, Shin-ing all a-long the way?
2. Have you heard the wild birds sing-ing, Sing-ing all a-long the way?
3. Have you seen the flow-ers grow-ing, Grow-ing all a-long the way?
Have you ev-er stopped to lis-ten What they al-ways seem to say?
Have you ev-er stopped to lis-ten What they al-ways seem to say?
Have you ev-er stopped to lis-ten What they al-ways seem to say?
Ev-'ry beam of beau-ty gives us Just a glimpse of heav'n a-bove;
Ev-'ry lit-tle song-ster gives us Just a glimpse of heav'n a-bove;
Ev-'ry pret-ty blos-som gives us Just a glimpse of heav'n a-bove;
FINE.
Ev-'ry lit-tle sunbeam whispers: God is wis-dom, God is love.
Ev-'ry lit-tle wild bird whispers: God is wis-dom, God is love.
Ev-'ry lit-tle flow-er whispers: God is wis-dom, God is love.
D. S.—May the children's hearts re-ech-o: God is wis-dom, God is love.
CHORUS.
D. S.
God is wis-dom, God is love; Read it in the stars a-bove;

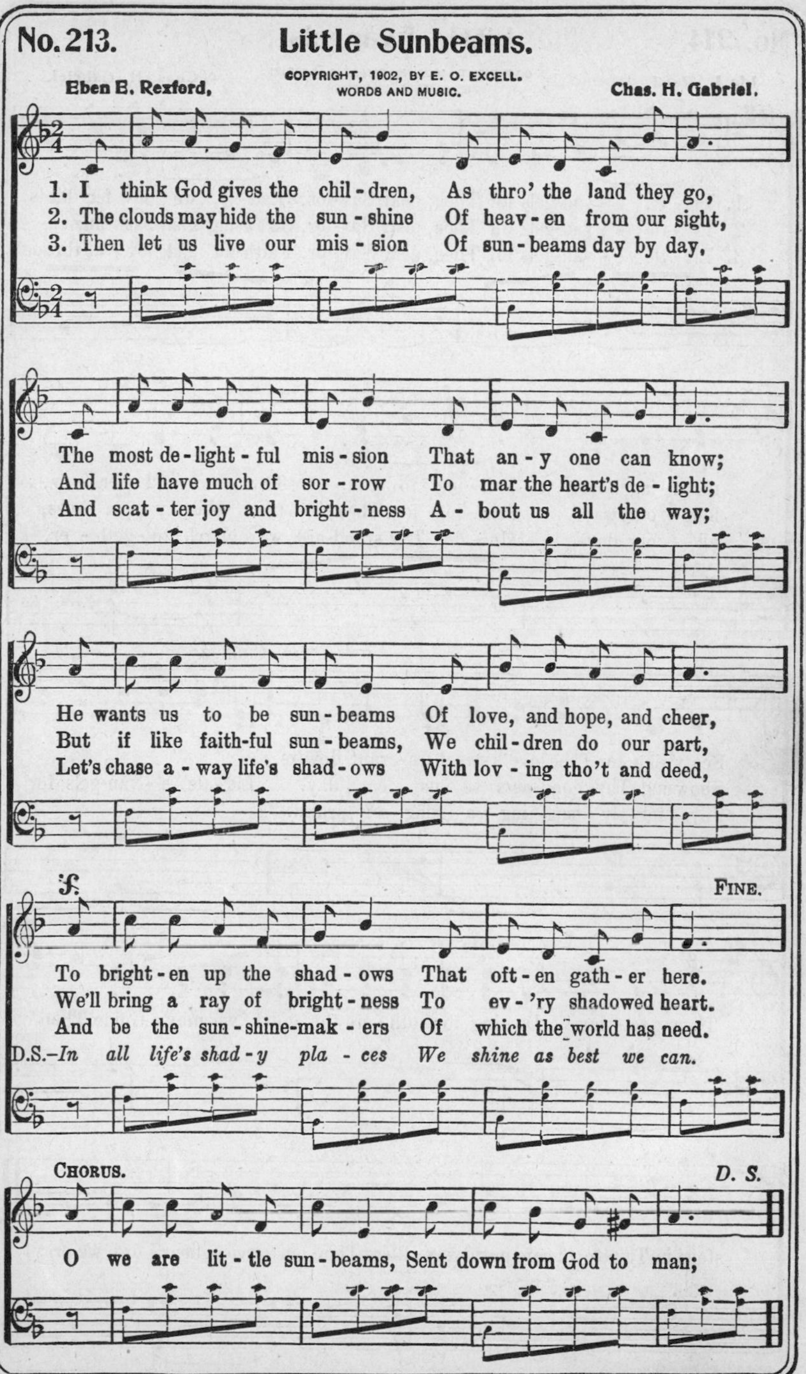
No. 213.
Little Sunbeams.
COPYRIGHT, 1902, BY E. O. EXCELL.
WORDS AND MUSIC.
Eben E. Rexford,
Chas. H. Gabriel.
1. I think God gives the chil-dren, As thro' the land they go,
2. The clouds may hide the sun-shine Of heav-en from our sight,
3. Then let us live our mis-sion Of sun-beams day by day,
The most de-light-ful mis-sion That an-y one can know;
And life have much of sor-row To mar the heart's de-light;
And scat-ter joy and bright-ness A-bout us all the way;
He wants us to be sun-beams Of love, and hope, and cheer,
But if like faith-ful sun-beams, We chil-dren do our part,
Let's chase a-way life's shad-ows With lov-ing tho't and deed,
FINE.
To bright-en up the shad-ows That oft-en gath-er here.
We'll bring a ray of bright-ness To ev-'ry shadowed heart.
And be the sun-shine-mak-ers Of which the world has need.
D.S.–In all life's shad-y pla-ces We shine as best we can.
CHORUS.
D. S.
O we are lit-tle sun-beams, Sent down from God to man;

No. 214.
Little Evangels.
Ida L. Reed.
COPYRIGHT, 1906, BY CHAS. H. GABRIEL.
E. O. EXCELL, OWNER.
Chas. H. Gabriel.
1. Lit-tle e-van-gels for Thee, dear Sav-ior, Glad-ly we of-fer life's morn-ing hours, Tell-ing to oth-ers Thy grace and mer-cy, Scatt'ring for Thee love's sweet fra-grant flow'rs.
2. Lit-tle e-van-gels for Thee, dear Sav-ior, Strew-ing glad bless-ings a-long our way, Shin-ing for Thee in the shad-y pla-ces, Show-ing Thy good-ness to us each day.
3. Lit-tle e-van-gels for Thee, dear Sav-ior, Faith-ful and loy-al through all our days, Un-der Thy stand-ard we march to-geth-er, Joy-ful-ly sing-ing a song of praise.
CHORUS.
Lit-tle e-van-gels for Thee to-day, Do-ing for oth-ers the good we may; Guide Thou our steps in Thine own safe path-way, Bless Thou our service, dear Lord, we pray!

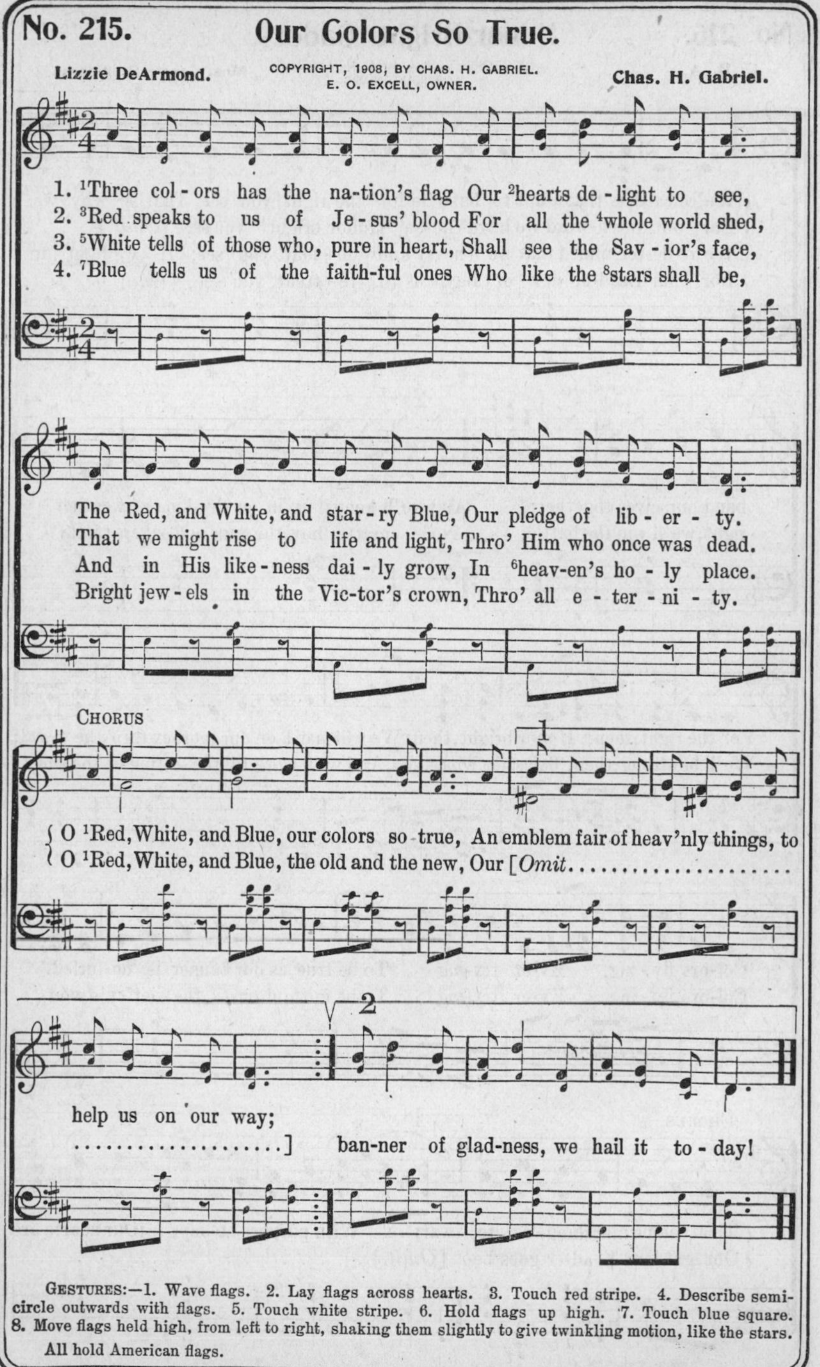
No. 215. Our Colors So True.
Lizzie DeArmond.
COPYRIGHT, 1908, BY CHAS. H. GABRIEL. E. O. EXCELL, OWNER.
Chas. H. Gabriel.
1. [1]Three col-ors has the na-tion's flag Our [2]hearts de-light to see,
2. [3]Red speaks to us of Je-sus' blood For all the [4]whole world shed,
3. [5]White tells of those who, pure in heart, Shall see the Sav-ior's face,
4. [7]Blue tells us of the faith-ful ones Who like the [8]stars shall be,
The Red, and White, and star-ry Blue, Our pledge of lib-er-ty.
That we might rise to life and light, Thro' Him who once was dead.
And in His like-ness dai-ly grow, In [6]heav-en's ho-ly place.
Bright jew-els in the Vic-tor's crown, Thro' all e-ter-ni-ty.
CHORUS
O [1]Red, White, and Blue, our colors so true, An emblem fair of heav'nly things, to help us on our way;
O [1]Red, White, and Blue, the old and the new, Our [Omit.......................] ban-ner of glad-ness, we hail it to-day!
GESTURES:—1. Wave flags. 2. Lay flags across hearts. 3. Touch red stripe. 4. Describe semi-circle outwards with flags. 5. Touch white stripe. 6. Hold flags up high. 7. Touch blue square. 8. Move flags held high, from left to right, shaking them slightly to give twinkling motion, like the stars.
All hold American flags.

No. 216. Honor-Bright Cadets.
C. B. A.
COPYRIGHT, 1802, BY E. O. EXCELL. WORDS AND MUSIC.
Mrs. Carrie B. Adams.
1
1. We're ca-dets that want to bat - tle for the right, you see; That is why we
For our watch-word we have chosen "Honor bright!" you see, [Omit.] . . . .
2. We're de-ter-mined that we'll never know de - feat, you see; If we fight for
For our Lead-er nev - er taught us to re - treat, you see, [Omit.] . . . ,
2
band ourselves together; And we'll keep it up in ev-'ry kind of weather.
right, we'll win the battle; No matter how the guns and sabers rattle.
For the right, then; Honor bright, then; We will march on our journey thro' the world;
We'll be strong, then, 'Gainst the wrong, then, And we'll work till the setting of the sun;
Col-ors fly - ing, Ev-er try-ing To be true, as our banner is un-furled.
Col-ors fly - ing, Ev-er try-ing To be faithful un-til the vict'ry's won.
CHORUS.
1
Then see us marching as to war; . . . With purpose steady, Our hearts are
Our gal-lant Lead-er goes be- [Omit.] . . . .

Honor-Bright Cadets.
2
read-y; fore: Then see us march! We are "Honor-Bright Cadets!"
No. 217. Dear Little Stranger.
C. H. G.
COPYRIGHT, 1900, BY E. O. EXCELL.
WORDS AND MUSIC.
Chas. H. Gabriel.
1. Low in a man - ger—dear lit - tle Stran - ger, Je - sus, the won-der - ful
2. An - gels de-scend - ing, o - ver Him bend - ing, Chant-ed a ten - der and
3. Dear lit - tle Stran - ger, born in a man - ger, Mak - er and Monarch, and
Savior, was born; There was none to receive Him, none to believe Him, None but the
si - lent refrain; Then a won-der-ful sto - ry told of His glo - ry, Un - to the
Sav-ior of all; I will love Thee for-ev - er! grieve Thee? no, never! Thou didst for
CHORUS.
an-gels were watching that morn.
shepherds on Beth-le-hem's plain.
me make Thy bed in a stall.
Dear lit - tle Stranger, slept in a man - ger,
But with the poor He slumbered se-cure, The
1
2
No down-y pil - low un-der His head; dear lit - tle Babe in His bed.

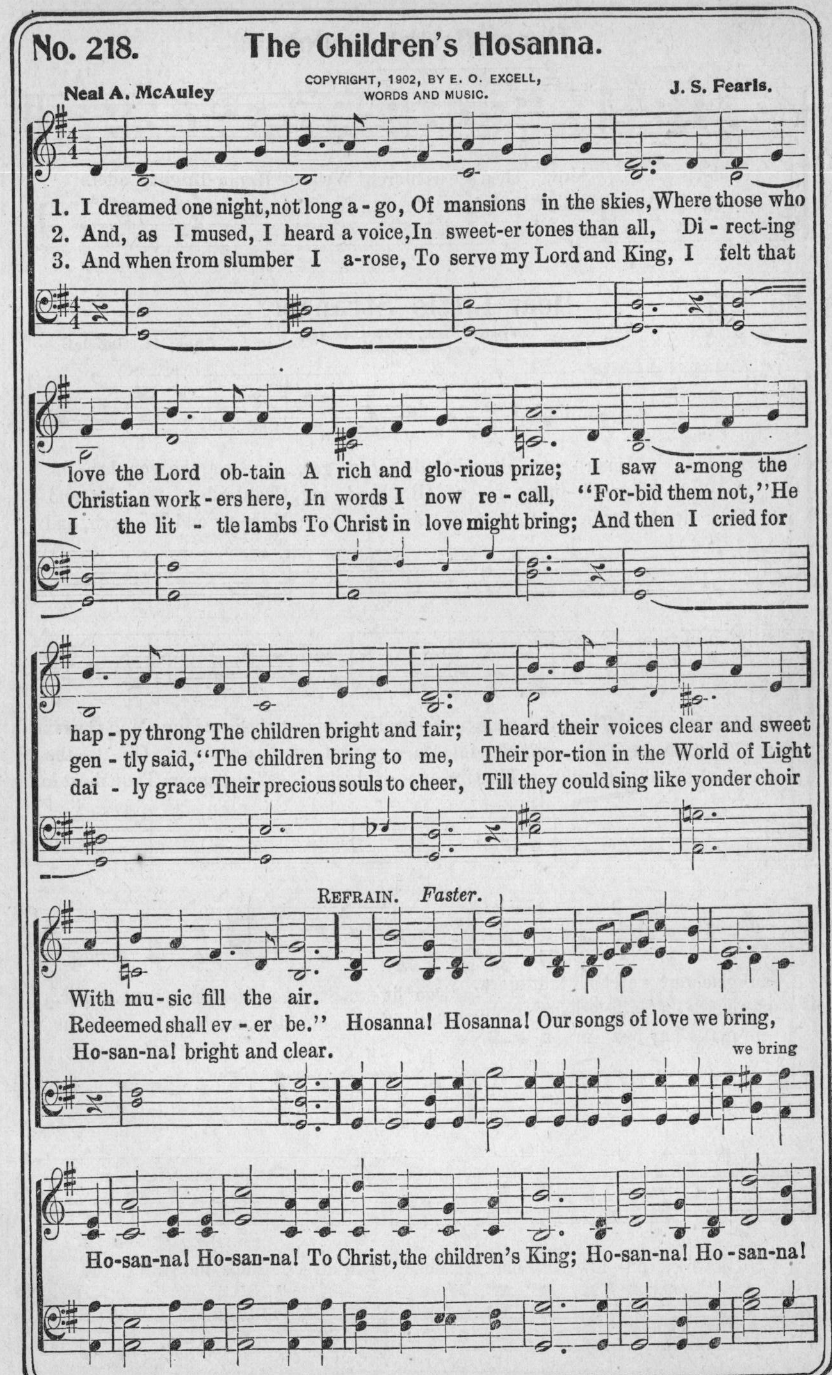
No. 218. The Children's Hosanna.
COPYRIGHT, 1902, BY E. O. EXCELL, WORDS AND MUSIC.
Neal A. McAuley
J. S. Fearls.
1. I dreamed one night, not long a - go, Of mansions in the skies, Where those who love the Lord ob-tain A rich and glo-rious prize; I saw a-mong the hap - py throng The children bright and fair; I heard their voices clear and sweet With mu - sic fill the air.
2. And, as I mused, I heard a voice, In sweet-er tones than all, Di - rect-ing Christian work - ers here, In words I now re - call, "For-bid them not," He gen - tly said, "The children bring to me, Their por-tion in the World of Light Redeemed shall ev - er be."
3. And when from slumber I a-rose, To serve my Lord and King, I felt that I the lit - tle lambs To Christ in love might bring; And then I cried for dai - ly grace Their precious souls to cheer, Till they could sing like yonder choir Ho-san-na! bright and clear.
REFRAIN. Faster.
Hosanna! Hosanna! Our songs of love we bring,
we bring
Ho-san-na! Ho-san-na! To Christ, the children's King; Ho-san-na! Ho - san-na!

The Children's Hosanna.
Our songs of love we bring, Ho-san-na! Ho-san-na! to Christ, the children's King.
we bring,
No 219.
Bring Them In.
Alexcenah Thomas.
COPYRIGHT, 1885, BY W. A. OGDEN. USED BY PERMISSION.
W. A. Ogden.
1. Hark! 't is the Shepherd's voice I hear, Out in the des-ert dark and drear,
2. Who'll go and help this Shepherd kind, Help Him the wand'ring ones to find?
3. Out in the des-ert hear their cry, Out on the mountains wild and high;
Call-ing the sheep who've gone astray Far from the Shepherd's fold a-way.
Who'll bring the lost ones to the fold, Where they'll be sheltered from the cold?
Hark! 't is the Mas-ter speaks to thee, "Go find my sheep wher-e'er they be."
CHORUS.
Bring them in, bring them in, Bring them in from the fields of sin;
Bring them in, bring them in, Bring the wand'ring ones to Je-sus.

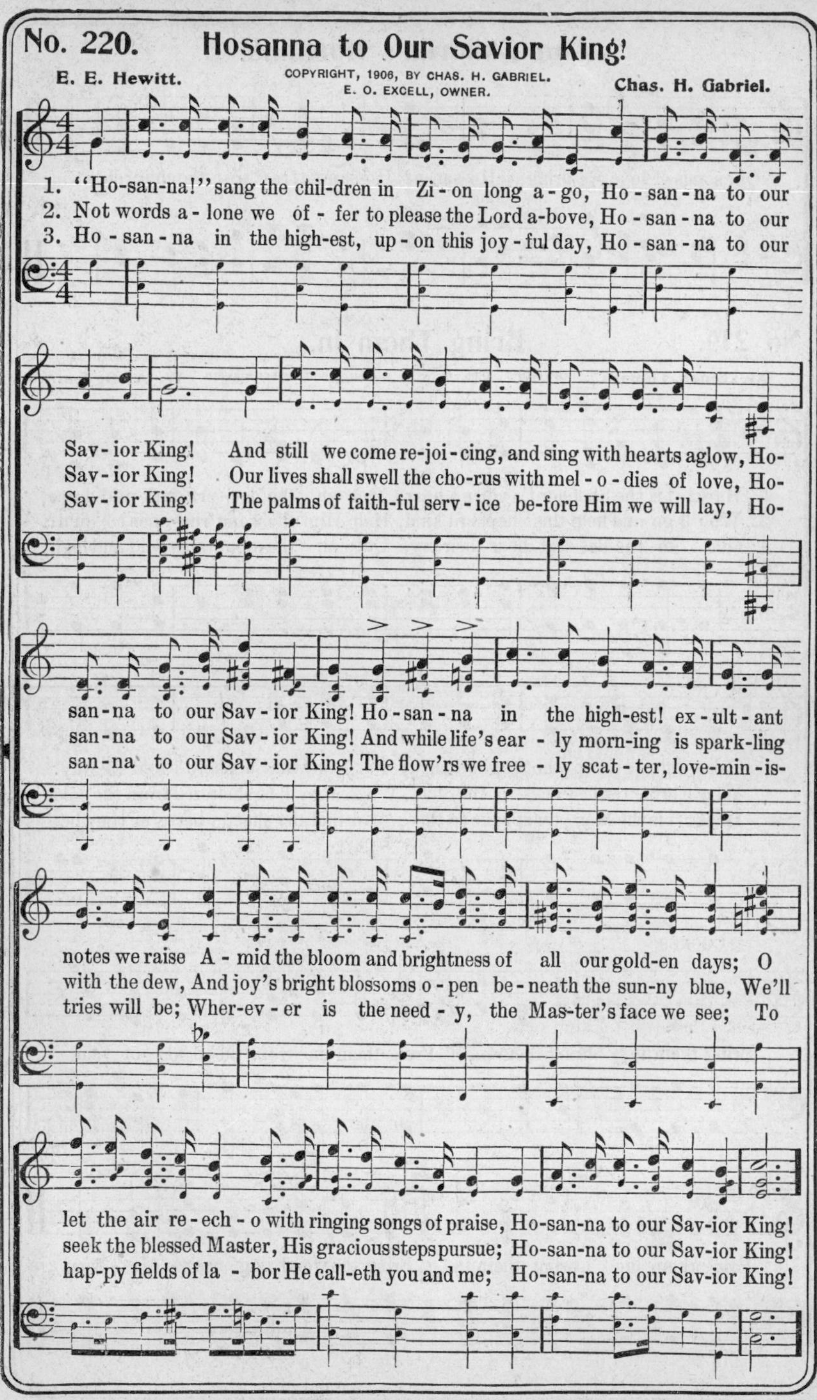

No. 220. Hosanna to Our Savior King!
E. E. Hewitt.
COPYRIGHT, 1906, BY CHAS. H. GABRIEL.
E. O. EXCELL, OWNER.
Chas. H. Gabriel.
1. "Ho-san-na!" sang the chil-dren in Zi-on long a-go, Ho-san-na to our
2. Not words a-lone we of-fer to please the Lord a-bove, Ho-san-na to our
3. Ho-san-na in the high-est, up-on this joy-ful day, Ho-san-na to our
Sav-ior King! And still we come re-joi-cing, and sing with hearts aglow, Ho-
Sav-ior King! Our lives shall swell the cho-rus with mel-o-dies of love, Ho-
Sav-ior King! The palms of faith-ful serv-ice be-fore Him we will lay, Ho-
san-na to our Sav-ior King! Ho-san-na in the high-est! ex-ult-ant
san-na to our Sav-ior King! And while life's ear-ly morn-ing is spark-ling
san-na to our Sav-ior King! The flow'rs we free-ly scat-ter, love-min-is-
notes we raise A-mid the bloom and brightness of all our gold-en days; O
with the dew, And joy's bright blossoms o-pen be-neath the sun-ny blue, We'll
tries will be; Wher-ev-er is the need-y, the Mas-ter's face we see; To
let the air re-ech-o with ringing songs of praise, Ho-san-na to our Sav-ior King!
seek the blessed Master, His gracious steps pursue; Ho-san-na to our Sav-ior King!
hap-py fields of la-bor He call-eth you and me; Ho-san-na to our Sav-ior King!

Hosanna to Our Savior King!
CHORUS.
1
2
Ho-san - na! ho - san - na! Ho-san-na to our Sav-ior King!
King!
No. 221.
Little Sowers.
James Rowe.
COPYRIGHT, 1906, BY CHAS. H. GABRIEL.
E. O. EXCELL, OWNER.
Chas. H. Gabriel.
1. We are lit - tle sow-ers, Sow-ing seeds of love, To be reaped and gathered
2. We are lit - tle sow-ers, Sow-ing here and there Lit - tle seeds that comfort
3. We are lit - tle sow-ers, And we pray that we May, as years pass o'er us,
In the fields a - bove; Je - sus helps us dai - ly, Shows us where to sow,
Hearts of grief and care; Oh, what joy it gives us Just to sow each day
Bet - ter sow-ers be; That when comes the whisper—"Reaping-time has come!"
And His love is with us Ev-'ry-where we go.
Lit - tle seeds of kind-ness As we go our way.
Man - y sheaves for Je - sus We may car - ry home.
CHORUS.
We are lit-tle sow - ers,
Sow-ing seeds of love, To be reaped and gathered In the fields a - bove.

No. 222. Jesus Bids Us Shine.

 E. O. Excell.

No. 223. Jesus Loves Me.

Wm. B. Bradbury.

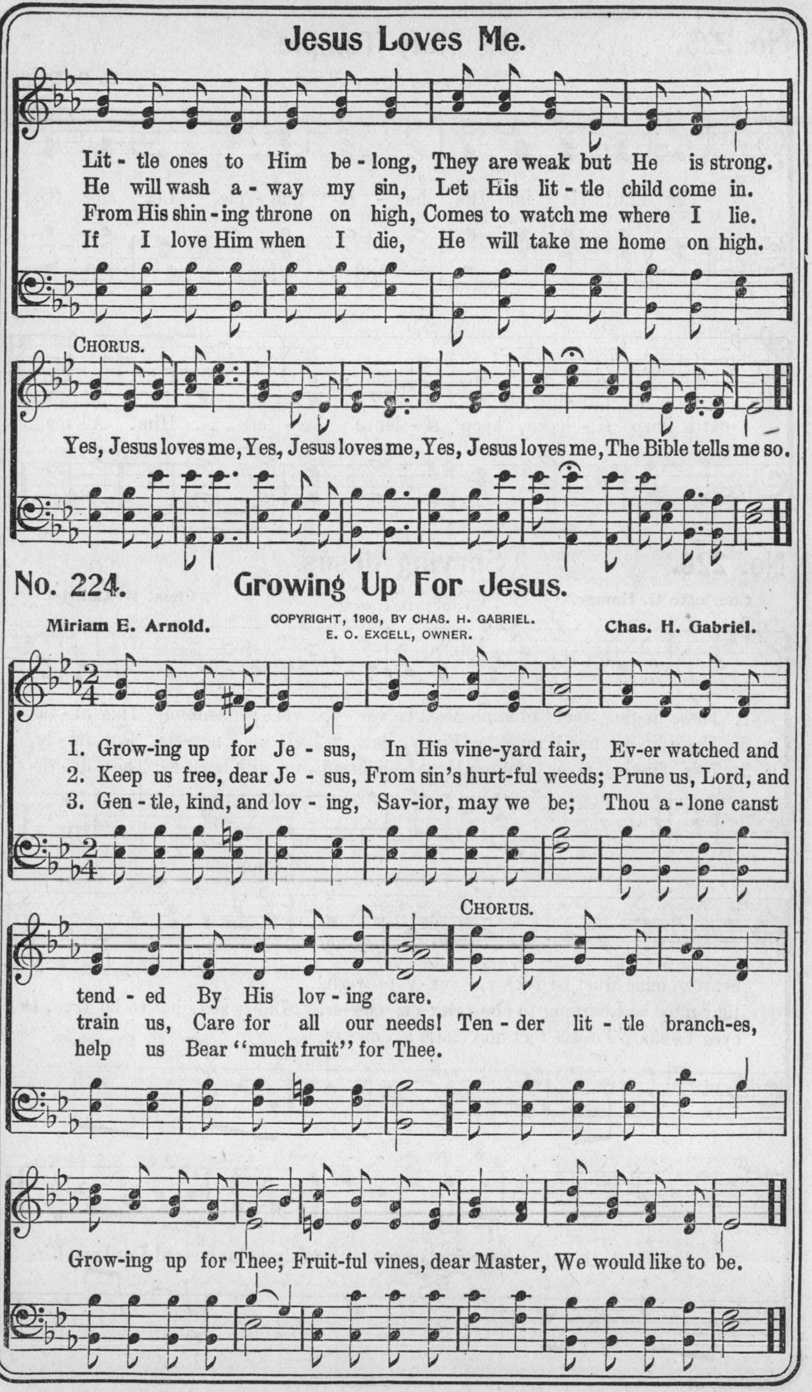
Jesus Loves Me.
Lit - tle ones to Him be - long, They are weak but He is strong.
He will wash a - way my sin, Let His lit - tle child come in.
From His shin - ing throne on high, Comes to watch me where I lie.
If I love Him when I die, He will take me home on high.
CHORUS.
Yes, Jesus loves me, Yes, Jesus loves me, Yes, Jesus loves me, The Bible tells me so.
No. 224. Growing Up For Jesus.
Miriam E. Arnold.
COPYRIGHT, 1906, BY CHAS. H. GABRIEL.
E. O. EXCELL, OWNER.
Chas. H. Gabriel.
1. Grow-ing up for Je - sus, In His vine-yard fair, Ev-er watched and tend - ed By His lov - ing care.
2. Keep us free, dear Je - sus, From sin's hurt-ful weeds; Prune us, Lord, and train us, Care for all our needs!
3. Gen - tle, kind, and lov - ing, Sav-ior, may we be; Thou a - lone canst help us Bear "much fruit" for Thee.
CHORUS.
Ten - der lit - tle branch-es, Grow-ing up for Thee; Fruit-ful vines, dear Master, We would like to be.

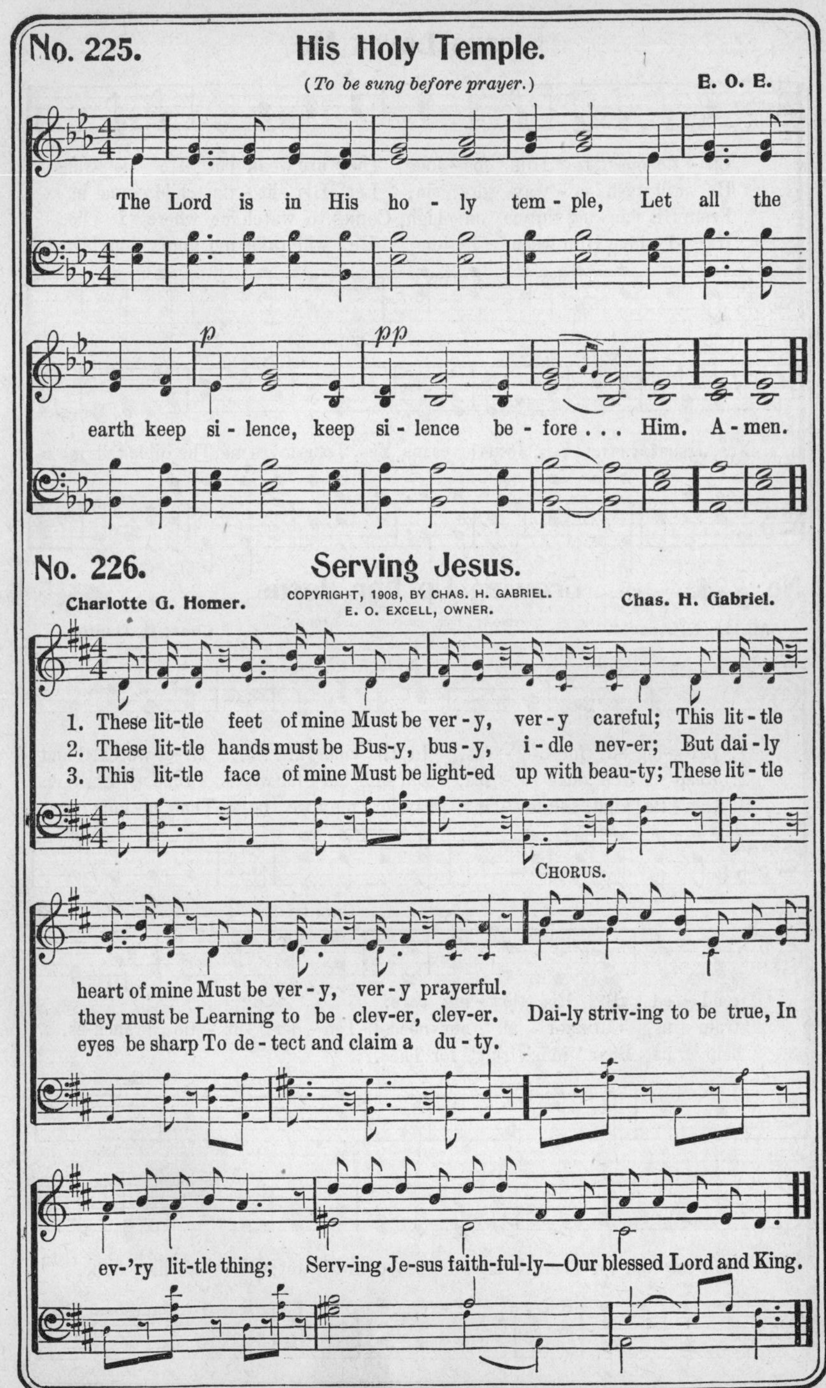
No. 225.
His Holy Temple.
(To be sung before prayer.)
E. O. E.
The Lord is in His ho - ly tem - ple, Let all the
p
pp
earth keep si - lence, keep si - lence be - fore . . . Him. A - men.
No. 226.
Serving Jesus.
Charlotte G. Homer.
COPYRIGHT, 1908, BY CHAS. H. GABRIEL.
E. O. EXCELL, OWNER.
Chas. H. Gabriel.
1. These lit-tle feet of mine Must be ver-y, ver-y careful; This lit-tle
2. These lit-tle hands must be Bus-y, bus-y, i-dle nev-er; But dai-ly
3. This lit-tle face of mine Must be light-ed up with beau-ty; These lit-tle
CHORUS.
heart of mine Must be ver - y, ver - y prayerful.
they must be Learning to be clev-er, clev-er.
eyes be sharp To de - tect and claim a du - ty.
Dai-ly striv-ing to be true, In
ev-'ry lit-tle thing; Serv-ing Je-sus faith-ful-ly—Our blessed Lord and King.

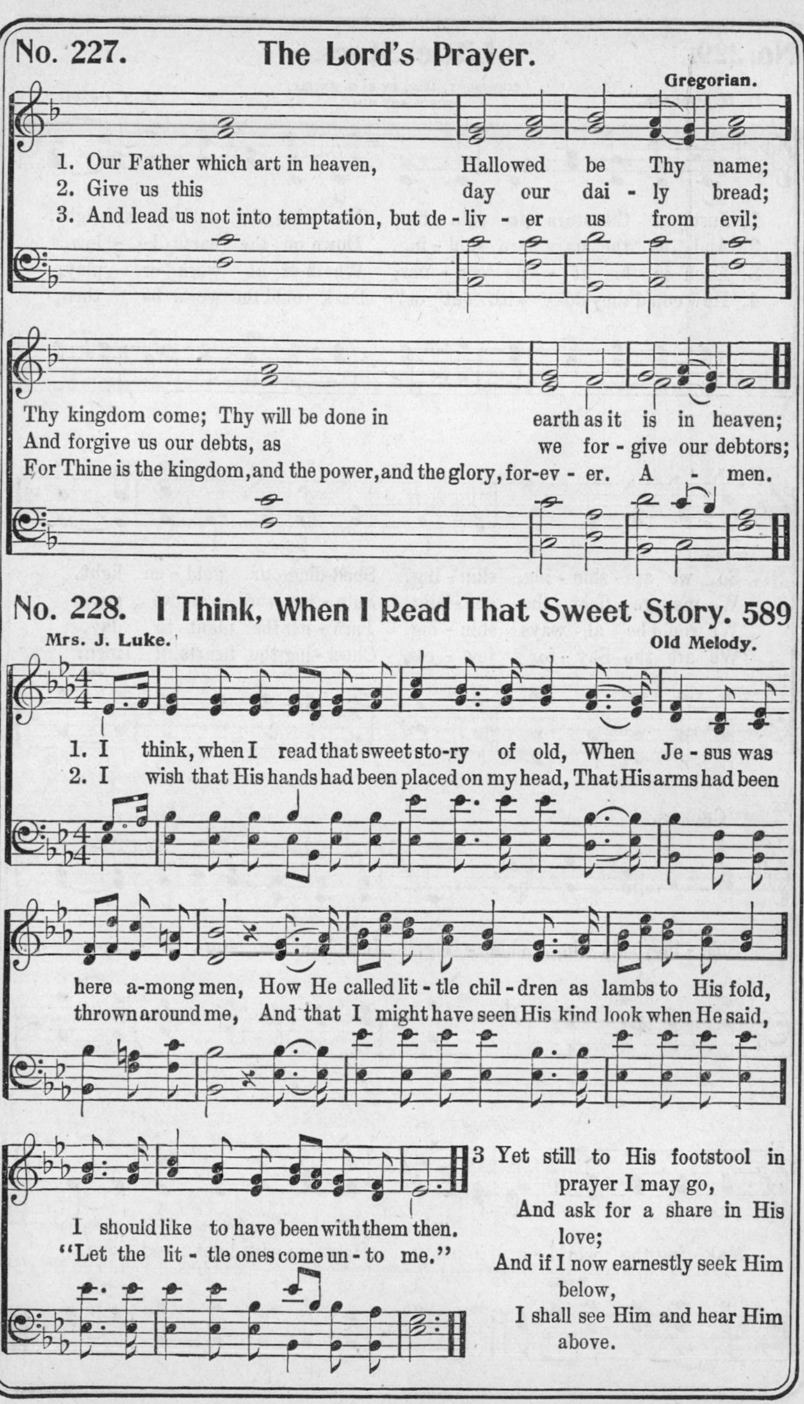
No. 227. The Lord's Prayer.
Gregorian.
1. Our Father which art in heaven, Hallowed be Thy name;
2. Give us this day our dai - ly bread;
3. And lead us not into temptation, but de - liv - er us from evil;
Thy kingdom come; Thy will be done in earth as it is in heaven;
And forgive us our debts, as we for - give our debtors;
For Thine is the kingdom, and the power, and the glory, for-ev - er. A - men.
No. 228. I Think, When I Read That Sweet Story. 589
Mrs. J. Luke.
Old Melody.
1. I think, when I read that sweet sto-ry of old, When Je - sus was
2. I wish that His hands had been placed on my head, That His arms had been
here a-mong men, How He called lit - tle chil - dren as lambs to His fold,
thrown around me, And that I might have seen His kind look when He said,
I should like to have been with them then.
"Let the lit - tle ones come un - to me."
3 Yet still to His footstool in prayer I may go,
And ask for a share in His love;
And if I now earnestly seek Him below,
I shall see Him and hear Him above.

No. 229. Little Stars.

Chorus Selections

No. 231. Jehovah is King.
C. H. G.
COPYRIGHT, 1910, BY E. O. EXCELL.
WORDS AND MUSIC.
Chas. H. Gabriel.
1. I will sing the praise of Je - ho - vah while I live; I will
2. Where He bids me, I, His am - bas - sa - dor, will go; His com-
3. I shall fear no ill, tho' the pow'rs of sin as - sail; He is
crown Him in my heart and life the King of kings; All there is with-
mand shall be my law, His word my guide and stay; All of self I
a - ble to de - liv - er, faith - ful to de - fend; He is just and
in me of good to Him I give, For He hides me 'neath His shelt'ring wings.
yield, sat-is - fied His will to know, As I walk beside Him day by day.
true, and His love shall nev-er fail; He will guide and keep me to the end.
CHORUS.
He is the King . . . . for-ev-er - more; . . . . . . He rules in
Je - ho - vah is King!
for - ev - er is King!
love . . . . . . from shore to shore; . . . . . His mandates shall . . . . . .
Je - ho - vah is King!
His glo - ry we sing!
The word of His law

Jehovah is King.

No. 232. Onward, Christian Soldiers!
To Prof. Chas. F. Allen.
Sabine Baring-Gould.
COPYRIGHT, 1907, BY E. O. EXCELL.
E. O. Excell.
1. On - ward, Chris-tian sol - diers! March - ing as to war, With the cross of Je - sus Go - ing on be - fore. Christ, the roy - al
2. At the sign of tri - umph Sa - tan's host doth flee; On, then, Chris - tian sol - diers, On to vic - to - ry! Hell's foun - da - tions
3. Like a might - y ar - my Moves the church of God; Broth - ers, we are tread - ing Where the saints have trod; We are not di-
4. On - ward, then, ye peo - ple! Join our hap - py throng, Blend with ours your voic - es In the tri - umph song; Glo - ry, laud, and

Onward, Christian Soldiers.
Mas - ter, Leads a - gainst the foe;...........
quiv - er At the shout of praise;.........
vid - ed, All one bod - y we,............
hon - or Un - to Christ the King,..........
For-ward in - to bat - tle, See His ban - ners go!
Broth-ers, lift your voi - ces, Loud your an - thems raise.
One in hope and doc - trine, One in char - i - ty.
This thro' count-less a - ges Men and an - gels sing.
Chorus.
Arthur S. Sullivan.
On-ward, Christian sol - diers! March-ing as to war, With the cross of
Je - sus Go - ing on be - fore. Interlude.

No. 233.
Marching in His Name.
COPYRIGHT, 1907, BY CHAS. H. GABRIEL.
COPYRIGHT, 1909, BY E. O. EXCELL.
Charlotte G. Homer.
Chas. H. Gabriel.
1. Like an ar - my we are mov - ing Stead - i - ly, and at com - mand,
2. Ma - ny foes concealed a - bout us, Would in - vade our ranks to - day,
3. In the light our ban - ner gleaming, Fills the heart with love and cheer,
Thro' a strange and hos - tile coun - try, To a bet - ter, bright - er land;
And with sub - tile ag - i - ta - tion, Seek to turn us from the way;
And the voice of our Re - deem - er, Qui - ets ev - 'ry doubt and fear;
Full e - quip'd, cour - age - ous, loy - al, With the gos - pel firm - ly shod,
But our Lead - er, on be - fore us, All their se - cret cun - ning knows,
Shoulder pressed to shoulder ev - er, With a tramp, tramp, tramp we move,
We are march - ing on to glo - ry, To the cit - y of our God.
And His wis - dom is for - ev - er Proof a - gainst the chief of foes.
On - ward, up - ward to the cit - y Built for us thro' Je - sus' love.

Marching in His Name.

No. 234. Crown Him King of Kings.
E. E. Rexford.
COPYRIGHT, 1909, BY E. O. EXCELL. WORDS AND MUSIC.
DeLoss Smith.
INTRODUCTION.
VOICES IN UNISON.
1. Crown Him, crown Him with glo - ry the King of kings;
2. He who reigns o'er the king-doms of earth to - day,
3. Praise Him, praise Him, the King on the great white throne;
Praise and hom-age each heart as its trib - ute brings;
Sends His bless-ings to those in the heav'n-ward way;
Love Him, serve Him, who rul - eth by love a - lone;
Sing, O earth, and u - nite in the might - y re - frain—
Sing we prais-es with hearts that with love o - ver - flow—
Up to heav - en the shout of the glo - ri - fied rings—

Crown Him King of Kings.

No. 235. A Song of Victory.
Charlotte G. Homer
COPYRIGHT, 1904, BY CHAS. H. GABRIEL.
COPYRIGHT, 1907, BY E. O. EXCELL.
Chas. H. Gabriel.
1. Loud - ly un - to the world is a cho - rus re - sound - ing,
2. Press - ing on to the bat - tle, each sol - dier re - joic - es,
3. Glo - ry! glo - ry to God in the high - est for - ev - er!
From the hosts of the Lord as they march a - long,
Sing - ing joy - ful - ly un - to the gra - cious King,
For the King in His beau - ty shall yet ap - pear;
Rich in har - mo - ny, send - ing the ech - oes re - bound - ing,
Earth is join - ing her praise with the tu - mult of voic - es,
Shout a - loud, for Je - ho - vah, our God, will de - liv - er;
Swell - ing might - i - ly from the vic - to - rious throng.
While the arch - es of heav - en with mu - sic ring.
His the bat - tle, and vic - to - ry draw - eth near.

A Song of Victory.
Chorus.
Vic - to - ry! rings aloud the bat - tle cry, bat - tle cry! Till the glad
Vic - to - ry! vic - to - ry! rings aloud the bat - tle cry, . . . Un - til the glo - ri - ous
echoes reach the vaulted sky, vaulted sky; O'er the world be un - furled
ech - oes reach the vault - ed sky; . . . . O - ver the world now be unfurl'd His
now His flag from shore to shore; Loy - al, true, in the ranks each
flag from shore to shore; , ... Loy - al and true, in the ranks each faith - ful
soldier stands, bravely stands, Glad - ly His will o - bey - ing in whate'er
sol - - - dier stands, ... Glad - ly o - bey - ing in what - so - ev - er He . . . com -
He commands; He the King, the kingdom His for - ev - er - more.
mands; . . . . . . He is the King, and the king - dom His for - ev - er - more.

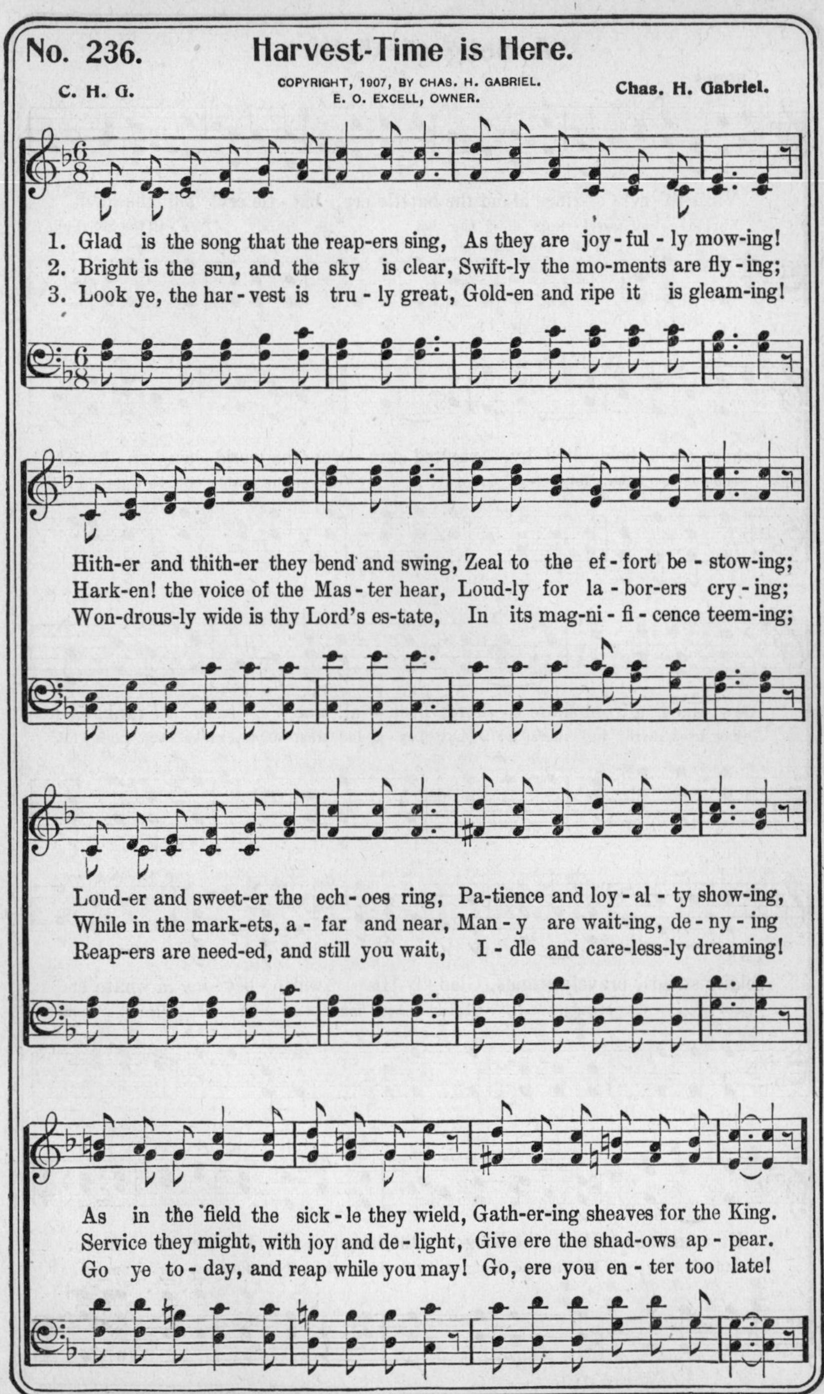

No. 236.
Harvest-Time is Here.
C. H. G.
COPYRIGHT, 1907, BY CHAS. H. GABRIEL.
E. O. EXCELL, OWNER.
Chas. H. Gabriel.
1. Glad is the song that the reap-ers sing, As they are joy-ful-ly mow-ing!
2. Bright is the sun, and the sky is clear, Swift-ly the mo-ments are fly-ing;
3. Look ye, the har-vest is tru-ly great, Gold-en and ripe it is gleam-ing!
Hith-er and thith-er they bend and swing, Zeal to the ef-fort be-stow-ing;
Hark-en! the voice of the Mas-ter hear, Loud-ly for la-bor-ers cry-ing;
Won-drous-ly wide is thy Lord's es-tate, In its mag-ni-fi-cence teem-ing;
Loud-er and sweet-er the ech-oes ring, Pa-tience and loy-al-ty show-ing,
While in the mark-ets, a-far and near, Man-y are wait-ing, de-ny-ing
Reap-ers are need-ed, and still you wait, I-dle and care-less-ly dreaming!
As in the field the sick-le they wield, Gath-er-ing sheaves for the King.
Service they might, with joy and de-light, Give ere the shad-ows ap-pear.
Go ye to-day, and reap while you may! Go, ere you en-ter too late!

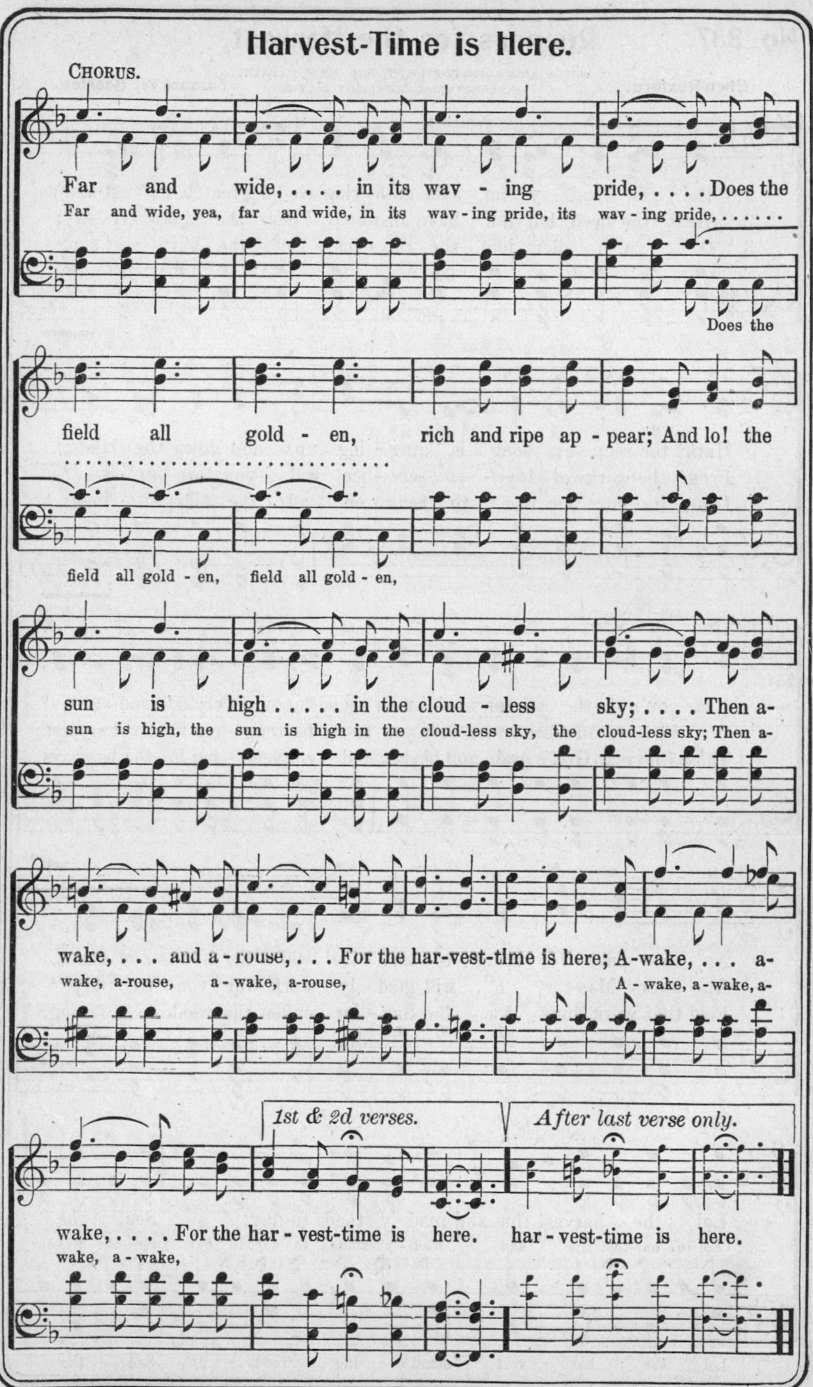
Harvest-Time is Here.
CHORUS.
Far and wide, ... in its wav - ing pride, ... Does the
Far and wide, yea, far and wide, in its wav - ing pride, its wav - ing pride, ...
Does the
field all gold - en, rich and ripe ap - pear; And lo! the
field all gold - en, field all gold - en,
sun is high . . . . in the cloud - less sky; . . . . Then a-
sun is high, the sun is high in the cloud-less sky, the cloud-less sky; Then a-
wake, . . . and a - rouse, . . . For the har-vest-time is here; A-wake, . . . a-
wake, a-rouse, a-wake, a-rouse, A - wake, a-wake, a-
wake, ... For the har - vest-time is here. har - vest-time is here.
wake, a - wake,
1st & 2d verses.
After last verse only.

No. 237. Reapers for the Harvest.
Eben Rexford.
WORDS AND MUSIC COPYRIGHT, 1905, BY E. O. EXCELL.
INTERNATIONAL COPYRIGHT SECURED.
Samuel W. Beasley.
1. Lo! all read - y for the gath-'ring God's great har - vest stands;
2. "Great the need but few have answered," hear the Mas - ter say;
3. O ye i - dlers join the cho - rus of the har - vest song,
Hark! the reap - ers' song is ring - ing up and down the lands;
From the work of loy - al serv - ice will you turn a - way?
Let its mu - sic rise to heav - en all the hills a - long;
Hear you not the call for work - men sound-ing o - ver hill and val-ley?
O for love of Christ who calls you to be reap - ers in His har-vest,
Those who reap God's grain and bind it, and go glean - ing in the by-ways,
An - swer quick - ly, bring to serv - ice will - ing hearts and hands.
An - swer "Mas-ter, I will glad - ly work for you to - day."
Find that work done for the Sav - ior makes the weak - est strong.
CHORUS.
Lo! the harvest ripe and read - y stands to-day; See, the
Lo! the har-vest ripe and read - y stands to - day, to - day; See the Mas-ter
Lo! the har - vest stand - ing read - y, See the

Reapers for the Harvest.
Master cometh, and He comes this way, Seeking for reapers, let us
com - eth, and He comes, He comes this way,
Mas - ter comes this way; He seek - eth reap - ers;
answer one and all, For a great reward is offered if we heed His call.
quickly,
an - swer quick - ly,
A-wake, a-wake, the harvest waits on ev - 'ry hill and plain;
See, the har-vest waits on ev - 'ry hill, on hill and plain;
See, the har - vest waits for reap - ers;
Go, and gath-er in the sheaves of golden grain; Reap-ing and bind-ing
Go and gather in the sheaves of gold - en grain, quickly;
Go, and gath - er for the Mas - ter; Reap - ing, bind-
rit.
ere the harvest pass a - way, Answer quickly, "We will work to-day."
go ye,
ing ere the harvest pass a - way,

No. 238. The Tramp of the Host.
COPYRIGHT, 1908, BY CHAS. H. GABRIEL.
COPYRIGHT, 1909, BY E. O. EXCELL.
C. H. G.
Chas. H. Gabriel.
1. Like an ar - my we are march-ing Un - der a ban - ner grand and glo - rious,
2. Sin and er - ror are ap - pall - ing! Per - ish-ing souls are all a - round us;
3. Man - y dan - gers lie be - fore us, Wearisome marches, sorrows, loss - es;
Ev - 'ry sol - dier true and loy - al In the serv - ice of the King.
Hea-then na - tions on be - fore us For the gos - pel watch and pray.
Heav - y bur - dens, lone - ly vig - ils To be kept by day and night;
For-ward ev - er on to bat - tle, Fol - low-ing Christ, who goes before us,
Nothing daunt - ed, noth-ing fear - ing, Joy - ful - ly on - ward to the res - cue,
Yet de - ter-mined and u - ni - ted, Shar-ing a - like in cares and sor - rows,

The Tramp of the Host.

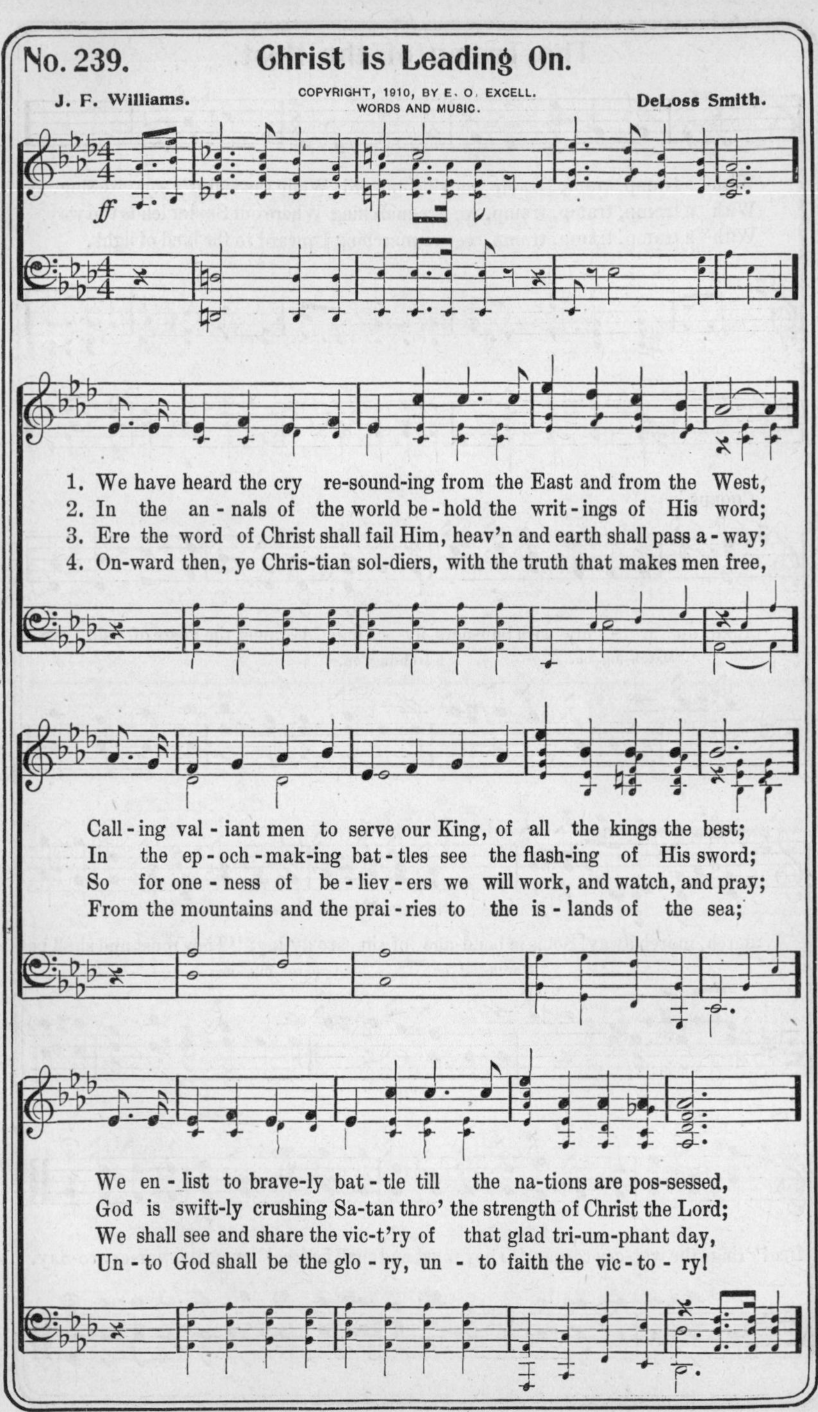
No. 239.
Christ is Leading On.
J. F. Williams.
COPYRIGHT, 1910, BY E. O. EXCELL.
WORDS AND MUSIC.
DeLoss Smith.
ff
1. We have heard the cry re-sound-ing from the East and from the West,
2. In the an - nals of the world be - hold the writ - ings of His word;
3. Ere the word of Christ shall fail Him, heav'n and earth shall pass a - way;
4. On-ward then, ye Chris-tian sol-diers, with the truth that makes men free,
Call - ing val - iant men to serve our King, of all the kings the best;
In the ep - och - mak-ing bat - tles see the flash-ing of His sword;
So for one - ness of be - liev - ers we will work, and watch, and pray;
From the mountains and the prai - ries to the is - lands of the sea;
We en - list to brave-ly bat - tle till the na-tions are pos-sessed,
God is swift-ly crushing Sa-tan thro' the strength of Christ the Lord;
We shall see and share the vic-t'ry of that glad tri-um-phant day,
Un - to God shall be the glo - ry, un - to faith the vic - to - ry!

Christ is Leading On.

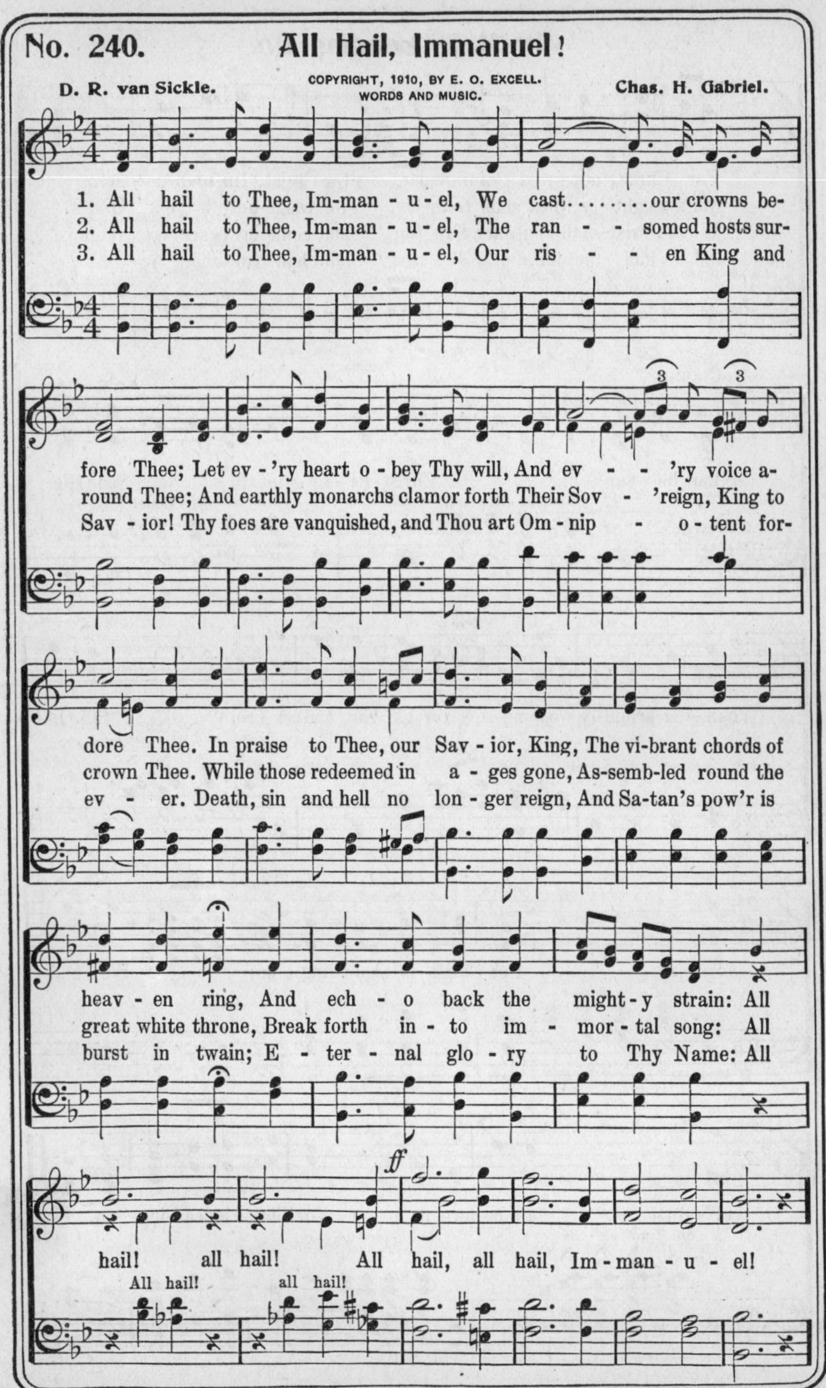
No. 240. All Hail, Immanuel!
D. R. van Sickle.
COPYRIGHT, 1910, BY E. O. EXCELL.
WORDS AND MUSIC.
Chas. H. Gabriel.
1. All hail to Thee, Im-man - u - el, We cast........our crowns be-fore Thee; Let ev - 'ry heart o - bey Thy will, And ev - - 'ry voice a-dore Thee. In praise to Thee, our Sav - ior, King, The vi-brant chords of heav - en ring, And ech - o back the might - y strain: All
2. All hail to Thee, Im-man - u - el, The ran - - somed hosts sur-round Thee; And earthly monarchs clamor forth Their Sov - 'reign, King to crown Thee. While those redeemed in a - ges gone, As-sem-bled round the great white throne, Break forth in - to im - mor - tal song: All
3. All hail to Thee, Im-man - u - el, Our ris - - en King and Sav - ior! Thy foes are vanquished, and Thou art Om - nip - o - tent for-ev - er. Death, sin and hell no lon - ger reign, And Sa-tan's pow'r is burst in twain; E - ter - nal glo - ry to Thy Name: All
3
3
hail! all hail! All hail, all hail, Im - man - u - el!
All hail! all hail!
ff

All Hail, Immanuel!

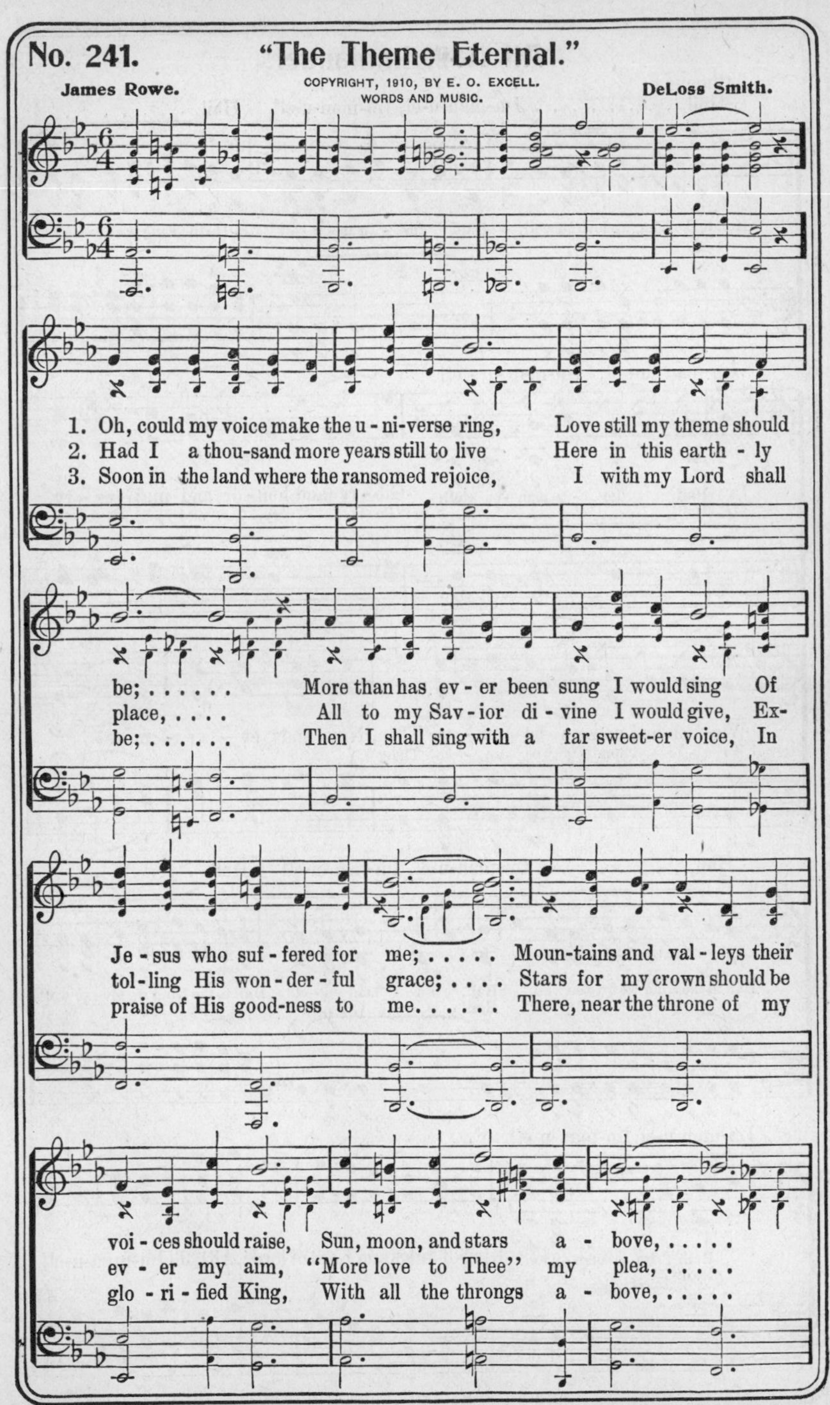
No. 241. "The Theme Eternal."
James Rowe.
COPYRIGHT, 1910, BY E. O. EXCELL.
WORDS AND MUSIC.
DeLoss Smith.
1. Oh, could my voice make the u - ni-verse ring, Love still my theme should
2. Had I a thou-sand more years still to live Here in this earth - ly
3. Soon in the land where the ransomed rejoice, I with my Lord shall
be; . . . . . . More than has ev - er been sung I would sing Of
place, ... All to my Sav - ior di - vine I would give, Ex-
be; . . . . . . Then I shall sing with a far sweet-er voice, In
Je - sus who suf - fered for me; . . . . . Moun-tains and val - leys their
tol-ling His won - der - ful grace; . . . . Stars for my crown should be
praise of His good-ness to me. . . . . . There, near the throne of my
voi - ces should raise, Sun, moon, and stars a - bove, ...
ev - er my aim, "More love to Thee" my plea, ...
glo - ri - fied King, With all the throngs a - bove, ...

"The Theme Eternal."
All should repeat thro' the ages my praise Of Christ and His wonderful love.
Sweeter and sweeter my voice should proclaim The Savior who suffered for me.
Sweet-er as age fol-lows age, I shall sing Of Christ and His wonderful love.
Chorus.
Praise Him, praise Him, Je - sus the King a - bove;
Praise Him, ye nations, ye throngs on high, Sing of His mer-cy and love;
Hon - or, glo - ry, His thro' the a - ges shall be,
Honor, and glo-ry, and praise to the Lamb Who suffered death for me.

No. 242. The Song of Triumph.
Charlotte G. Homer.
COPYRIGHT, 1897, BY E. O. EXCELL. WORDS AND MUSIC.
Chas. H. Gabriel.
D. C.–1. We are march - ing un - der the ban - ner vic - to - rious;
2. God is with us, strong to sup - port and de - liv - er;
3. On-ward, on - ward! an - swer the call of the Lead - er;
Leav - ing all at the call of the Com-man-der we love;
In His might day and night stead - i - ly on - ward we move;
For the right we will fight, fear - less - ly en - ter the fray,
Tramp! tramp! Sa - tan's bat - tle - ments trem-ble be - fore us,
Where He leads, thro' val - ley, o'er mount-ain or riv - er,
Brave - ly, tru - ly heed - ing the sum-mons to serv - ice,
"Vic - to - ry! vic - to - ry!" ech - o the courts a - bove!
We will go for we know in - fi - nite is His love.
Val - iant - ly, loy - al - ly bat - tle for Christ to - day.
FINE.

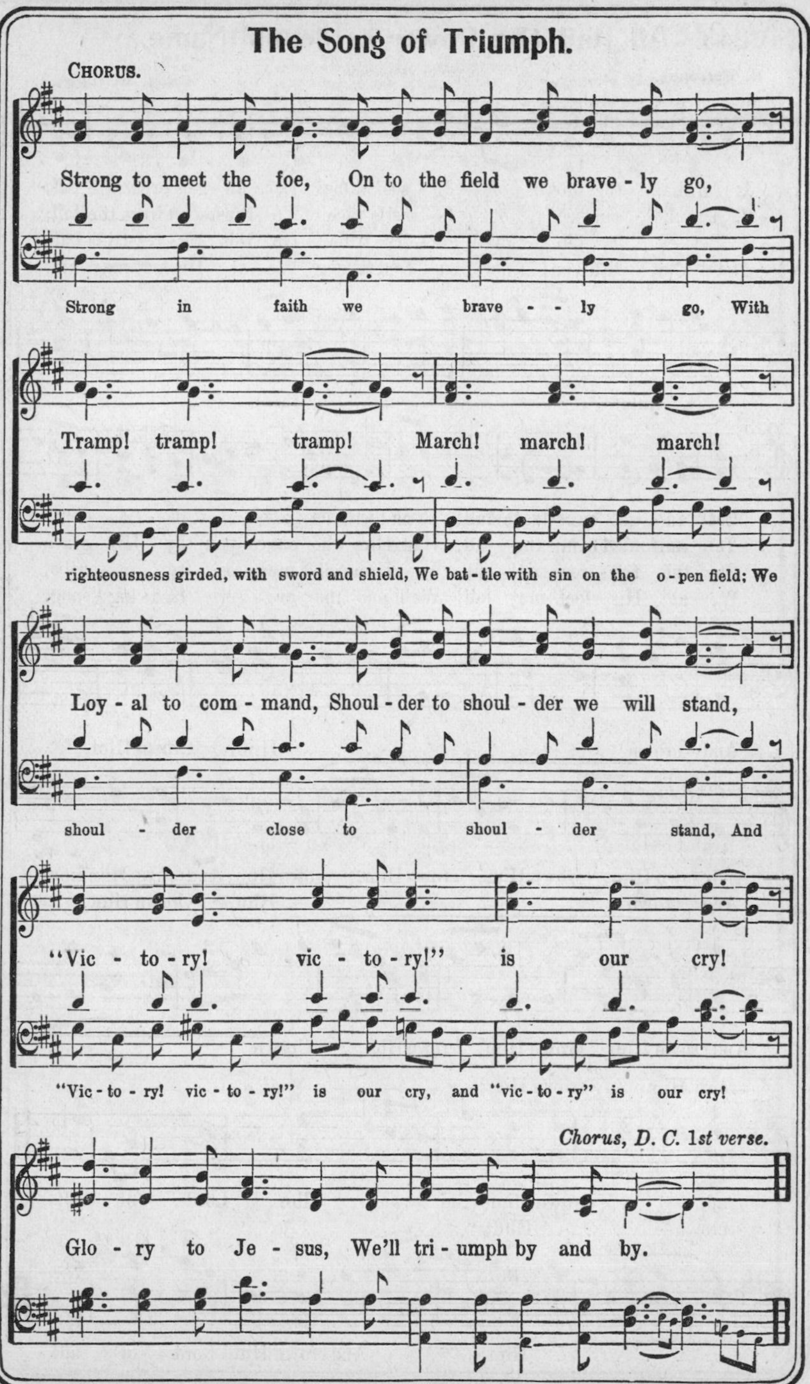
The Song of Triumph.
Chorus.
Strong to meet the foe, On to the field we brave - ly go,
Strong in faith we brave - - ly go, With
Tramp! tramp! tramp! March! march! march!
righteousness girded, with sword and shield, We bat - tle with sin on the o - pen field; We
Loy - al to com - mand, Shoul - der to shoul - der we will stand,
shoul - der close to shoul - der stand, And
"Vic - to - ry! vic - to - ry!" is our cry!
"Vic - to - ry! vic - to - ry!" is our cry, and "vic - to - ry" is our cry!
Chorus, D. C. 1st verse.
Glo - ry to Je - sus, We'll tri - umph by and by.

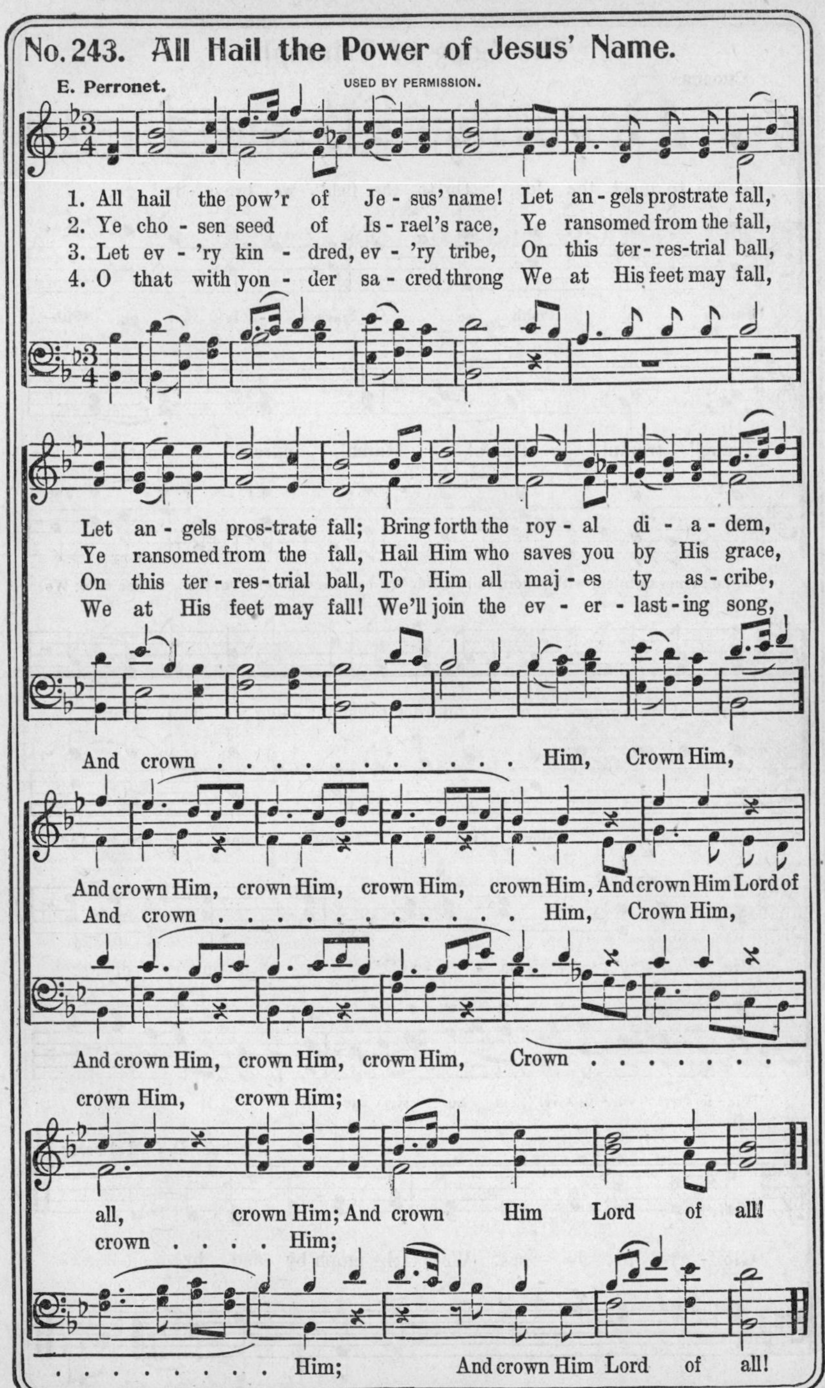
No. 243. All Hail the Power of Jesus' Name.
E. Perronet.
USED BY PERMISSION.
1. All hail the pow'r of Je - sus' name! Let an - gels prostrate fall,
2. Ye cho - sen seed of Is - rael's race, Ye ransomed from the fall,
3. Let ev - 'ry kin - dred, ev - 'ry tribe, On this ter - res - trial ball,
4. O that with yon - der sa - cred throng We at His feet may fall,
Let an - gels pros - trate fall; Bring forth the roy - al di - a - dem,
Ye ransomed from the fall, Hail Him who saves you by His grace,
On this ter - res - trial ball, To Him all maj - es ty as - cribe,
We at His feet may fall! We'll join the ev - er - last - ing song,
And crown . . . . Him, Crown Him,
And crown Him, crown Him, crown Him, crown Him, And crown Him Lord of
And crown . . . . Him, Crown Him,
And crown Him, crown Him, crown Him, Crown . . . .
crown Him, crown Him;
all, crown Him; And crown Him Lord of all!
crown . . . . Him;
. . . . Him; And crown Him Lord of all!

Devotional Hymns

No. 244. Glorious Things of Thee are Spoken.

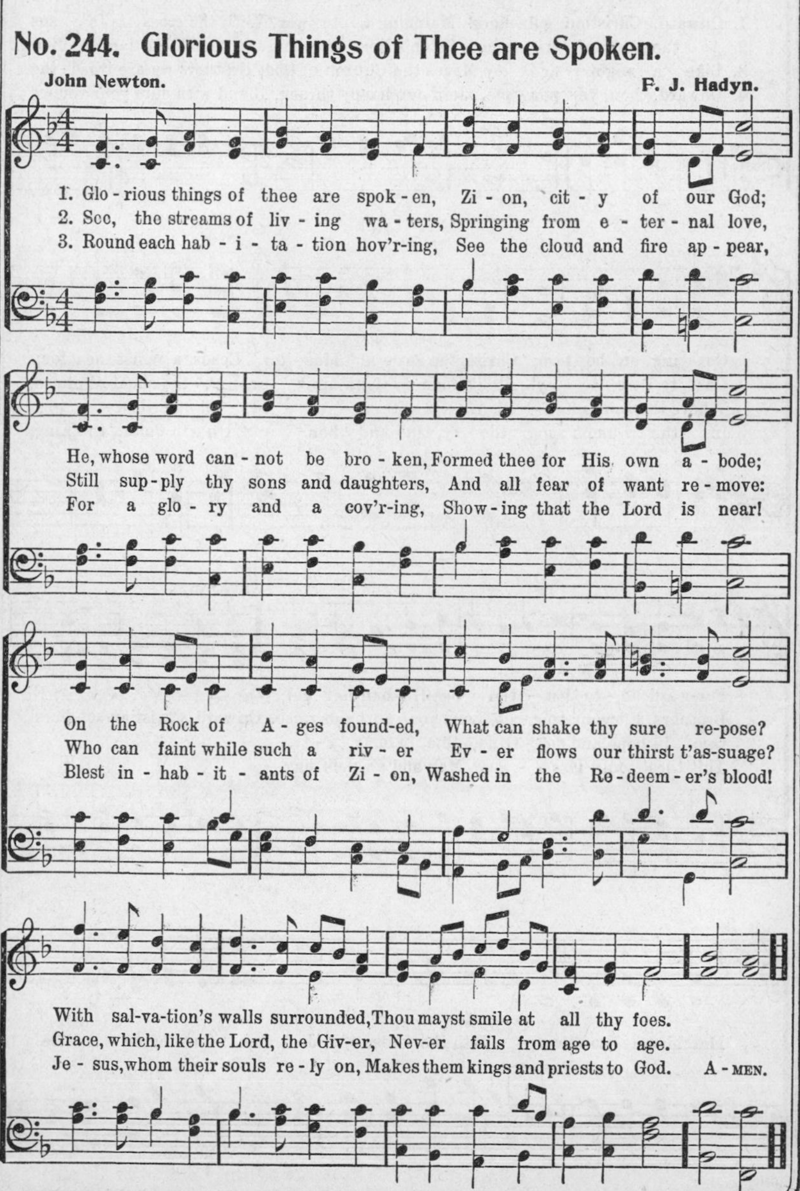

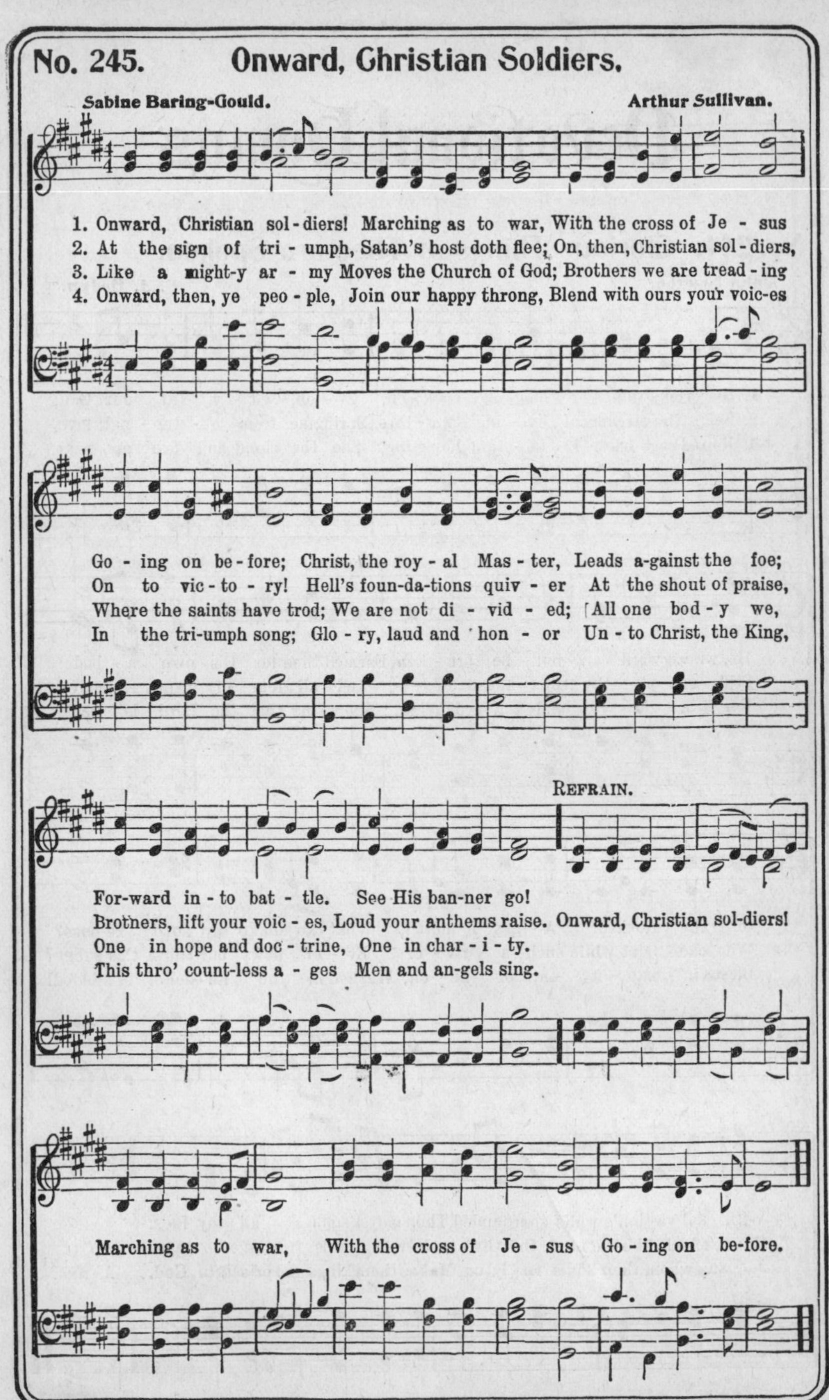
No. 245. Onward, Christian Soldiers.
Sabine Baring-Gould.
Arthur Sullivan.
1. Onward, Christian sol - diers! Marching as to war, With the cross of Je - sus
2. At the sign of tri - umph, Satan's host doth flee; On, then, Christian sol - diers,
3. Like a might-y ar - my Moves the Church of God; Brothers we are tread - ing
4. Onward, then, ye peo - ple, Join our happy throng, Blend with ours your voic-es
Go - ing on be - fore; Christ, the roy - al Mas - ter, Leads a-gainst the foe;
On to vic - to - ry! Hell's foun-da-tions quiv - er At the shout of praise,
Where the saints have trod; We are not di - vid - ed; All one bod - y we,
In the tri-umph song; Glo - ry, laud and hon - or Un - to Christ, the King,
For-ward in - to bat - tle. See His ban-ner go!
Brothers, lift your voic - es, Loud your anthems raise.
One in hope and doc - trine, One in char - i - ty.
This thro' count-less a - ges Men and an-gels sing.
Refrain.
Onward, Christian sol-diers!
Marching as to war, With the cross of Je - sus Go - ing on be-fore.

No. 246. How Firm a Foundation.
George Keith.
Unknown.
1. How firm a foun-da-tion, ye saints of the Lord, Is laid for your faith in His
2. "Fear not, I am with thee, O be not dis-mayed, For I am thy God, I will
3. "When thro' the deep waters I call thee to go, The riv-ers of sor-row shall
4. "When thro' fiery tri-als thy path-way shall lie, My grace, all-suf-fi-cient, shall
ex-cel-lent word! What more can He say than to you He hath said, To you, who for
still give thee aid; I'll strengthen thee, help thee, and cause thee to stand, Up-held by my
not o-ver-flow; For I will be with thee thy tri-als to bless, And sanc-ti-fy
be thy sup-ply, The flames shall not hurt thee; I on-ly de-sign Thy dross to con-
ref-uge to Je-sus have fled? To you, who for ref-uge to Je-sus have fled?
gra-cious, om-nip-o-tent hand, Up-held by my gra-cious, om-nip-o-tent hand.
to thee thy deep-est dis-tress, And sanc-ti-fy to thee thy deep-est dis-tress.
sume, and thy gold to re-fine, Thy dross to con-sume, and thy gold to re-fine."
No. 247. How Firm a Foundation.
George Keith.
(Second tune.)
Anne Steele.

No. 248. Love Divine.
Charles Wesley.
John Zundel.
1. Love di - vine, all love ex - cell - ing, Joy of heav'n, to earth come down!
Fix in us Thy hum - ble dwell - ing; All Thy faith - ful mer - cies crown.
D. S.—Vis - it us with Thy sal - va - tion, En - ter ev - 'ry trem - bling heart!
FINE.
Je - sus, Thou art all com - pas - sion, Pure, un - bound - ed love Thou art;
D. S.
2 Breathe, oh, breathe Thy loving Spirit
Into every troubled breast!
Let us all in Thee inherit,
Let us find the promised rest.
Take away the love of sinning;
Alpha and Omega be;
End of faith, as its beginning,
Set our hearts at liberty!
3 Come, Almighty to deliver,
Let us all Thy grace receive;
Suddenly return, and never,
Never more Thy temples leave:
Thee we would be always blessing,
Serve Thee as Thy hosts above,
Pray, and praise Thee without ceasing,
Glory in Thy perfect love!
No. 249. The Son of God Goes Forth to War.
R. Heber.
H. S. Cutler.
1. The Son of God goes forth to war, A king - ly crown to gain; His blood - red ban - ner
2. That martyr first, whose eagle eye Could pierce beyond the grave; Who saw his Mas - ter
3. A no - ble band, the chosen few On whom the Spir - it came; Twelve valiant saints, their

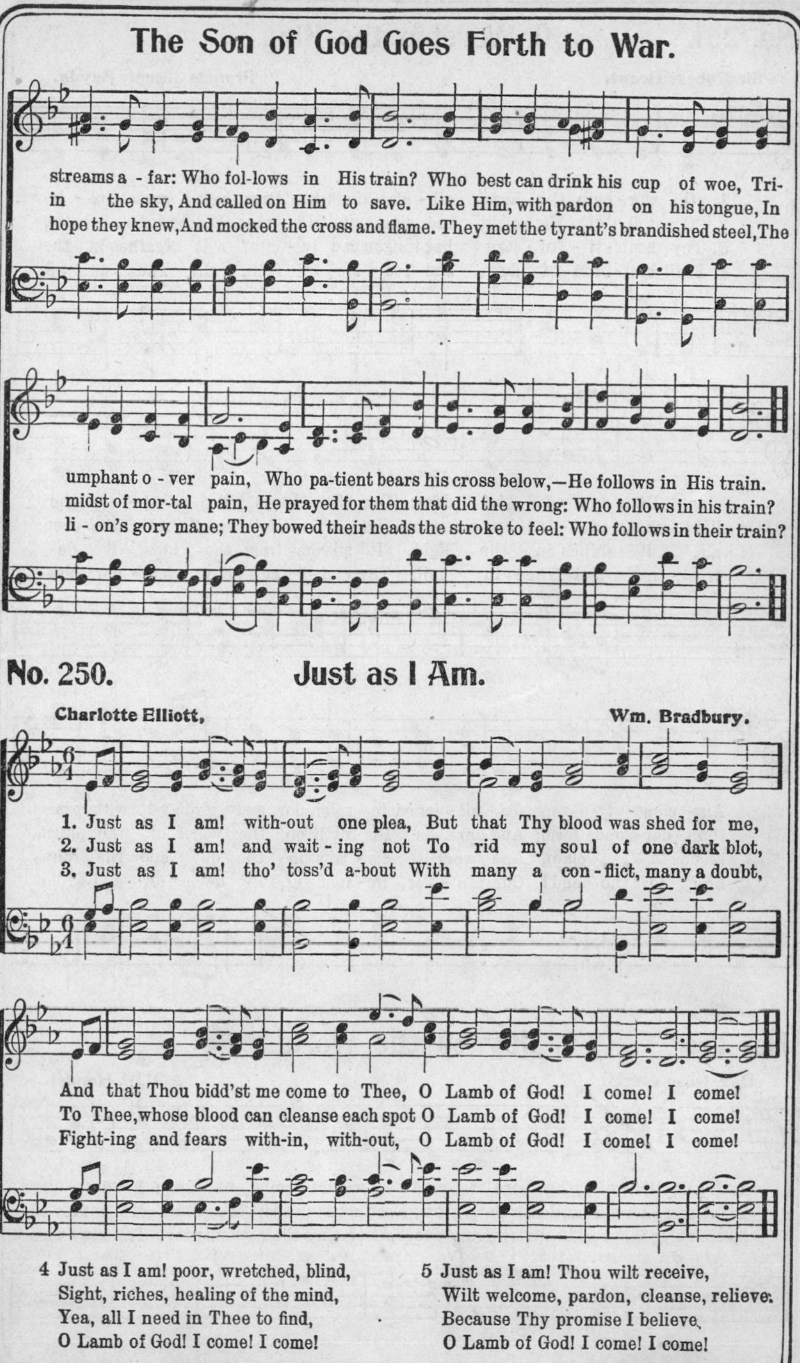
The Son of God Goes Forth to War.
streams a - far: Who fol-lows in His train? Who best can drink his cup of woe, Tri-
in the sky, And called on Him to save. Like Him, with pardon on his tongue, In
hope they knew, And mocked the cross and flame. They met the tyrant's brandished steel, The
umphant o - ver pain, Who pa-tient bears his cross below,—He follows in His train.
midst of mor-tal pain, He prayed for them that did the wrong: Who follows in his train?
li - on's gory mane; They bowed their heads the stroke to feel: Who follows in their train?
No. 250. Just as I Am.
Charlotte Elliott,
Wm. Bradbury.
1. Just as I am! with-out one plea, But that Thy blood was shed for me,
2. Just as I am! and wait - ing not To rid my soul of one dark blot,
3. Just as I am! tho' toss'd a-bout With many a con - flict, many a doubt,
And that Thou bidd'st me come to Thee, O Lamb of God! I come! I come!
To Thee, whose blood can cleanse each spot O Lamb of God! I come! I come!
Fight-ing and fears with-in, with-out, O Lamb of God! I come! I come!
4 Just as I am! poor, wretched, blind,
Sight, riches, healing of the mind,
Yea, all I need in Thee to find,
O Lamb of God! I come! I come!
5 Just as I am! Thou wilt receive,
Wilt welcome, pardon, cleanse, relieve:
Because Thy promise I believe,
O Lamb of God! I come! I come!

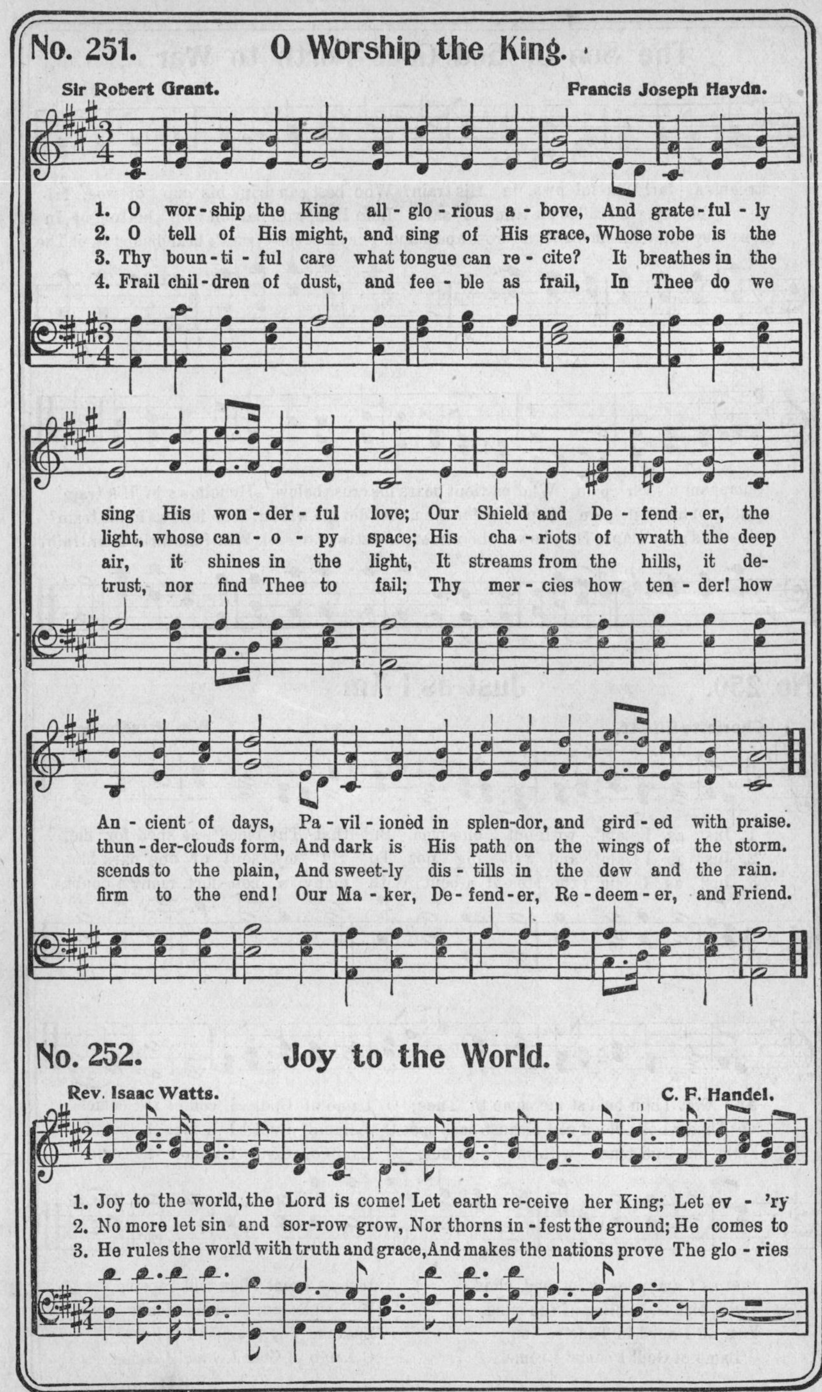
No. 251. O Worship the King.
Sir Robert Grant.
Francis Joseph Haydn.
1. O wor - ship the King all - glo - rious a - bove, And grate - ful - ly
2. O tell of His might, and sing of His grace, Whose robe is the
3. Thy boun - ti - ful care what tongue can re - cite? It breathes in the
4. Frail chil - dren of dust, and fee - ble as frail, In Thee do we
sing His won - der - ful love; Our Shield and De - fend - er, the
light, whose can - o - py space; His cha - riots of wrath the deep
air, it shines in the light, It streams from the hills, it de-
trust, nor find Thee to fail; Thy mer - cies how ten - der! how
An - cient of days, Pa - vil - ioned in splen - dor, and gird - ed with praise.
thun - der - clouds form, And dark is His path on the wings of the storm.
scends to the plain, And sweet - ly dis - tills in the dew and the rain.
firm to the end! Our Ma - ker, De - fend - er, Re - deem - er, and Friend.
No. 252. Joy to the World.
Rev. Isaac Watts.
C. F. Handel.
1. Joy to the world, the Lord is come! Let earth re - ceive her King; Let ev - 'ry
2. No more let sin and sor - row grow, Nor thorns in - fest the ground; He comes to
3. He rules the world with truth and grace, And makes the nations prove The glo - ries

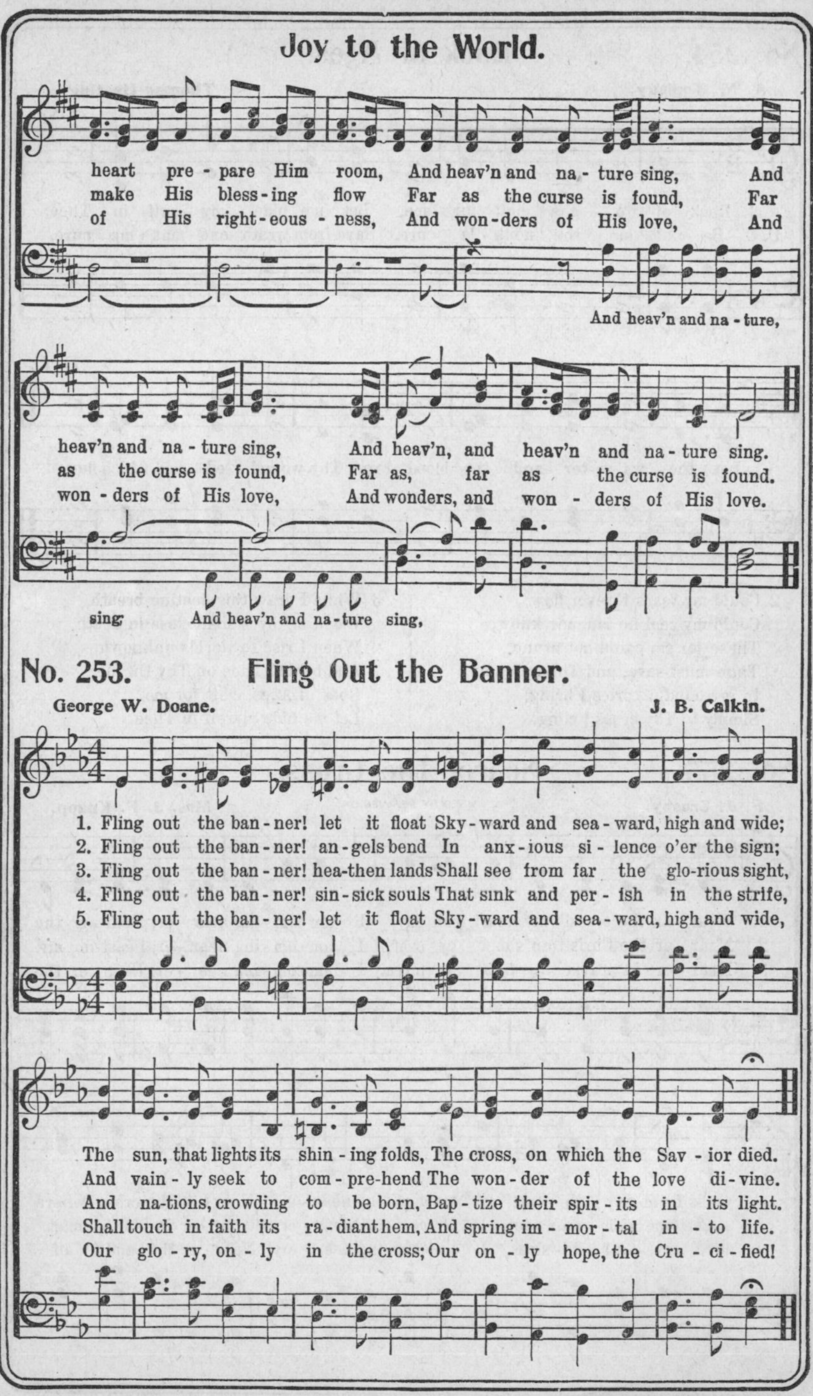
Joy to the World.
heart pre - pare Him room, And heav'n and na - ture sing, And
make His bless - ing flow Far as the curse is found, Far
of His right - eous - ness, And won - ders of His love, And
And heav'n and na - ture,
heav'n and na - ture sing, And heav'n, and heav'n and na - ture sing.
as the curse is found, Far as, far as the curse is found.
won - ders of His love, And wonders, and won - ders of His love.
sing, And heav'n and na - ture sing,
No. 253. Fling Out the Banner.
George W. Doane.
J. B. Calkin.
1. Fling out the ban - ner! let it float Sky - ward and sea - ward, high and wide;
2. Fling out the ban - ner! an - gels bend In anx - ious si - lence o'er the sign;
3. Fling out the ban - ner! hea-then lands Shall see from far the glo-rious sight,
4. Fling out the ban - ner! sin - sick souls That sink and per - ish in the strife,
5. Fling out the ban - ner! let it float Sky - ward and sea - ward, high and wide,
The sun, that lights its shin - ing folds, The cross, on which the Sav - ior died.
And vain - ly seek to com - pre - hend The won - der of the love di - vine.
And na - tions, crowding to be born, Bap - tize their spir - its in its light.
Shall touch in faith its ra - diant hem, And spring im - mor - tal in - to life.
Our glo - ry, on - ly in the cross; Our on - ly hope, the Cru - ci - fied!

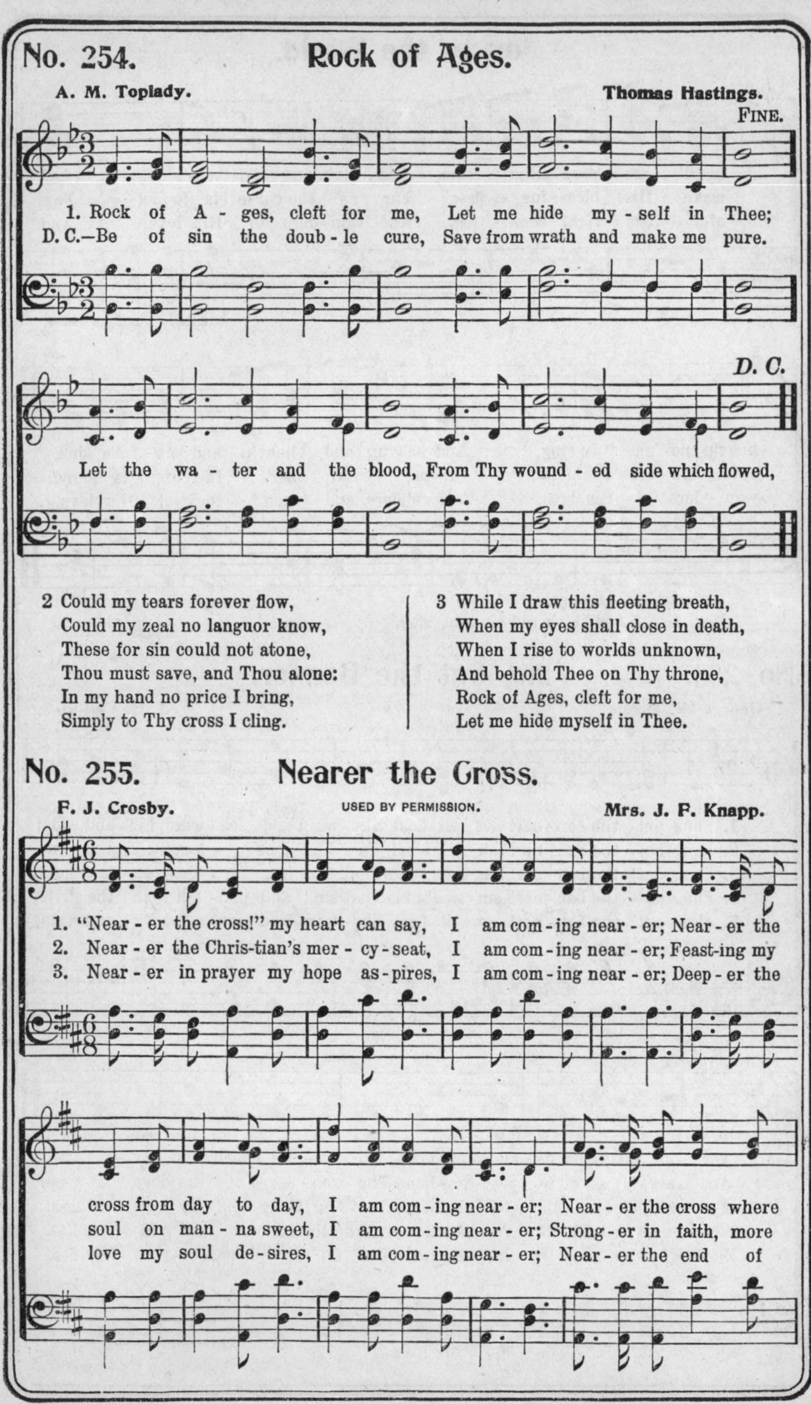
No. 254. Rock of Ages.
A. M. Toplady.
Thomas Hastings.
FINE.
1. Rock of A - ges, cleft for me, Let me hide my - self in Thee;
D. C.—Be of sin the doub - le cure, Save from wrath and make me pure.
D. C.
Let the wa - ter and the blood, From Thy wound - ed side which flowed,
2 Could my tears forever flow,
Could my zeal no languor know,
These for sin could not atone,
Thou must save, and Thou alone:
In my hand no price I bring,
Simply to Thy cross I cling.
3 While I draw this fleeting breath,
When my eyes shall close in death,
When I rise to worlds unknown,
And behold Thee on Thy throne,
Rock of Ages, cleft for me,
Let me hide myself in Thee.
No. 255. Nearer the Cross.
F. J. Crosby.
USED BY PERMISSION.
Mrs. J. F. Knapp.
1. "Near - er the cross!" my heart can say, I am com - ing near - er; Near - er the
2. Near - er the Chris - tian's mer - cy - seat, I am com - ing near - er; Feast - ing my
3. Near - er in prayer my hope as - pires, I am com - ing near - er; Deep - er the
cross from day to day, I am com - ing near - er; Near - er the cross where
soul on man - na sweet, I am com - ing near - er; Strong - er in faith, more
love my soul de - sires, I am com - ing near - er; Near - er the end of

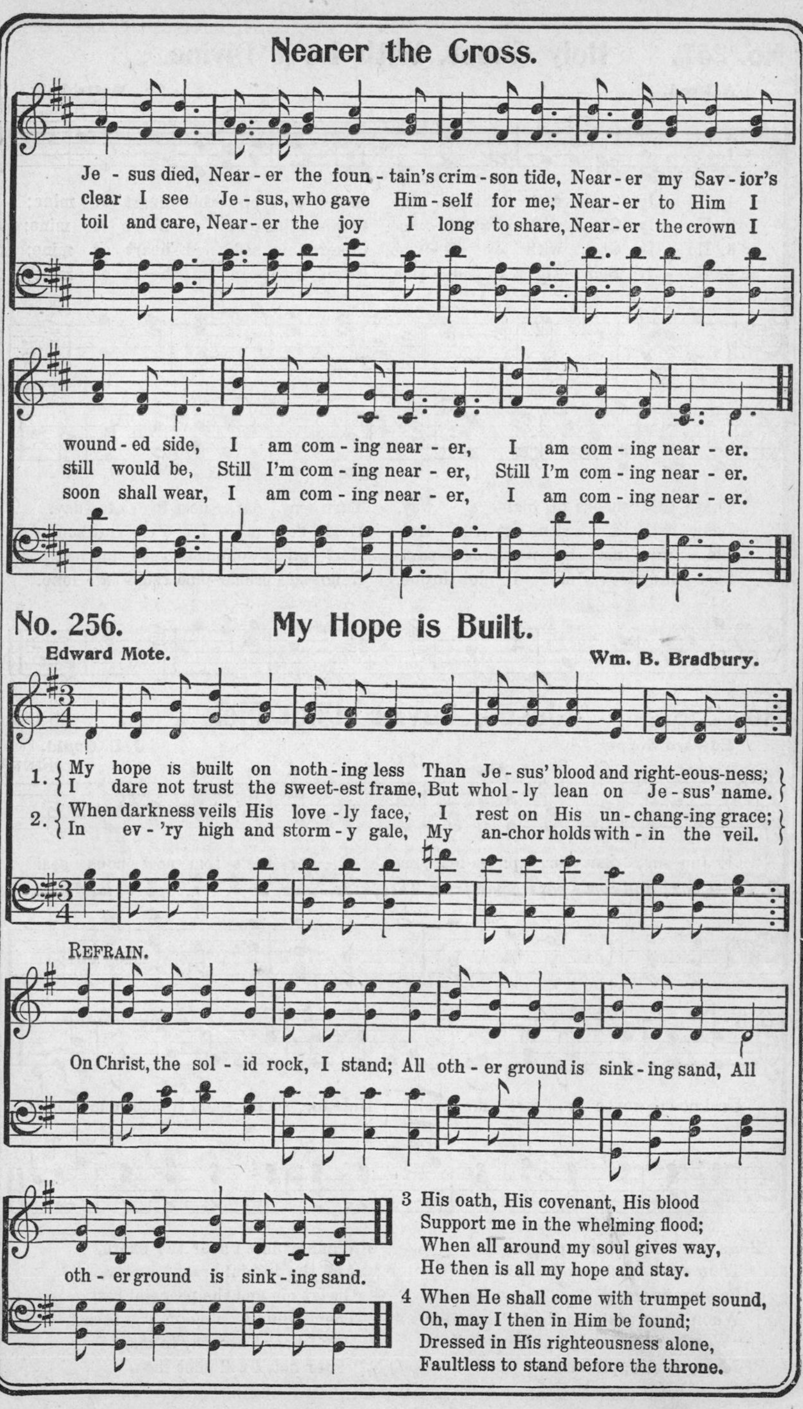
Nearer the Cross.
Je - sus died, Near - er the foun - tain's crim - son tide, Near - er my Sav - ior's
clear I see Je - sus, who gave Him - self for me; Near - er to Him I
toil and care, Near - er the joy I long to share, Near - er the crown I
wound - ed side, I am com - ing near - er, I am com - ing near - er.
still would be, Still I'm com - ing near - er, Still I'm com - ing near - er.
soon shall wear, I am com - ing near - er, I am com - ing near - er.
No. 256. My Hope is Built.
Edward Mote.
Wm. B. Bradbury.
1. My hope is built on noth - ing less Than Je - sus' blood and right - eous - ness;
I dare not trust the sweet - est frame, But whol - ly lean on Je - sus' name.
2. When darkness veils His love - ly face, I rest on His un - chang - ing grace;
In ev - 'ry high and storm - y gale, My an - chor holds with - in the veil.
REFRAIN.
On Christ, the sol - id rock, I stand; All oth - er ground is sink - ing sand, All
oth - er ground is sink - ing sand.
3 His oath, His covenant, His blood
Support me in the whelming flood;
When all around my soul gives way,
He then is all my hope and stay.
4 When He shall come with trumpet sound,
Oh, may I then in Him be found;
Dressed in His righteousness alone,
Faultless to stand before the throne.

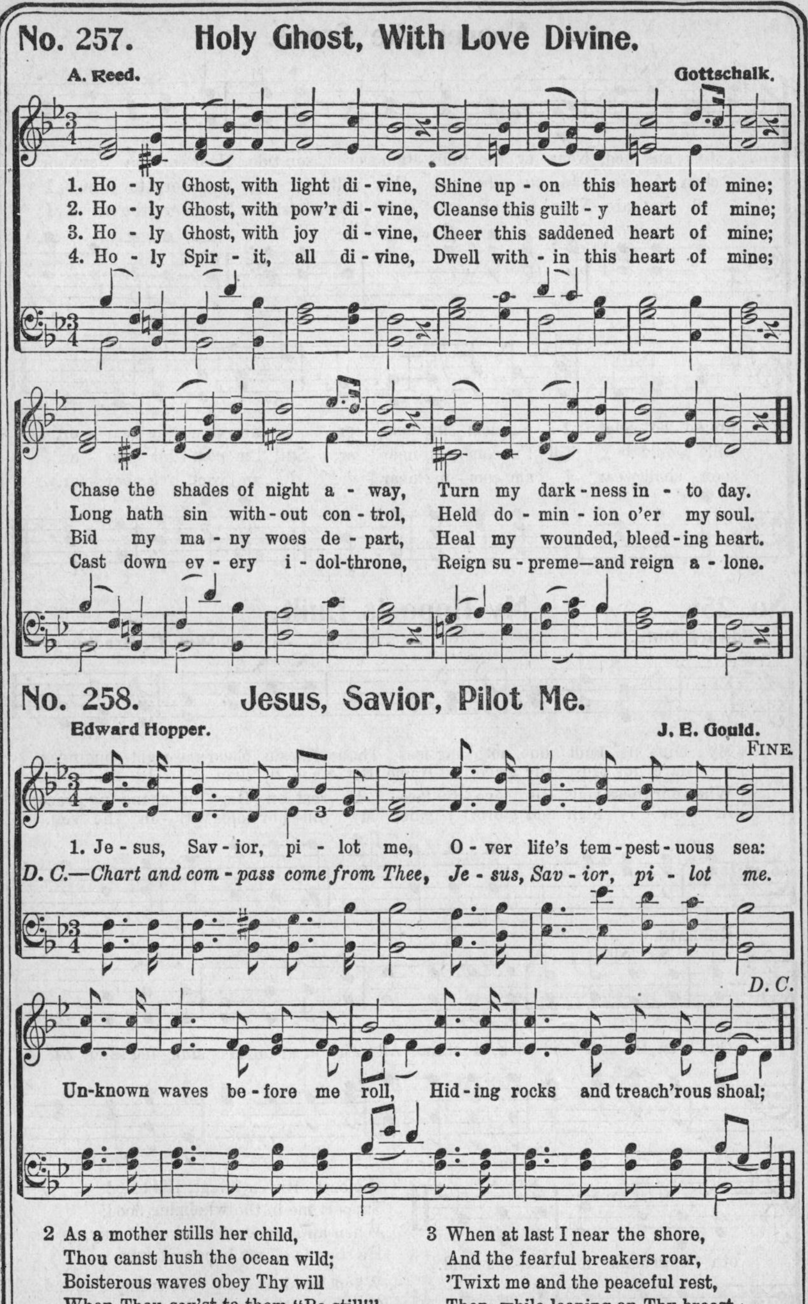

2 As a mother stills her child,
Thou canst hush the ocean wild;
Boisterous waves obey Thy will
When Thou say'st to them "Be still!"
"Wondrous Sovereign of the sea."
Jesus, Savior, pilot me.

3 When at last I near the shore,
And the fearful breakers roar,
'Twixt me and the peaceful rest,
Then, while leaning on Thy breast,
May I hear Thee say to me,
"Fear not, I will pilot thee."

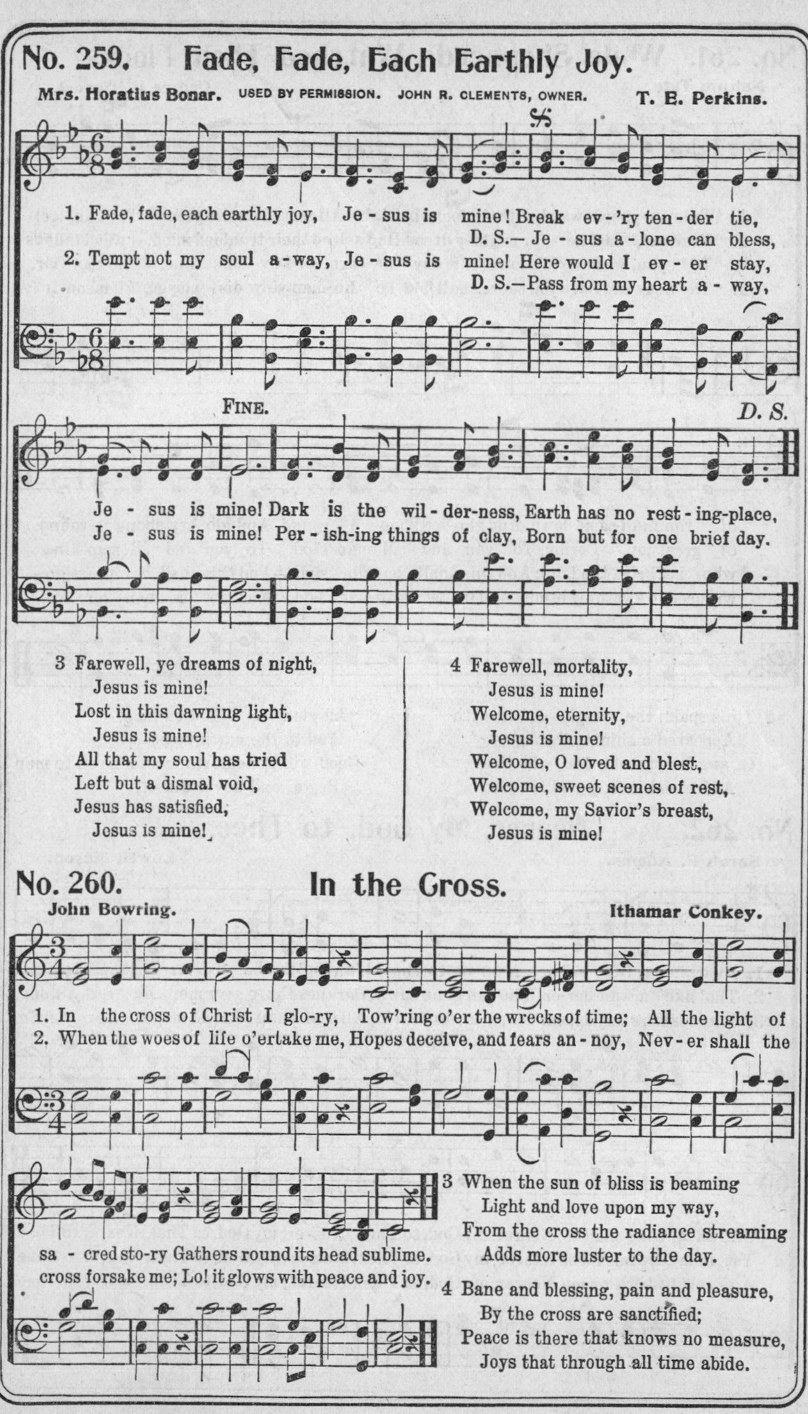
No. 259. Fade, Fade, Each Earthly Joy.
Mrs. Horatius Bonar. USED BY PERMISSION. JOHN R. CLEMENTS, OWNER. T. E. Perkins.
1. Fade, fade, each earthly joy, Je - sus is mine! Break ev - 'ry ten - der tie,
D. S.— Je - sus a - lone can bless,
2. Tempt not my soul a - way, Je - sus is mine! Here would I ev - er stay,
D. S.—Pass from my heart a - way,
FINE. D. S.
Je - sus is mine! Dark is the wil - der-ness, Earth has no rest - ing-place,
Je - sus is mine! Per - ish-ing things of clay, Born but for one brief day.
3 Farewell, ye dreams of night,
Jesus is mine!
Lost in this dawning light,
Jesus is mine!
All that my soul has tried
Left but a dismal void,
Jesus has satisfied,
Jesus is mine!
4 Farewell, mortality,
Jesus is mine!
Welcome, eternity,
Jesus is mine!
Welcome, O loved and blest,
Welcome, sweet scenes of rest,
Welcome, my Savior's breast,
Jesus is mine!
No. 260. In the Cross.
John Bowring. Ithamar Conkey.
1. In the cross of Christ I glo-ry, Tow'ring o'er the wrecks of time; All the light of
2. When the woes of life o'ertake me, Hopes deceive, and fears an - noy, Nev - er shall the
sa - cred sto-ry Gathers round its head sublime.
cross forsake me; Lo! it glows with peace and joy.
3 When the sun of bliss is beaming
Light and love upon my way,
From the cross the radiance streaming
Adds more luster to the day.
4 Bane and blessing, pain and pleasure,
By the cross are sanctified;
Peace is there that knows no measure,
Joys that through all time abide.

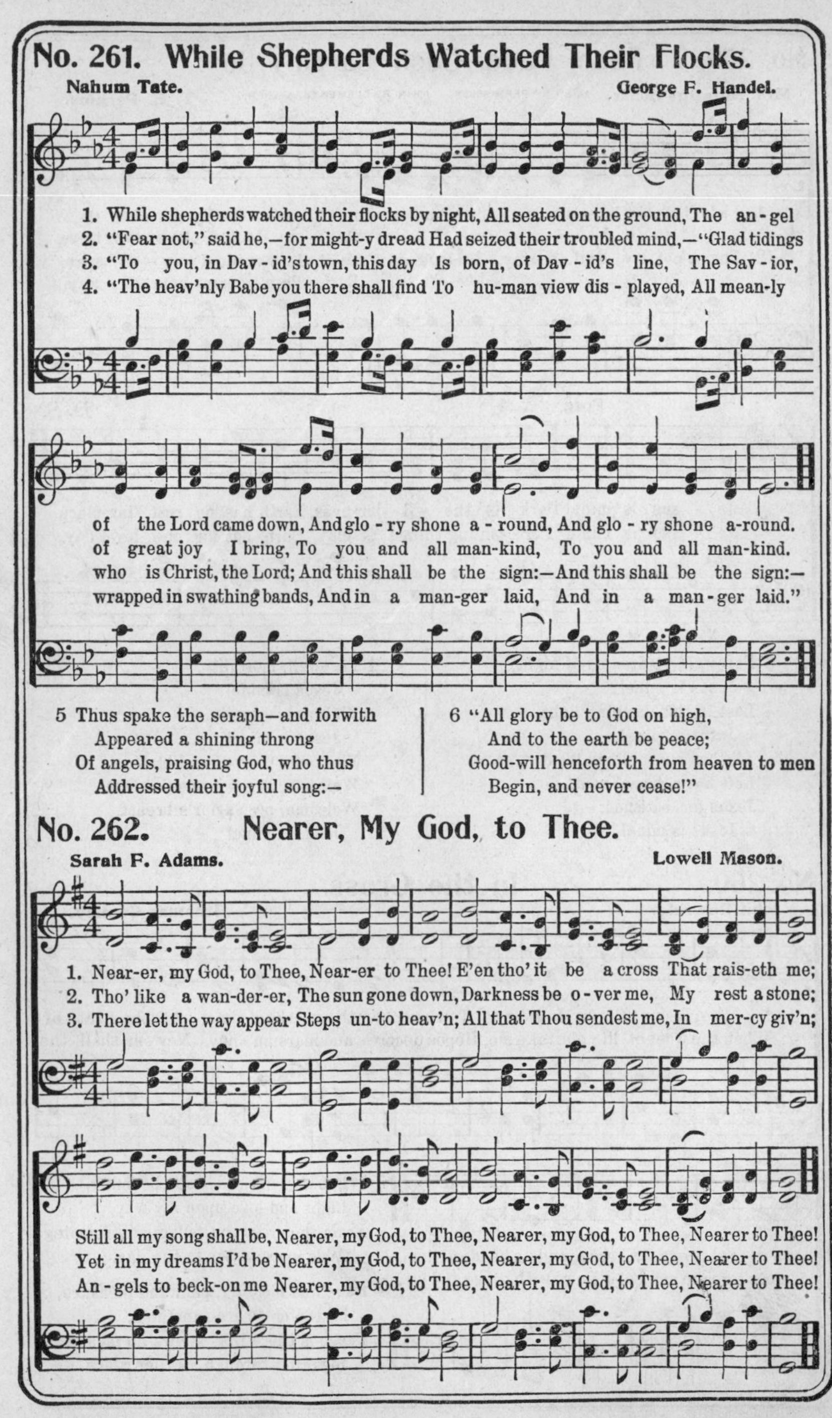

No. 261. While Shepherds Watched Their Flocks.
Nahum Tate.
George F. Handel.
1. While shepherds watched their flocks by night, All seated on the ground, The an - gel
2. "Fear not," said he,—for might-y dread Had seized their troubled mind,—"Glad tidings
3. "To you, in Dav - id's town, this day Is born, of Dav - id's line, The Sav - ior,
4. "The heav'nly Babe you there shall find To hu-man view dis - played, All mean-ly
of the Lord came down, And glo - ry shone a - round, And glo - ry shone a-round.
of great joy I bring, To you and all man-kind, To you and all man-kind.
who is Christ, the Lord; And this shall be the sign:—And this shall be the sign:—
wrapped in swathing bands, And in a man-ger laid, And in a man-ger laid."
5 Thus spake the seraph—and forwith
Appeared a shining throng
Of angels, praising God, who thus
Addressed their joyful song:—
6 "All glory be to God on high,
And to the earth be peace;
Good-will henceforth from heaven to men
Begin, and never cease!"
No. 262. Nearer, My God, to Thee.
Sarah F. Adams.
Lowell Mason.
1. Near-er, my God, to Thee, Near-er to Thee! E'en tho' it be a cross That rais-eth me;
2. Tho' like a wan-der-er, The sun gone down, Darkness be o - ver me, My rest a stone;
3. There let the way appear Steps un-to heav'n; All that Thou sendest me, In mer-cy giv'n;
Still all my song shall be, Nearer, my God, to Thee, Nearer, my God, to Thee, Nearer to Thee!
Yet in my dreams I'd be Nearer, my God, to Thee, Nearer, my God, to Thee, Nearer to Thee!
An - gels to beck-on me Nearer, my God, to Thee, Nearer, my God, to Thee, Nearer to Thee!

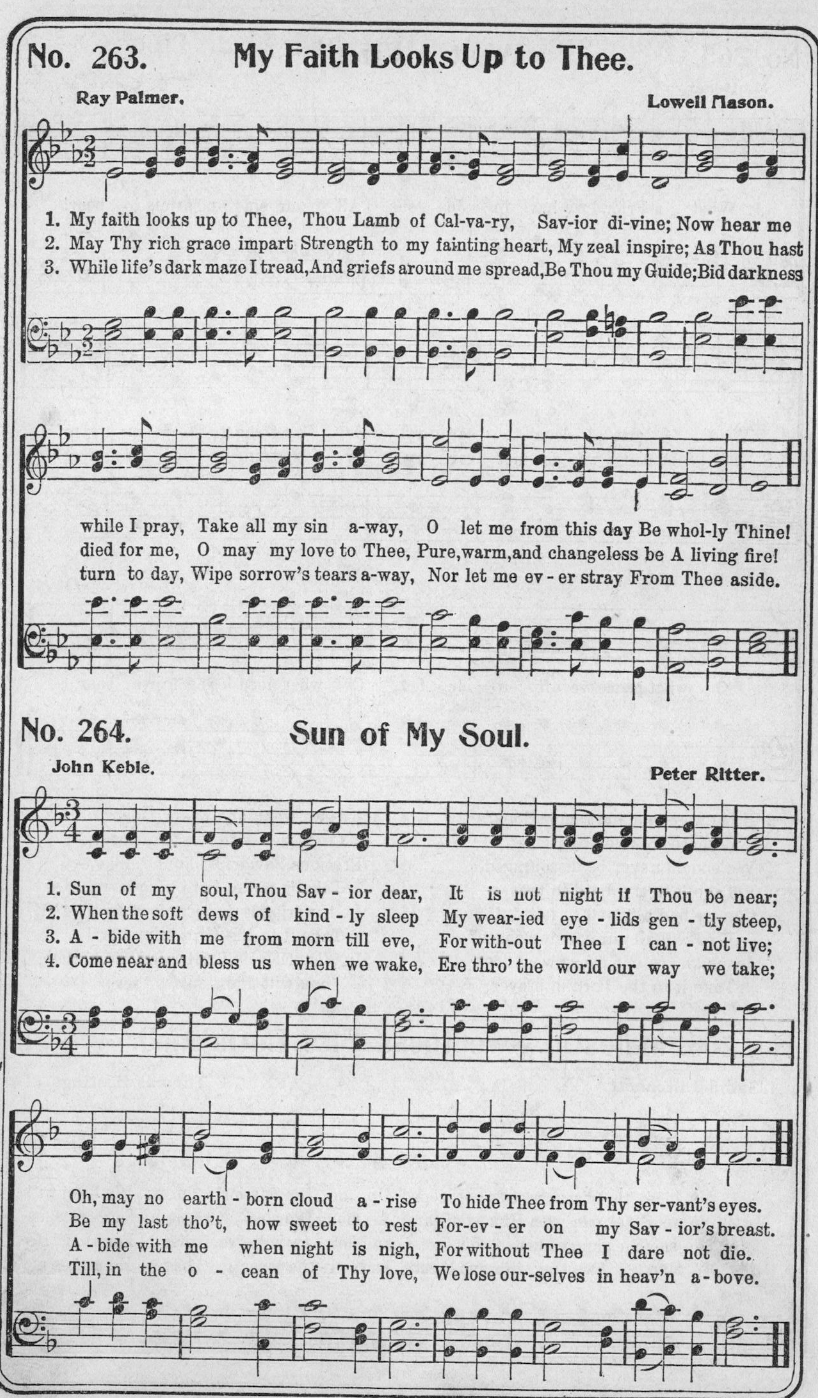
No. 263. My Faith Looks Up to Thee.
Ray Palmer.
Lowell Mason.
1. My faith looks up to Thee, Thou Lamb of Cal-va-ry, Sav-ior di-vine; Now hear me
2. May Thy rich grace impart Strength to my fainting heart, My zeal inspire; As Thou hast
3. While life's dark maze I tread, And griefs around me spread, Be Thou my Guide; Bid darkness
while I pray, Take all my sin a-way, O let me from this day Be whol-ly Thine!
died for me, O may my love to Thee, Pure, warm, and changeless be A living fire!
turn to day, Wipe sorrow's tears a-way, Nor let me ev - er stray From Thee aside.
No. 264. Sun of My Soul.
John Keble.
Peter Ritter.
1. Sun of my soul, Thou Sav - ior dear, It is not night if Thou be near;
2. When the soft dews of kind - ly sleep My wear-ied eye - lids gen - tly steep,
3. A - bide with me from morn till eve, For with-out Thee I can - not live;
4. Come near and bless us when we wake, Ere thro' the world our way we take;
Oh, may no earth - born cloud a - rise To hide Thee from Thy ser-vant's eyes.
Be my last tho't, how sweet to rest For-ev - er on my Sav - ior's breast.
A - bide with me when night is nigh, For without Thee I dare not die.
Till, in the o - cean of Thy love, We lose our-selves in heav'n a - bove.

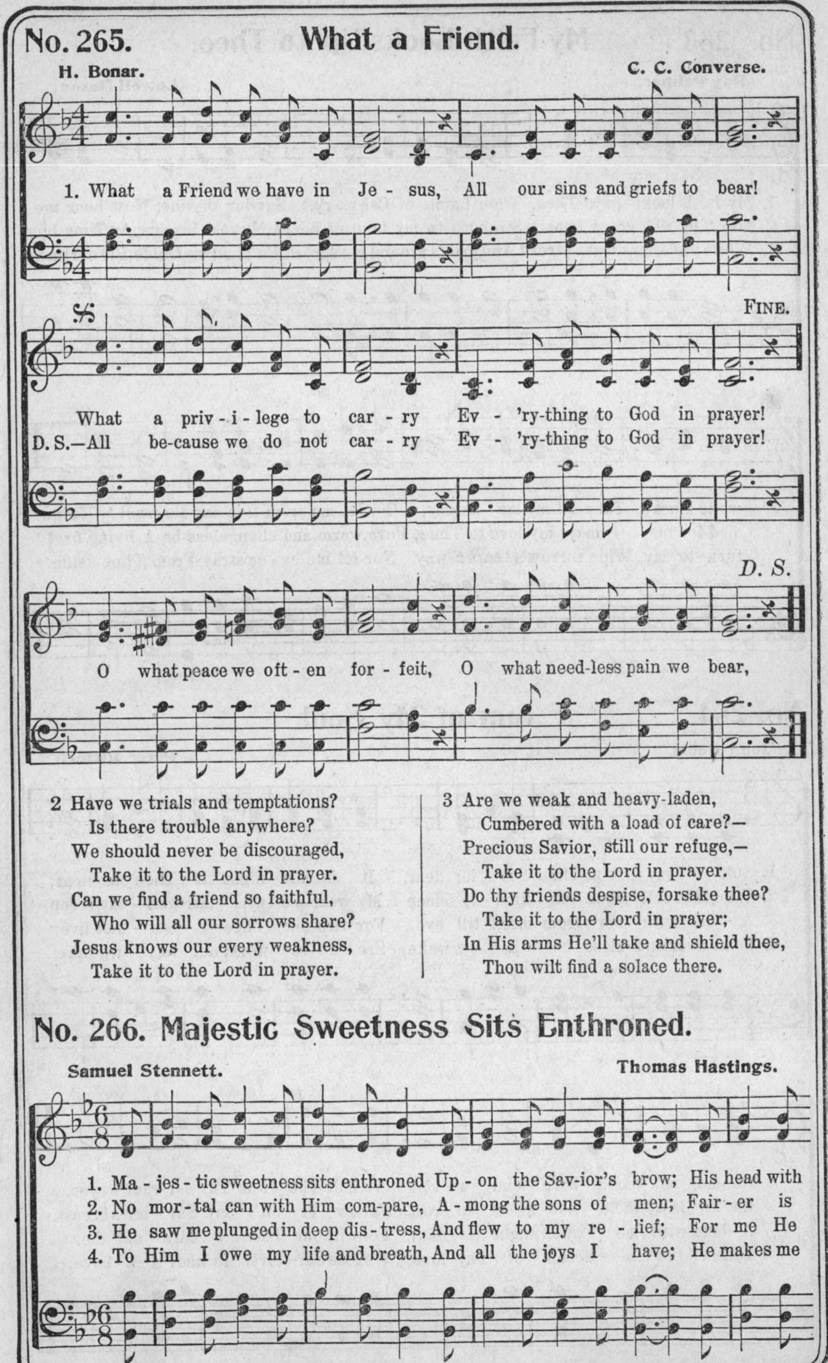
No. 265. What a Friend.
H. Bonar.
C. C. Converse.
1. What a Friend we have in Je - sus, All our sins and griefs to bear!
FINE.
What a priv - i - lege to car - ry Ev - 'ry-thing to God in prayer!
D. S.—All be-cause we do not car - ry Ev - 'ry-thing to God in prayer!
D. S.
O what peace we oft - en for - feit, O what need-less pain we bear,
2 Have we trials and temptations?
Is there trouble anywhere?
We should never be discouraged,
Take it to the Lord in prayer.
Can we find a friend so faithful,
Who will all our sorrows share?
Jesus knows our every weakness,
Take it to the Lord in prayer.
3 Are we weak and heavy-laden,
Cumbered with a load of care?—
Precious Savior, still our refuge,—
Take it to the Lord in prayer.
Do thy friends despise, forsake thee?
Take it to the Lord in prayer;
In His arms He'll take and shield thee,
Thou wilt find a solace there.
No. 266. Majestic Sweetness Sits Enthroned.
Samuel Stennett.
Thomas Hastings.
1. Ma - jes - tic sweetness sits enthroned Up - on the Sav-ior's brow; His head with
2. No mor-tal can with Him com-pare, A - mong the sons of men; Fair - er is
3. He saw me plunged in deep dis - tress, And flew to my re - lief; For me He
4. To Him I owe my life and breath, And all the joys I have; He makes me

Majestic Sweetness Sits Enthroned.
ra - diant glories crowned, His lips with grace o'erflow, His lips with grace o'er-flow.
He than all the fair That fill the heav'nly train, That fill the heav'nly train.
bore the shameful cross, And car - ried all my grief, And car-ried all my grief.
tri-umph o - ver death, And saves me from the grave, And saves me from the grave.
No. 267. Sweet Hour of Prayer.
W. W. Walford.
Wm. B. Bradbury.
1. Sweet hour of prayer, sweet hour of prayer, That calls me from a world of care,
FINE.
And bids me, at my Father's throne, Make all my wants and wish - es known!
D.S.—And oft es-caped the tempt-er's snare, By thy re - turn, sweet hour of prayer.
D. S.
In sea - sons of dis - tress and grief, My soul has oft - en found re - lief,
2 Sweet hour of prayer, sweet hour of prayer,
The joys I feel, the bliss I share,
Of those whose anxious spirits burn
With strong desires for thy return!
With such I hasten to the place
Where God, my Savior, shows His face,
And gladly take my station there,
And wait for thee, sweet hour of prayer.
3 Sweet hour of prayer, sweet hour of prayer,
Thy wings shall my petition bear
To Him, whose truth and faithfulness
Engage the waiting soul to bless:
And since He bids me seek His face,
Believe His word, and trust His grace,
I'll cast on Him my every care,
And wait for thee, sweet hour of prayer.

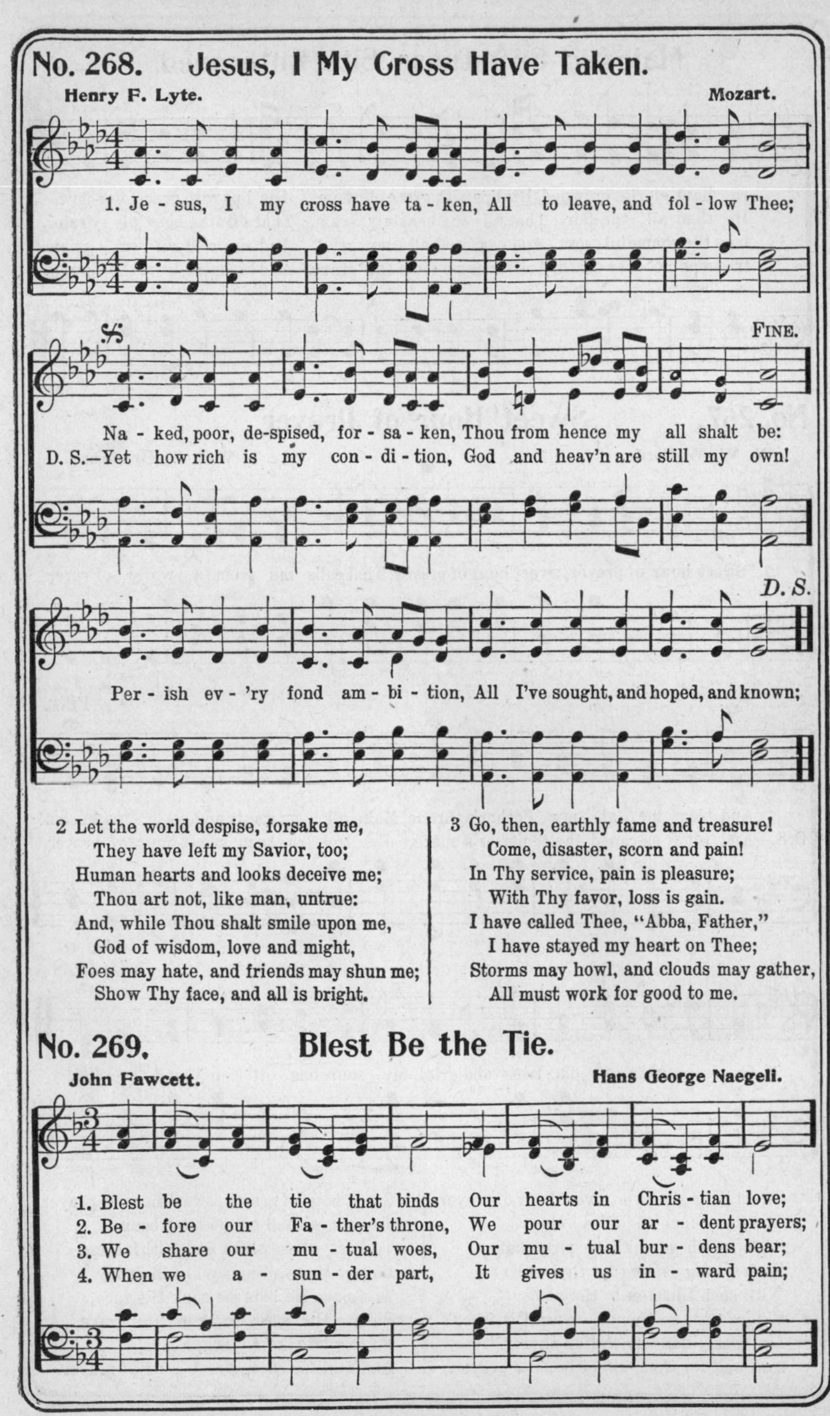
No. 268. Jesus, I My Cross Have Taken.
Henry F. Lyte.
Mozart.
1. Je - sus, I my cross have ta - ken, All to leave, and fol - low Thee;
FINE.
Na - ked, poor, de-spised, for - sa - ken, Thou from hence my all shalt be:
D. S.—Yet how rich is my con - di - tion, God and heav'n are still my own!
D. S.
Per - ish ev - 'ry fond am - bi - tion, All I've sought, and hoped, and known;
2 Let the world despise, forsake me,
They have left my Savior, too;
Human hearts and looks deceive me;
Thou art not, like man, untrue:
And, while Thou shalt smile upon me,
God of wisdom, love and might,
Foes may hate, and friends may shun me;
Show Thy face, and all is bright.
3 Go, then, earthly fame and treasure!
Come, disaster, scorn and pain!
In Thy service, pain is pleasure;
With Thy favor, loss is gain.
I have called Thee, "Abba, Father,"
I have stayed my heart on Thee;
Storms may howl, and clouds may gather,
All must work for good to me.
No. 269. Blest Be the Tie.
John Fawcett.
Hans George Naegeli.
1. Blest be the tie that binds Our hearts in Chris - tian love;
2. Be - fore our Fa - ther's throne, We pour our ar - dent prayers;
3. We share our mu - tual woes, Our mu - tual bur - dens bear;
4. When we a - sun - der part, It gives us in - ward pain;

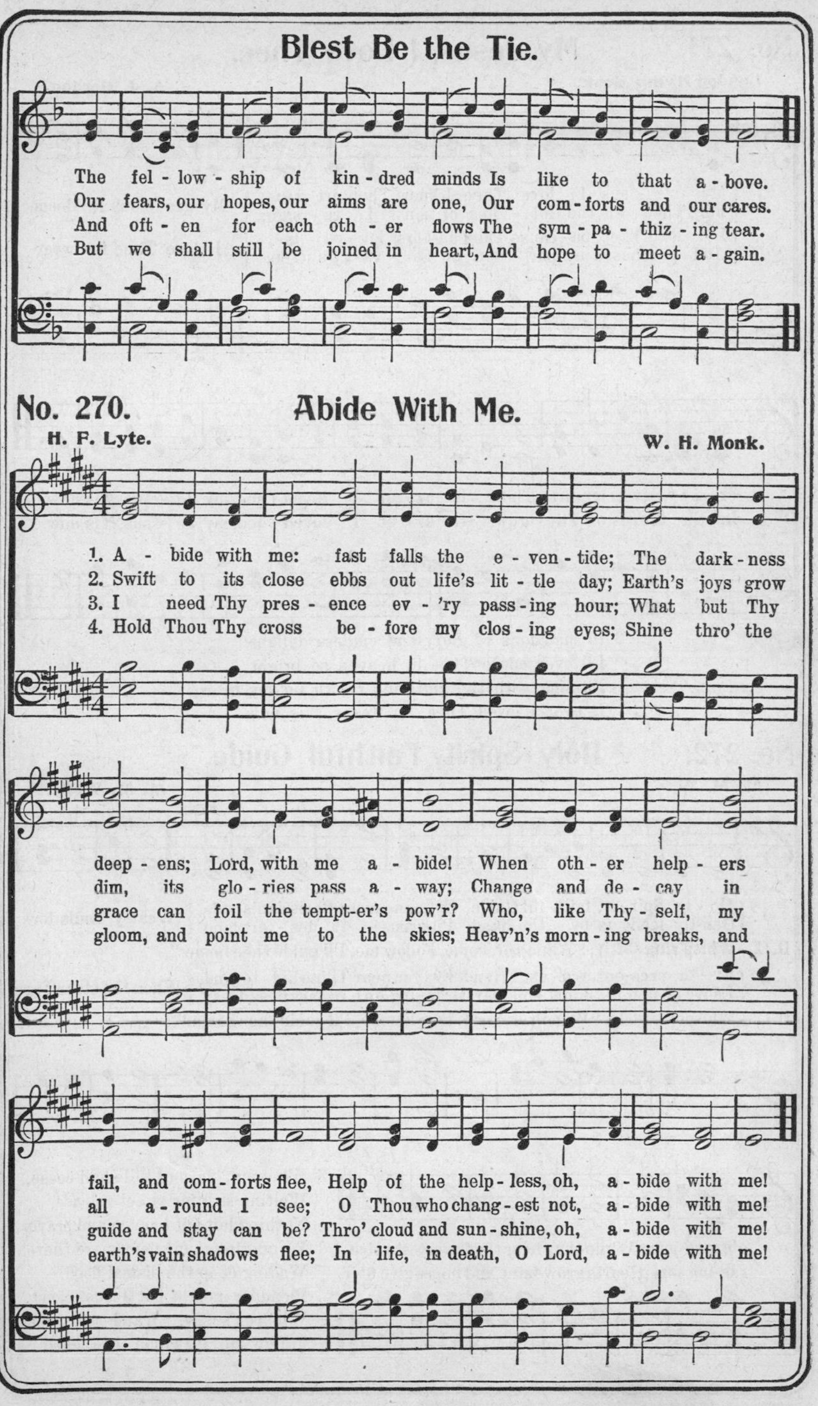
Blest Be the Tie.
The fel - low - ship of kin - dred minds Is like to that a - bove.
Our fears, our hopes, our aims are one, Our com - forts and our cares.
And oft - en for each oth - er flows The sym - pa - thiz - ing tear.
But we shall still be joined in heart, And hope to meet a - gain.
No. 270. Abide With Me.
H. F. Lyte.
W. H. Monk.
1. A - bide with me: fast falls the e - ven - tide; The dark - ness
2. Swift to its close ebbs out life's lit - tle day; Earth's joys grow
3. I need Thy pres - ence ev - 'ry pass - ing hour; What but Thy
4. Hold Thou Thy cross be - fore my clos - ing eyes; Shine thro' the
deep - ens; Lord, with me a - bide! When oth - er help - ers
dim, its glo - ries pass a - way; Change and de - cay in
grace can foil the tempt - er's pow'r? Who, like Thy - self, my
gloom, and point me to the skies; Heav'n's morn - ing breaks, and
fail, and com - forts flee, Help of the help - less, oh, a - bide with me!
all a - round I see; O Thou who chang - est not, a - bide with me!
guide and stay can be? Thro' cloud and sun - shine, oh, a - bide with me!
earth's vain shadows flee; In life, in death, O Lord, a - bide with me!

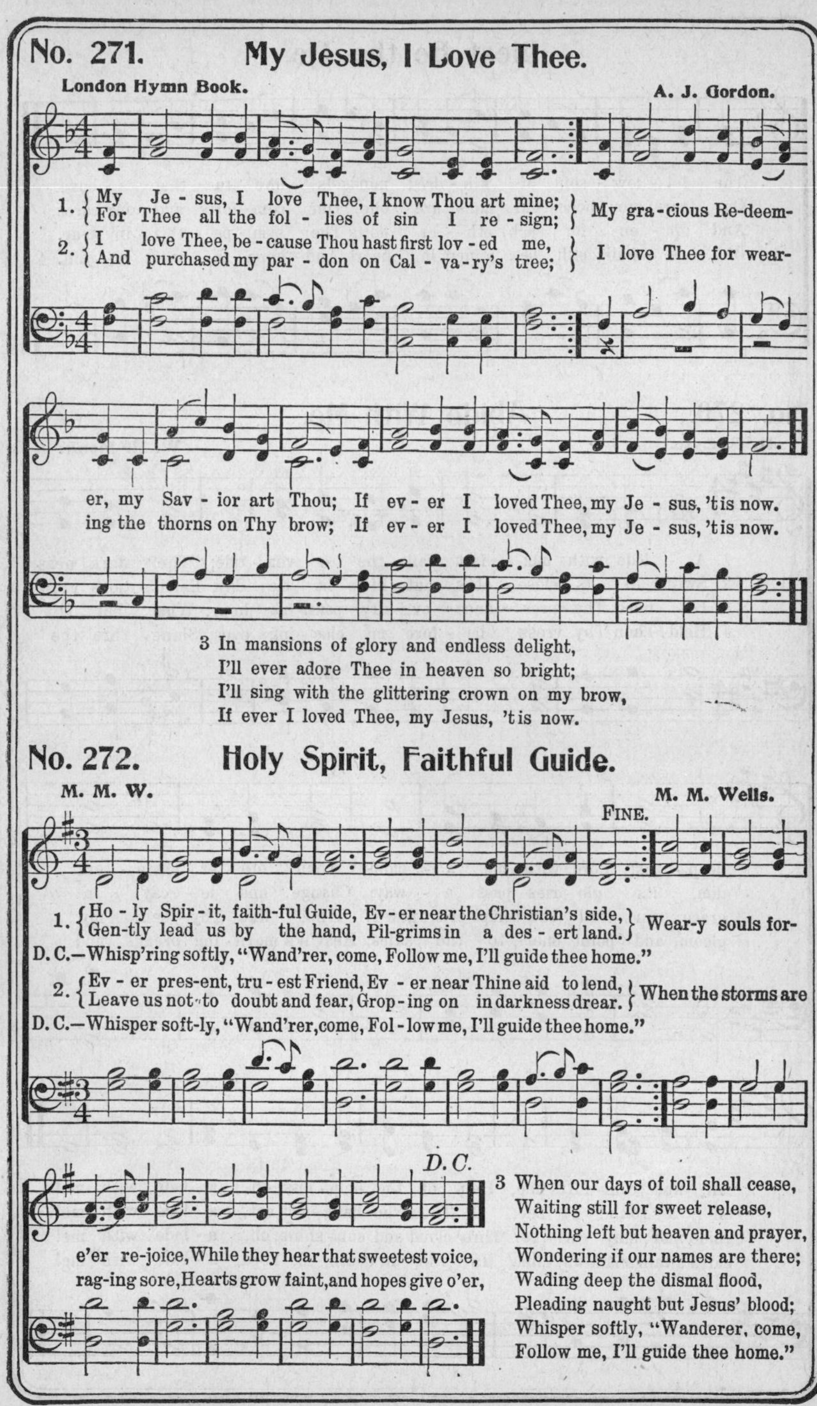
No. 271. My Jesus, I Love Thee.
London Hymn Book.
A. J. Gordon.
1. { My Je - sus, I love Thee, I know Thou art mine; For Thee all the fol - lies of sin I re - sign; } My gra - cious Re-deem-
2. { I love Thee, be - cause Thou hast first lov - ed me, And purchased my par - don on Cal - va - ry's tree; } I love Thee for wear-
er, my Sav - ior art Thou; If ev - er I loved Thee, my Je - sus, 'tis now.
ing the thorns on Thy brow; If ev - er I loved Thee, my Je - sus, 'tis now.
3 In mansions of glory and endless delight,
I'll ever adore Thee in heaven so bright;
I'll sing with the glittering crown on my brow,
If ever I loved Thee, my Jesus, 'tis now.
No. 272. Holy Spirit, Faithful Guide.
M. M. W.
M. M. Wells.
FINE.
1. { Ho - ly Spir - it, faith-ful Guide, Ev - er near the Christian's side, Gen-tly lead us by the hand, Pil-grims in a des - ert land. } Wear-y souls for-
D. C.—Whisp'ring softly, "Wand'rer, come, Follow me, I'll guide thee home."
2. { Ev - er pres-ent, tru - est Friend, Ev - er near Thine aid to lend, Leave us not to doubt and fear, Grop - ing on in darkness drear. } When the storms are
D. C.—Whisper soft-ly, "Wand'rer, come, Fol - low me, I'll guide thee home."
D. C.
e'er re-joice, While they hear that sweetest voice,
rag-ing sore, Hearts grow faint, and hopes give o'er,
3 When our days of toil shall cease,
Waiting still for sweet release,
Nothing left but heaven and prayer,
Wondering if our names are there;
Wading deep the dismal flood,
Pleading naught but Jesus' blood;
Whisper softly, "Wanderer, come,
Follow me, I'll guide thee home."

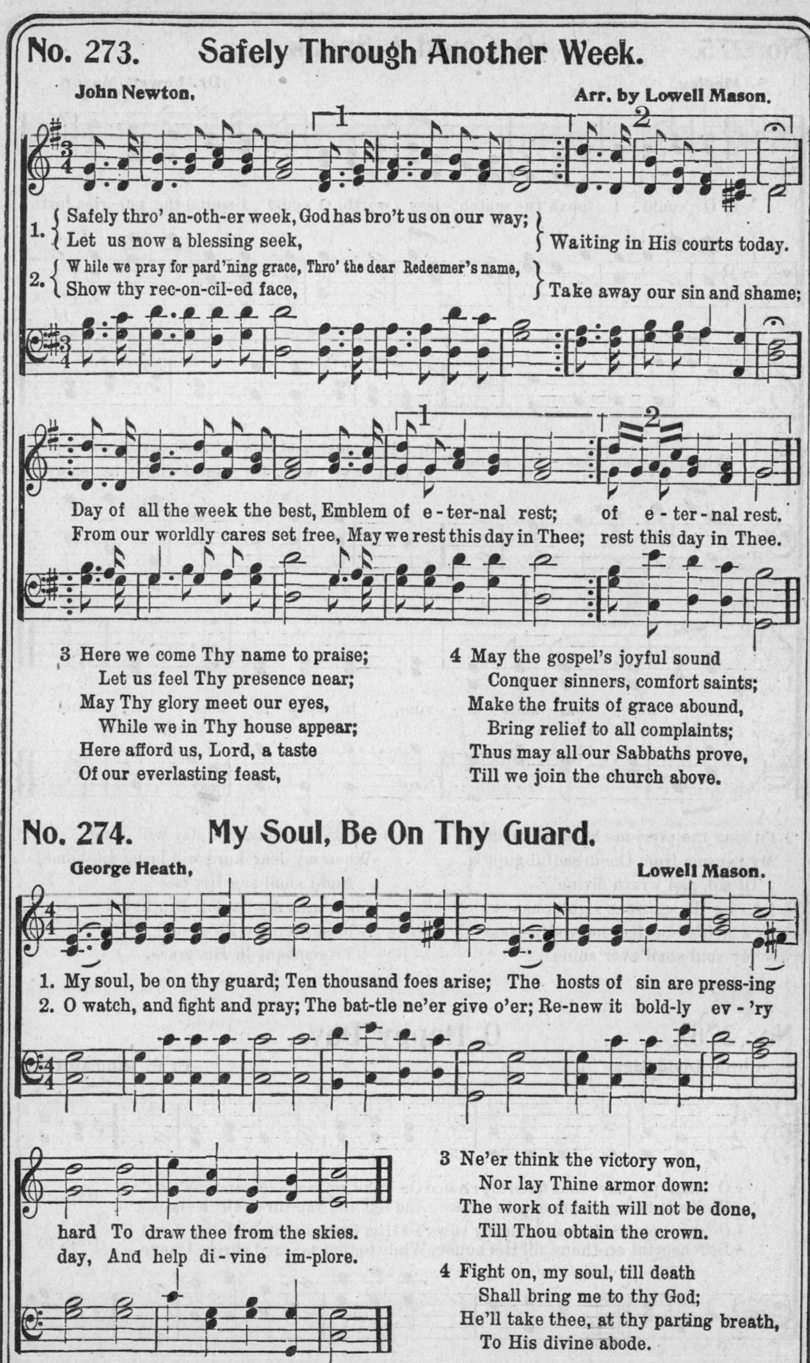
No. 273. Safely Through Another Week.
John Newton,
Arr. by Lowell Mason.
1
2
1. { Safely thro' an-oth-er week, God has bro't us on our way;
Let us now a blessing seek, } Waiting in His courts today.
2. { While we pray for pard'ning grace, Thro' the dear Redeemer's name,
Show thy rec-on-cil-ed face, } Take away our sin and shame;
1
2
Day of all the week the best, Emblem of e-ter-nal rest; of e-ter-nal rest.
From our worldly cares set free, May we rest this day in Thee; rest this day in Thee.
3 Here we come Thy name to praise;
Let us feel Thy presence near;
May Thy glory meet our eyes,
While we in Thy house appear;
Here afford us, Lord, a taste
Of our everlasting feast,
4 May the gospel's joyful sound
Conquer sinners, comfort saints;
Make the fruits of grace abound,
Bring relief to all complaints;
Thus may all our Sabbaths prove,
Till we join the church above.
No. 274. My Soul, Be On Thy Guard.
George Heath,
Lowell Mason.
1. My soul, be on thy guard; Ten thousand foes arise; The hosts of sin are press-ing
2. O watch, and fight and pray; The bat-tle ne'er give o'er; Re-new it bold-ly ev-'ry
hard To draw thee from the skies.
day, And help di-vine im-plore.
3 Ne'er think the victory won,
Nor lay Thine armor down:
The work of faith will not be done,
Till Thou obtain the crown.
4 Fight on, my soul, till death
Shall bring me to thy God;
He'll take thee, at thy parting breath,
To His divine abode.

No. 275. O Could I Speak.
S. Medley.
Dr. Lowell Mason.
1. O could I speak the match - less worth, O could I sound the glo - ries forth
Which in my Sav - ior shine,
I'd soar and touch the heav'n-ly strings,
And vie with Ga - briel while he sings
In notes al - most di - vine, In notes al - most di - vine.
2 I'd sing the precious blood He spilt,
My ransom from the dreadful guilt
Of sin, and wrath divine!
I'd sing His glorious righteousness,
In which all-perfect heavenly dress
My soul shall ever shine.
3 Well—the delightful day will come,
When my dear Lord will bring me home,
And I shall see His face:
Then with my Savior, Brother, Friend,
A blest eternity I'll spend,
Triumphant in His grace.
No. 276. O Happy Day.
Philip Doddridge.
E. F. Rimbault.
1. O hap - py day that fixed my choice On Thee, my Sav - ior and my God!
Well may this glowing heart re - joice, And tell its rap - tures all a - broad.
Hap - py
2. O hap - py bond, that seals my vows To Him who mer - its all my love!
Let cheerful an - thems fill His house, While to that sa - cred shrine I move.
Hap - py

O Happy Day.
Fine.
day, hap-py day, When Je-sus washed my sins a-way. He taught me how to watch and
D. S.
pray, And live re-joi-cing ev-'ry day;
3 'Tis done, the great transaction's done;
I am my Lord's, and He is mine;
He drew me, and I followed on,
Charmed to confess the voice divine.
4 Now rest, my long-divided heart,
Fixed on this blissful center, rest;
Nor ever from thy Lord depart,
With Him of every good possessed.
No. 277. Sweet By-and-By.
S. Fillmore Bennett.
By permission.
Jos. P. Webster.
1. {There's a land that is fair-er than day, And by faith we can see it a-far;}
{For the Fa-ther waits o-ver the way, To pre-[Omit.........................]}
pare us a dwelling-place there. In the sweet by-and-by, We shall meet on that
Chorus.
In the sweet by-and-by,
beau-ti-ful shore; by-and-by, We shall meet on that beautiful shore.
by-and-by; by-and-by,
2 We shall sing on that beautiful shore
The melodious songs of the blest,
And our spirits shall sorrow no more,
Not a sigh for the blessing of rest.
3 To our bountiful Father above,
We will offer our tribute of praise,
For the glorious gift of His love,
And the blessings that hallow our days.

No. 278. Lead, Kindly Light.

J. H. Newman. J. B. Dykes.

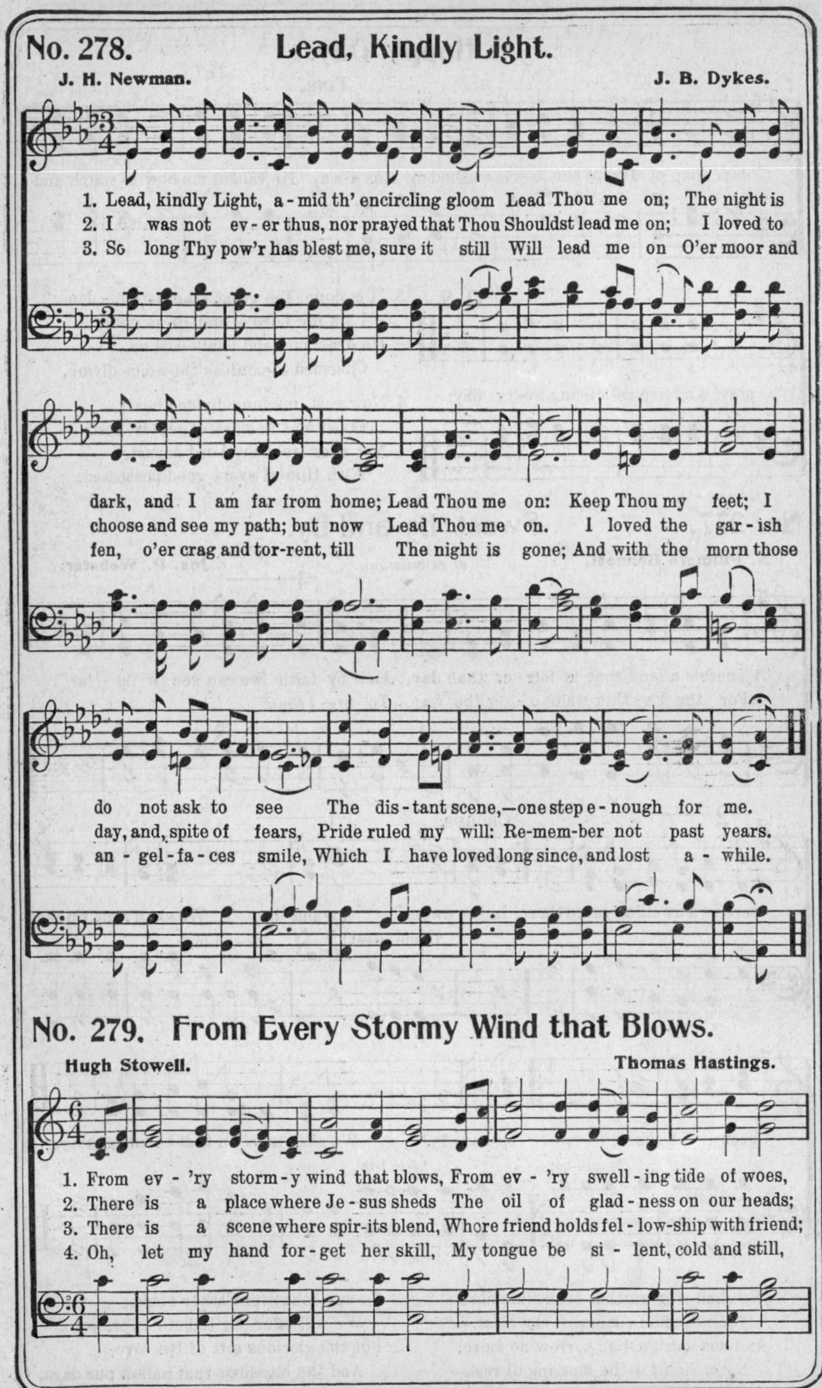

No. 279. From Every Stormy Wind that Blows.

Hugh Stowell. Thomas Hastings.

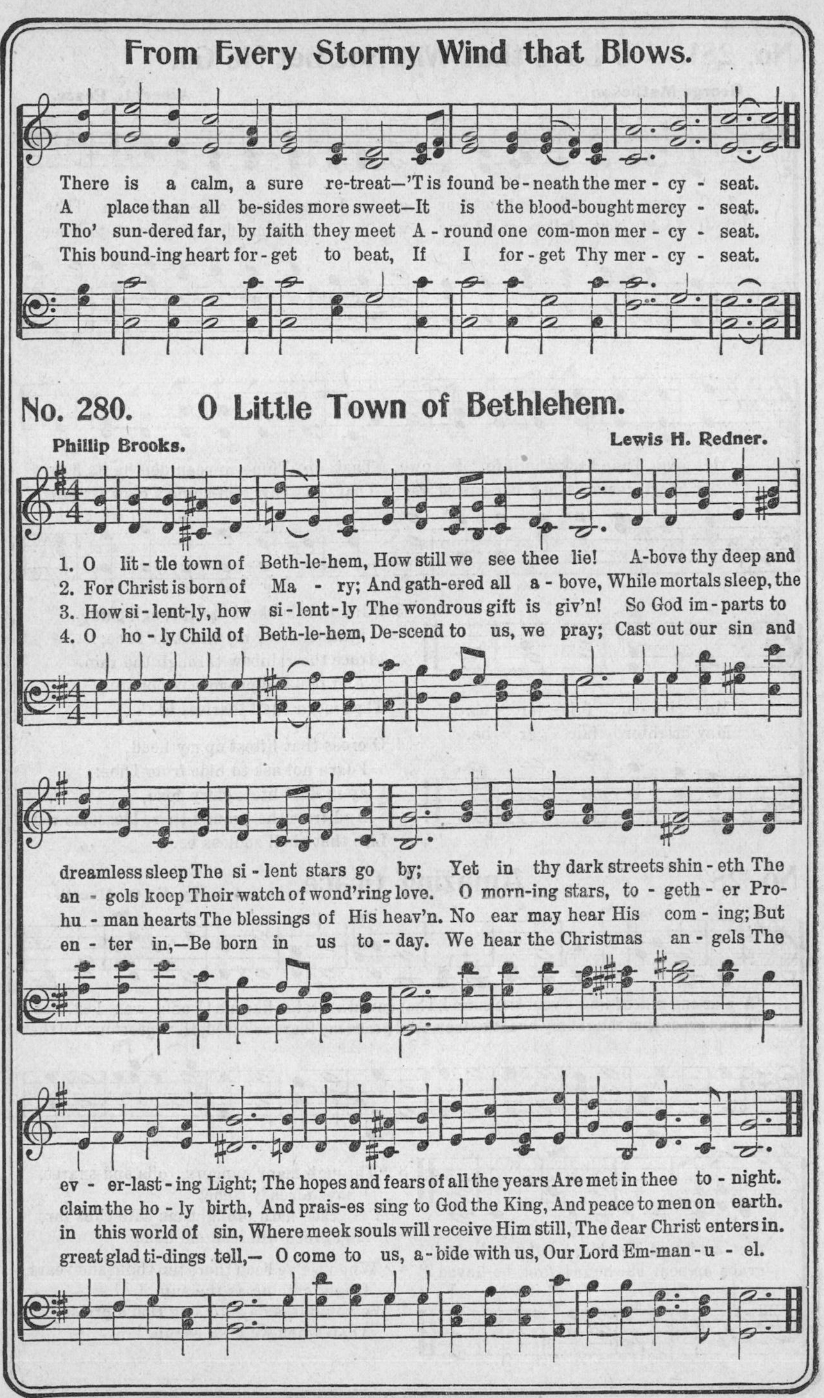
From Every Stormy Wind that Blows.
There is a calm, a sure re-treat—'T is found be - neath the mer - cy - seat.
A place than all be-sides more sweet—It is the blood-bought mercy - seat.
Tho' sun-dered far, by faith they meet A - round one com-mon mer - cy - seat.
This bound-ing heart for - get to beat, If I for - get Thy mer - cy - seat.
No. 280. O Little Town of Bethlehem.
Phillip Brooks.
Lewis H. Redner.
1. O lit - tle town of Beth-le-hem, How still we see thee lie! A-bove thy deep and
2. For Christ is born of Ma - ry; And gath-ered all a - bove, While mortals sleep, the
3. How si - lent-ly, how si - lent - ly The wondrous gift is giv'n! So God im - parts to
4. O ho - ly Child of Beth-le-hem, De-scend to us, we pray; Cast out our sin and
dreamless sleep The si - lent stars go by; Yet in thy dark streets shin - eth The
an - gels keep Their watch of wond'ring love. O morn-ing stars, to - geth - er Pro-
hu - man hearts The blessings of His heav'n. No ear may hear His com - ing; But
en - ter in,—Be born in us to - day. We hear the Christmas an - gels The
ev - er-last - ing Light; The hopes and fears of all the years Are met in thee to - night.
claim the ho - ly birth, And prais-es sing to God the King, And peace to men on earth.
in this world of sin, Where meek souls will receive Him still, The dear Christ enters in.
great glad ti-dings tell,— O come to us, a - bide with us, Our Lord Em-man - u - el.

No. 281. O Love that Wilt Not Let Me Go.
George Matheson.
Albert L. Peace.
1. O Love that wilt not let me go, I rest my wea-ry soul in Thee,
2. O Light that followest all my way, I yield my flickering torch to Thee;
I give Thee back the life I owe, That in Thine o-cean depths its flow
My heart restores its bor-rowed ray, That in Thy sun-shine's glow its day
May rich-er ful-ler be.
May brighter fair-er be.
3 O Joy that seekest me through pain,
I cannot close my heart to Thee;
I trace the rainbow through the rain,
And feel the promise is not vain
That morn shall tearless be.
4 O cross that liftest up my head,
I dare not ask to hide from Thee:
I lay in dust life's glory dead,
And from the ground there blossoms red
Life that shall endless be.
No. 282. Amazing Grace.
Arr. by E. O. Excell.
1. "A-maz-ing grace! how sweet the sound, That saved a wretch like me! I once was lost, but
2. "'T was grace that taught my heart to fear, And grace my fears relieved; How precious did that
now am found, Was blind, but now I see."
grace ap-pear The hour I first be-lieved!"
3 "Through many dangers, toils and snares,
I have already come;
'T is grace hath brought me safe thus far,
And grace will lead me home."
4 "When we've been there ten thousand years,
Bright shining as the sun,
We've no less days to sing God's praise
Than when we first begun."

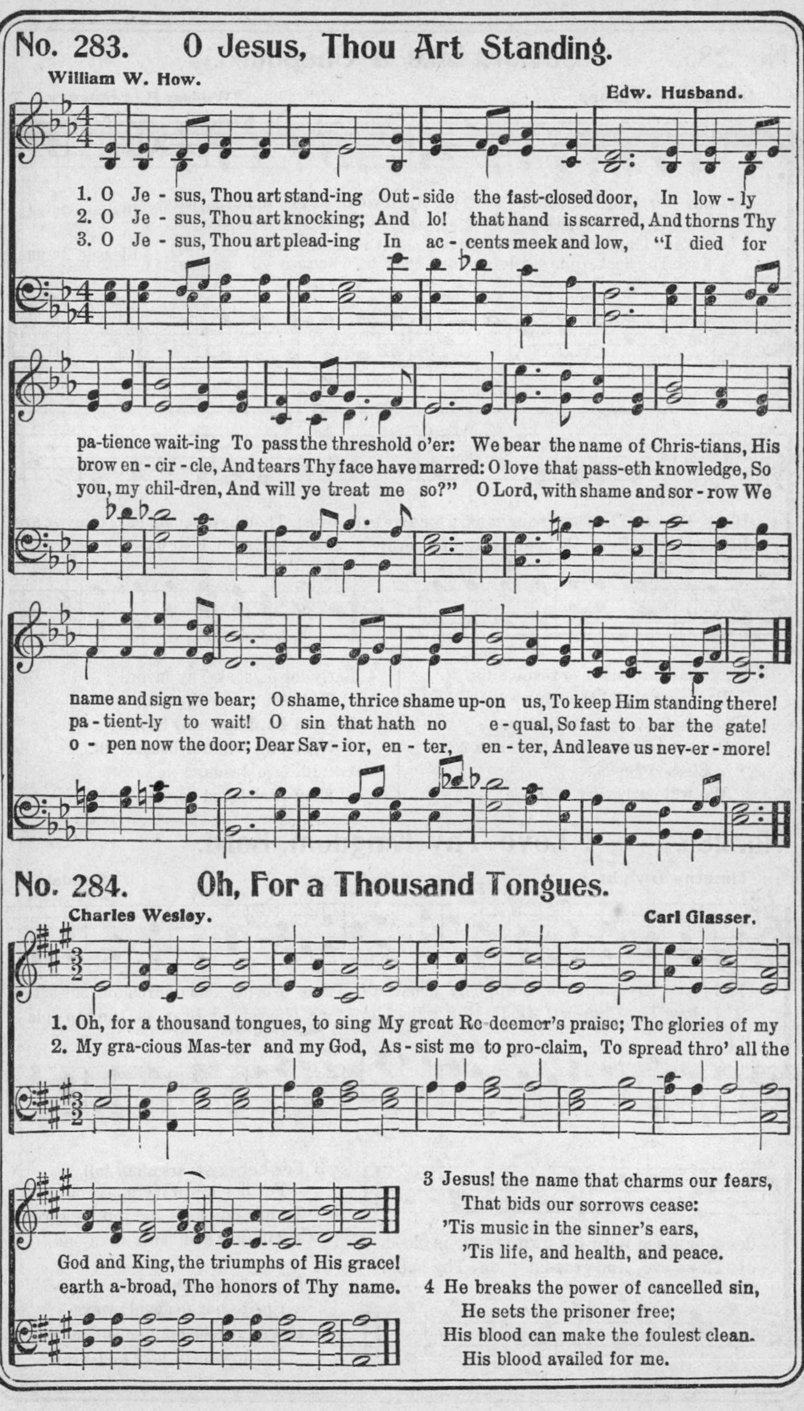
No. 283. O Jesus, Thou Art Standing.
William W. How.
Edw. Husband.
1. O Je - sus, Thou art stand-ing Out-side the fast-closed door, In low - ly
2. O Je - sus, Thou art knocking; And lo! that hand is scarred, And thorns Thy
3. O Je - sus, Thou art plead-ing In ac - cents meek and low, "I died for
pa-tience wait-ing To pass the threshold o'er: We bear the name of Chris-tians, His
brow en - cir - cle, And tears Thy face have marred: O love that pass-eth knowledge, So
you, my chil-dren, And will ye treat me so?" O Lord, with shame and sor - row We
name and sign we bear; O shame, thrice shame up-on us, To keep Him standing there!
pa - tient-ly to wait! O sin that hath no e - qual, So fast to bar the gate!
o - pen now the door; Dear Sav - ior, en - ter, en - ter, And leave us nev-er - more!
No. 284. Oh, For a Thousand Tongues.
Charles Wesley.
Carl Glasser.
1. Oh, for a thousand tongues, to sing My great Re-deemer's praise; The glories of my
2. My gra-cious Mas-ter and my God, As-sist me to pro-claim, To spread thro' all the
God and King, the triumphs of His grace!
earth a-broad, The honors of Thy name.
3 Jesus! the name that charms our fears,
That bids our sorrows cease:
'Tis music in the sinner's ears,
'Tis life, and health, and peace.
4 He breaks the power of cancelled sin,
He sets the prisoner free;
His blood can make the foulest clean.
His blood availed for me.

No. 285. Savior, Like a Shepherd.
Dorothy A. Thrupp.
William B. Bradbury.
1. Sav-ior, like a shepherd lead us, Much we need Thy tend'rest care;
In Thy pleasant pastures feed us, For our use Thy folds pre-pare:
Blessed Je-sus,
2. We are Thine; do Thou befriend us, Be the Guardian of our way;
Keep Thy flock, from sin defend us, Seek us when we go a-stray:
Blessed Je-sus,
1
2
Blessed Jesus, Thou hast bought us, Thine we are; Jesus, Thou hast bought us, Thine we are.
Blessed Jesus, Hear, oh, hear us when we pray; Jesus, Hear, oh, hear us when we pray.
3 Thou hast promised to receive us,
Poor and sinful though we be;
Thou hast mercy to relieve us,
Grace to cleanse, and power to free:
Blessed Jesus,
We will early turn to Thee.
4 Early let us seek Thy favor,
Early let us do Thy will;
Blessed Lord and only Savior,
With Thy love our bosoms fill:
Blessed Jesus,
Thou hast loved us, love us still.
No. 286. I Love Thy Kingdom, Lord.
Timothy Dwight.
Handel.
1. I love Thy king-dom, Lord, The house of Thine a-bode, The Church our blest Re-
2. I love Thy Church O God! Her walls be-fore Thee stand, Dear as the ap-ple
deem-er saved With His own pre-cious blood.
of Thine eye, And grav-en on Thy hand.
3 For her my tears shall fall,
For her my prayers ascend;
To her my cares and toil be given,
Till toils and cares shall end.
4 Beyond my highest joy
I prize her heavenly ways,
Her sweet communion, solemn vows,
Her hymns of love and praise.

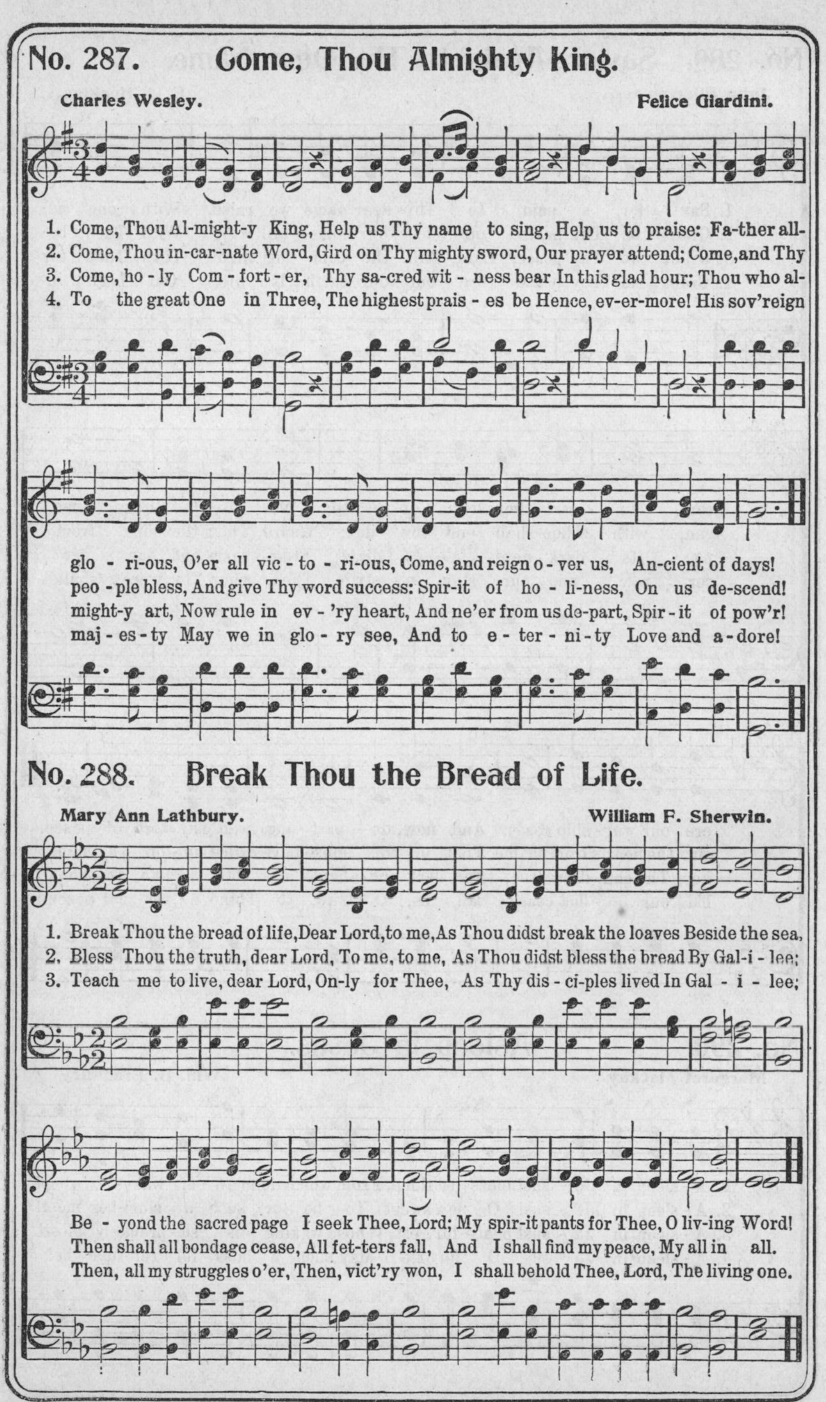
No. 287. Come, Thou Almighty King.
Charles Wesley.
Felice Giardini.
1. Come, Thou Al-might-y King, Help us Thy name to sing, Help us to praise: Fa-ther all-
2. Come, Thou in-car-nate Word, Gird on Thy mighty sword, Our prayer attend; Come, and Thy
3. Come, ho-ly Com-fort-er, Thy sa-cred wit-ness bear In this glad hour; Thou who al-
4. To the great One in Three, The highest prais-es be Hence, ev-er-more! His sov'reign
glo-ri-ous, O'er all vic-to-ri-ous, Come, and reign o-ver us, An-cient of days!
peo-ple bless, And give Thy word success: Spir-it of ho-li-ness, On us de-scend!
might-y art, Now rule in ev-'ry heart, And ne'er from us de-part, Spir-it of pow'r!
maj-es-ty May we in glo-ry see, And to e-ter-ni-ty Love and a-dore!
No. 288. Break Thou the Bread of Life.
Mary Ann Lathbury.
William F. Sherwin.
1. Break Thou the bread of life, Dear Lord, to me, As Thou didst break the loaves Beside the sea,
2. Bless Thou the truth, dear Lord, To me, to me, As Thou didst bless the bread By Gal-i-lee;
3. Teach me to live, dear Lord, On-ly for Thee, As Thy dis-ci-ples lived In Gal-i-lee;
Be-yond the sacred page I seek Thee, Lord; My spir-it pants for Thee, O liv-ing Word!
Then shall all bondage cease, All fet-ters fall, And I shall find my peace, My all in all.
Then, all my struggles o'er, Then, vict'ry won, I shall behold Thee, Lord, The living one.

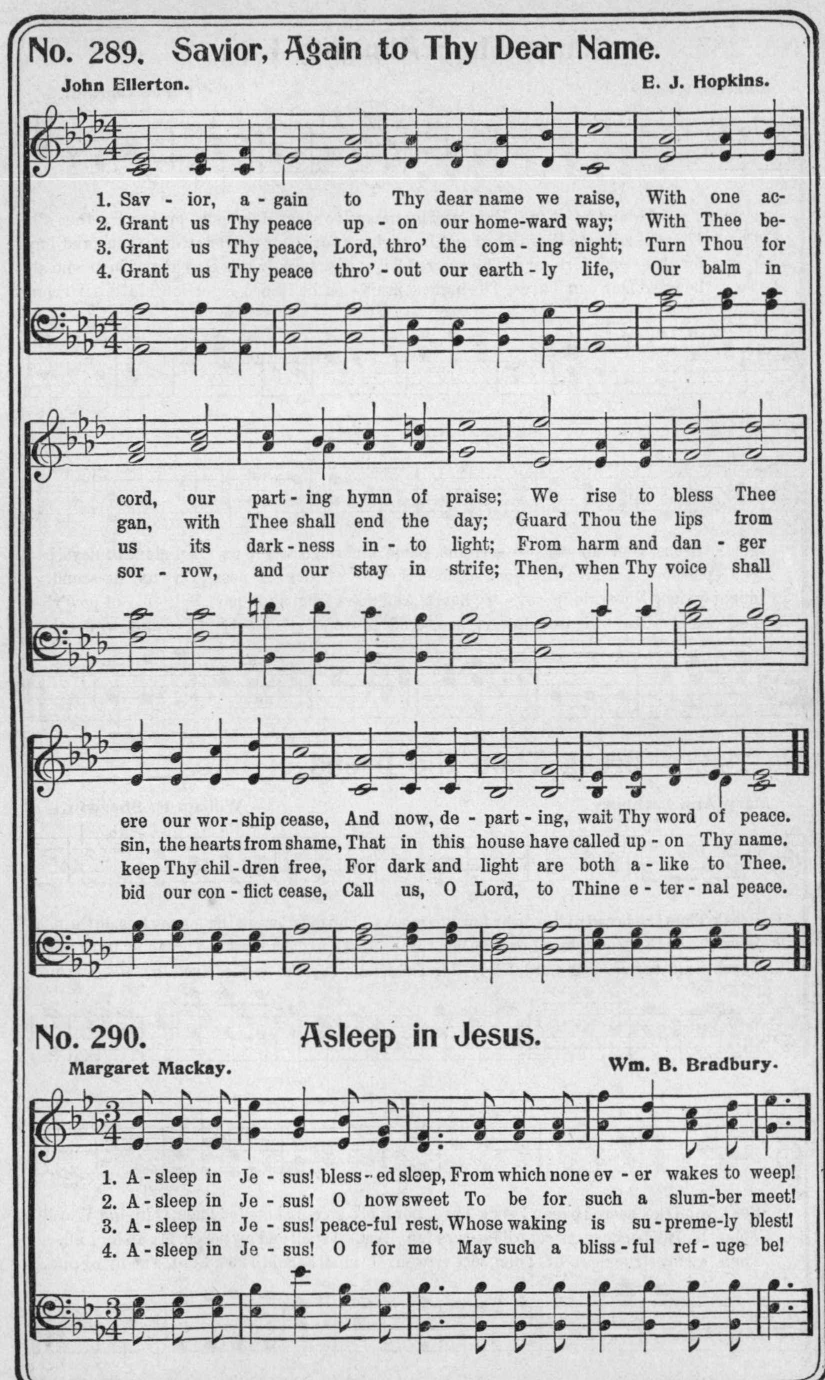
No. 289. Savior, Again to Thy Dear Name.
John Ellerton.
E. J. Hopkins.
1. Sav - ior, a - gain to Thy dear name we raise, With one ac-
2. Grant us Thy peace up - on our home-ward way; With Thee be-
3. Grant us Thy peace, Lord, thro' the com - ing night; Turn Thou for
4. Grant us Thy peace thro' - out our earth - ly life, Our balm in
cord, our part - ing hymn of praise; We rise to bless Thee
gan, with Thee shall end the day; Guard Thou the lips from
us its dark - ness in - to light; From harm and dan - ger
sor - row, and our stay in strife; Then, when Thy voice shall
ere our wor - ship cease, And now, de - part - ing, wait Thy word of peace.
sin, the hearts from shame, That in this house have called up - on Thy name.
keep Thy chil - dren free, For dark and light are both a - like to Thee.
bid our con - flict cease, Call us, O Lord, to Thine e - ter - nal peace.
No. 290. Asleep in Jesus.
Margaret Mackay.
Wm. B. Bradbury.
1. A - sleep in Je - sus! bless - ed sleep, From which none ev - er wakes to weep!
2. A - sleep in Je - sus! O how sweet To be for such a slum-ber meet!
3. A - sleep in Je - sus! peace-ful rest, Whose waking is su - preme-ly blest!
4. A - sleep in Je - sus! O for me May such a bliss - ful ref - uge be!

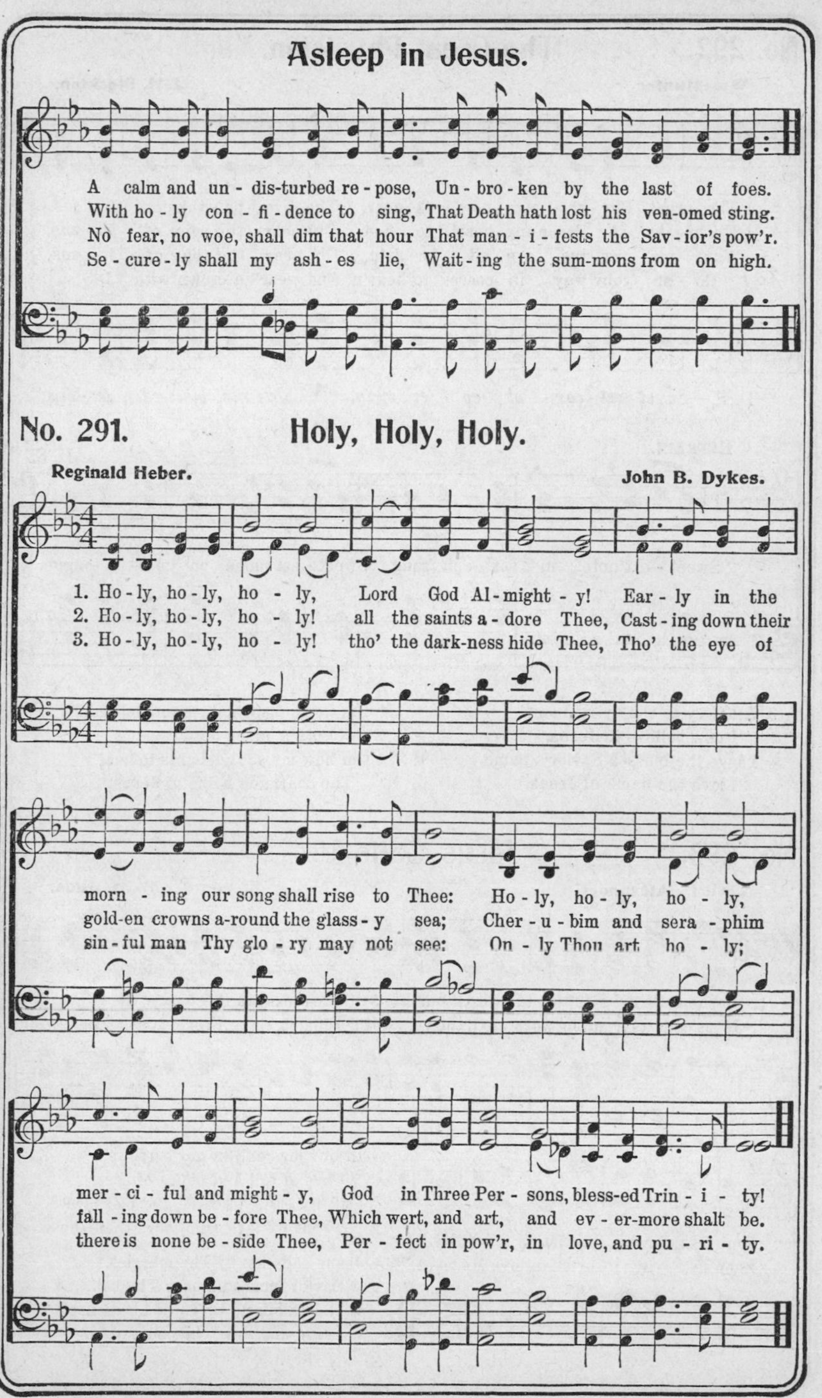
Asleep in Jesus.
A calm and un - dis-turbed re - pose, Un - bro - ken by the last of foes.
With ho - ly con - fi - dence to sing, That Death hath lost his ven-omed sting.
No fear, no woe, shall dim that hour That man - i - fests the Sav - ior's pow'r.
Se - cure - ly shall my ash - es lie, Wait - ing the sum-mons from on high.
No. 291. Holy, Holy, Holy.
Reginald Heber.
John B. Dykes.
1. Ho - ly, ho - ly, ho - ly, Lord God Al - might - y! Ear - ly in the
2. Ho - ly, ho - ly, ho - ly! all the saints a - dore Thee, Cast - ing down their
3. Ho - ly, ho - ly, ho - ly! tho' the dark-ness hide Thee, Tho' the eye of
morn - ing our song shall rise to Thee: Ho - ly, ho - ly, ho - ly,
gold-en crowns a-round the glass - y sea; Cher - u - bim and sera - phim
sin - ful man Thy glo - ry may not see: On - ly Thou art ho - ly;
mer - ci - ful and might - y, God in Three Per - sons, bless-ed Trin - i - ty!
fall - ing down be - fore Thee, Which wert, and art, and ev - er-more shalt be.
there is none be - side Thee, Per - fect in pow'r, in love, and pu - ri - ty.

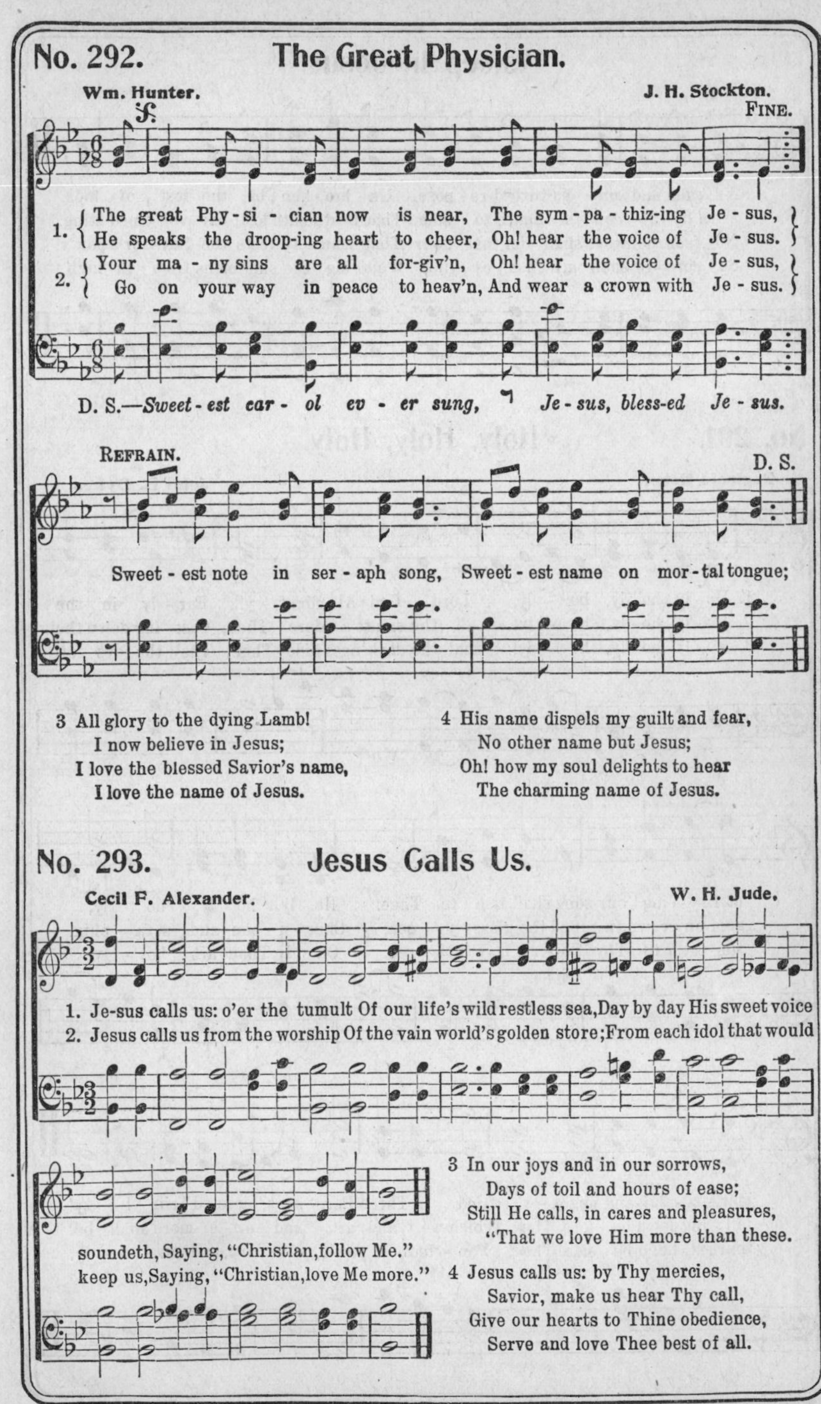
No. 292.
The Great Physician.
Wm. Hunter.
J. H. Stockton.
Fine.
1. The great Phy-si-cian now is near, The sym-pa-thiz-ing Je-sus,
He speaks the droop-ing heart to cheer, Oh! hear the voice of Je-sus.
2. Your ma-ny sins are all for-giv'n, Oh! hear the voice of Je-sus,
Go on your way in peace to heav'n, And wear a crown with Je-sus.
D. S.—Sweet-est car-ol ev-er sung, Jesus, bless-ed Je-sus.
Refrain.
D. S.
Sweet-est note in ser-aph song, Sweet-est name on mor-tal tongue;
3 All glory to the dying Lamb!
I now believe in Jesus;
I love the blessed Savior's name,
I love the name of Jesus.
4 His name dispels my guilt and fear,
No other name but Jesus;
Oh! how my soul delights to hear
The charming name of Jesus.
No. 293.
Jesus Calls Us.
Cecil F. Alexander.
W. H. Jude.
1. Je-sus calls us: o'er the tumult Of our life's wild restless sea, Day by day His sweet voice soundeth, Saying, "Christian, follow Me."
2. Jesus calls us from the worship Of the vain world's golden store; From each idol that would keep us, Saying, "Christian, love Me more."
3 In our joys and in our sorrows,
Days of toil and hours of ease;
Still He calls, in cares and pleasures,
"That we love Him more than these.
4 Jesus calls us: by Thy mercies,
Savior, make us hear Thy call,
Give our hearts to Thine obedience,
Serve and love Thee best of all.

No. 294.
I Am Coming, Lord.
L. H.
Rev. L. Hartsough.
1. I hear Thy wel-come voice, That calls me, Lord, to Thee, For cleans-ing in Thy pre-cious blood That flowed on Cal - va - ry.
2. Tho' com - ing weak and vile, Thou dost my strength assure; Thou dost my vile-ness ful - ly cleanse, Till spot - less all and pure.
3. 'Tis Je - sus calls me on To per-fect faith and love, To per-fect hope, and peace, and trust, For earth and heav'n a-bove.
Chorus.
I am com - ing, Lord! Com - ing now to Thee! Wash me, cleanse me, in the blood That flowed on Cal - va - ry!
No. 295.
Alas! and Did My Savior Bleed?
Isaac Watts.
Hugh Wilson.
1. A - las! and did my Savior bleed? And did my Sov'reign die? Would He devote that sa-cred head For such a worm as I?
2. Was it for crimes that I have done, He groan'd upon the tree? A-maz-ing pit - y! grace unknown! And love be-yond de-gree!
3 Well might the sun in darkness hide,
And shut his glories in,
When Christ, the mighty Maker, died,
For man, the creature's sin.
4 But drops of grief can ne'er repay
The debt of love I owe:
Here, Lord, I give myself away,—
'Tis all that I can do.

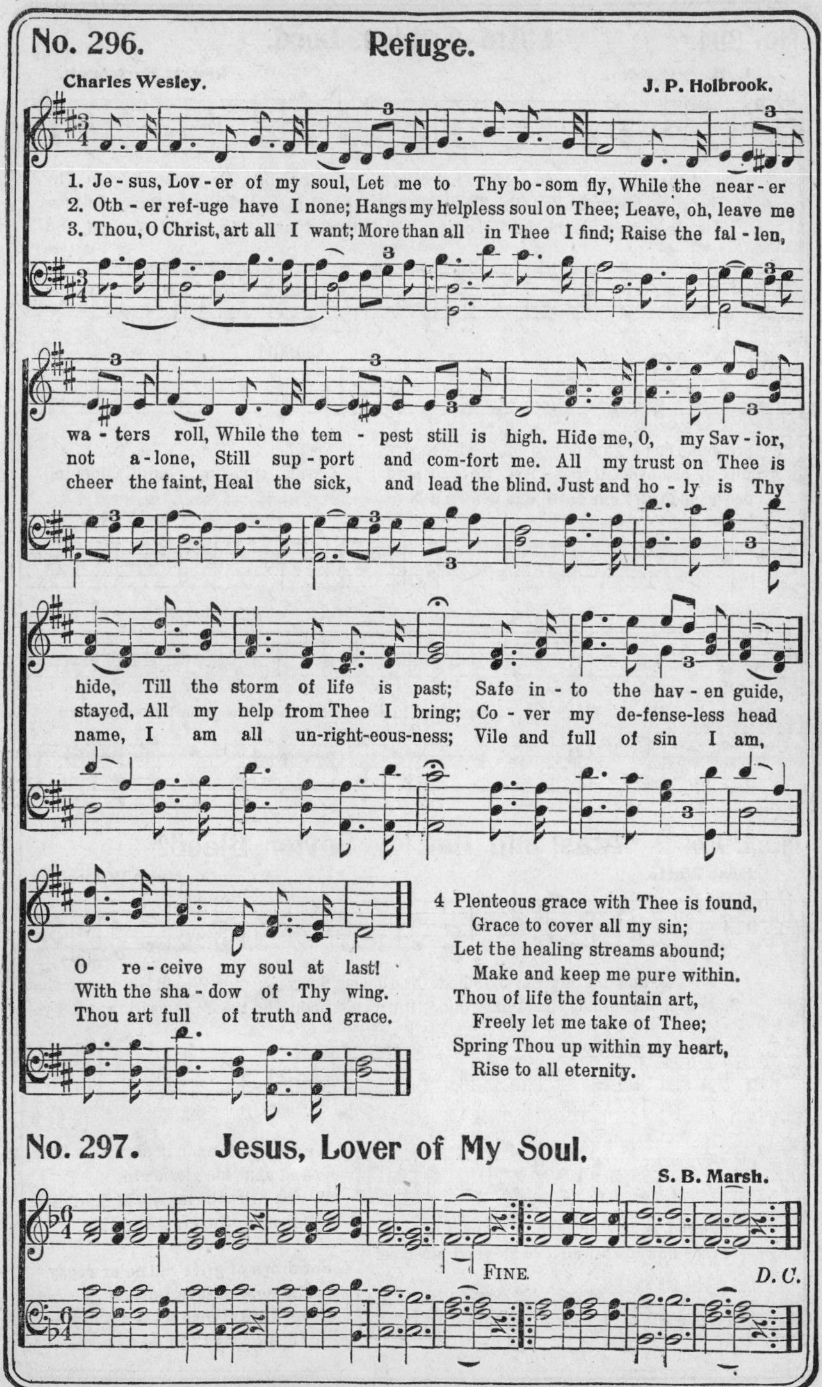
No. 296. Refuge.
Charles Wesley.
J. P. Holbrook.
1. Je - sus, Lov - er of my soul, Let me to Thy bo - som fly, While the near - er
2. Oth - er ref - uge have I none; Hangs my helpless soul on Thee; Leave, oh, leave me
3. Thou, O Christ, art all I want; More than all in Thee I find; Raise the fal - len,
wa - ters roll, While the tem - pest still is high. Hide me, O, my Sav - ior,
not a - lone, Still sup - port and com - fort me. All my trust on Thee is
cheer the faint, Heal the sick, and lead the blind. Just and ho - ly is Thy
hide, Till the storm of life is past; Safe in - to the hav - en guide,
stayed, All my help from Thee I bring; Co - ver my de - fense - less head
name, I am all un - right - eous - ness; Vile and full of sin I am,
O re - ceive my soul at last!
With the sha - dow of Thy wing.
Thou art full of truth and grace.
4 Plenteous grace with Thee is found,
Grace to cover all my sin;
Let the healing streams abound;
Make and keep me pure within.
Thou of life the fountain art,
Freely let me take of Thee;
Spring Thou up within my heart,
Rise to all eternity.
No. 297. Jesus, Lover of My Soul.
S. B. Marsh.
FINE.
D. C.

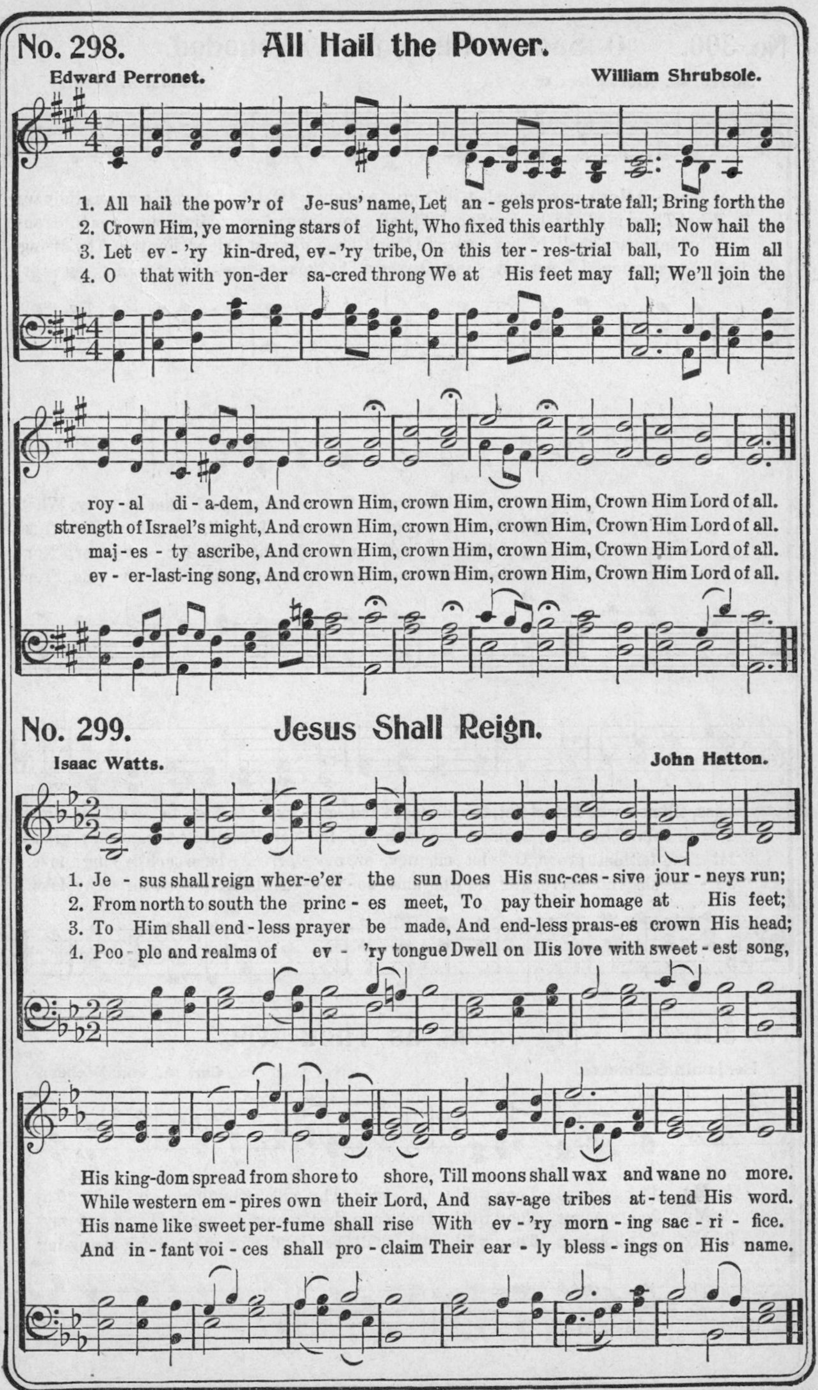
No. 298. All Hail the Power.
Edward Perronet.
William Shrubsole.
1. All hail the pow'r of Je-sus' name, Let an - gels pros-trate fall; Bring forth the
2. Crown Him, ye morning stars of light, Who fixed this earthly ball; Now hail the
3. Let ev - 'ry kin-dred, ev - 'ry tribe, On this ter - res-trial ball, To Him all
4. O that with yon-der sa-cred throng We at His feet may fall; We'll join the
roy - al di - a-dem, And crown Him, crown Him, crown Him, Crown Him Lord of all.
strength of Israel's might, And crown Him, crown Him, crown Him, Crown Him Lord of all.
maj - es - ty ascribe, And crown Him, crown Him, crown Him, Crown Him Lord of all.
ev - er-last-ing song, And crown Him, crown Him, crown Him, Crown Him Lord of all.
No. 299. Jesus Shall Reign.
Isaac Watts.
John Hatton.
1. Je - sus shall reign wher-e'er the sun Does His suc-ces - sive jour - neys run;
2. From north to south the princ - es meet, To pay their homage at His feet;
3. To Him shall end - less prayer be made, And end-less prais-es crown His head;
1. Peo - plo and realms of ev - 'ry tongue Dwell on His love with sweet - est song,
His king-dom spread from shore to shore, Till moons shall wax and wane no more.
While western em - pires own their Lord, And sav-age tribes at - tend His word.
His name like sweet per-fume shall rise With ev - 'ry morn - ing sac - ri - fice.
And in - fant voi - ces shall pro - claim Their ear - ly bless - ings on His name.

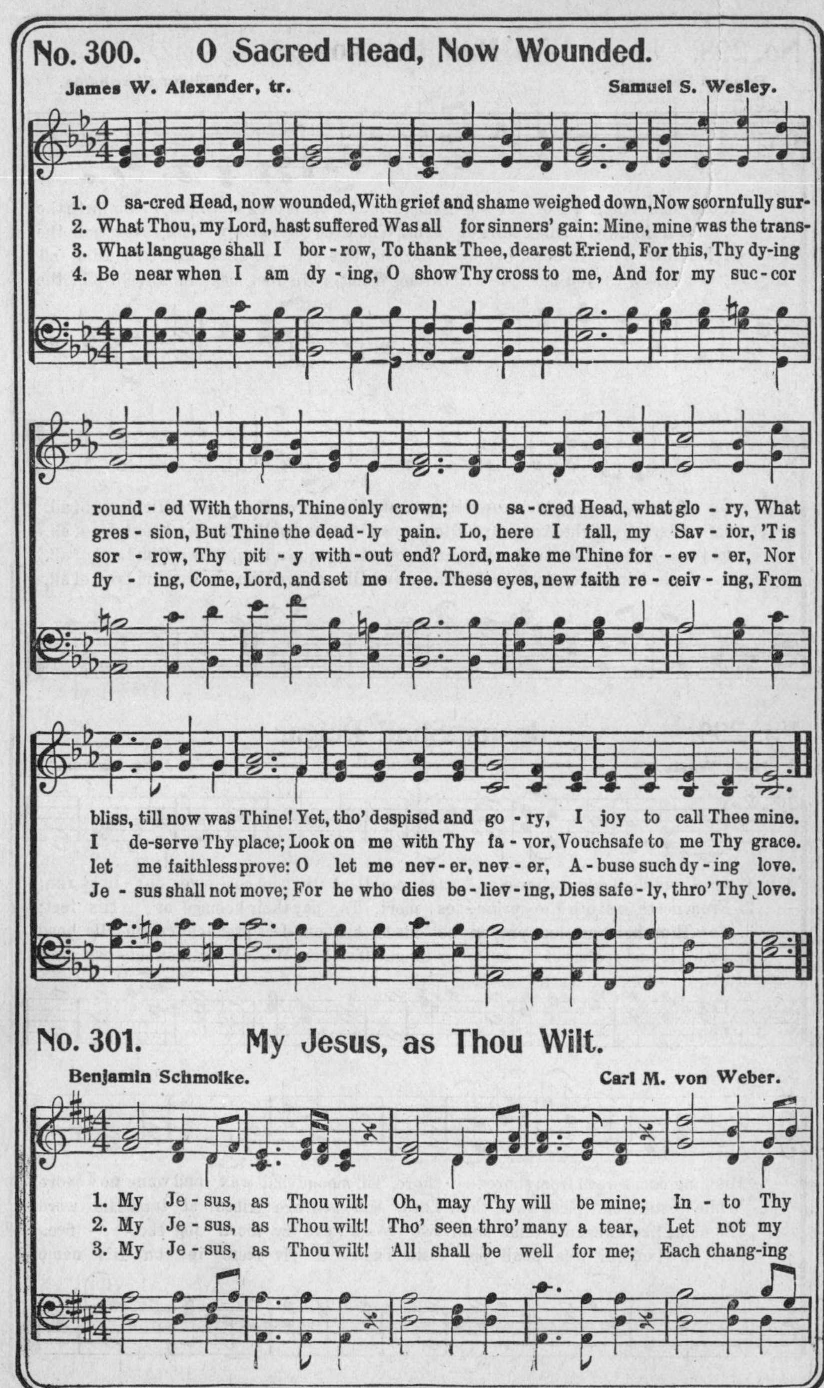

No. 300. O Sacred Head, Now Wounded.
James W. Alexander, tr.
Samuel S. Wesley.
1. O sa-cred Head, now wounded, With grief and shame weighed down, Now scornfully sur-round-ed With thorns, Thine only crown; O sa-cred Head, what glo-ry, What bliss, till now was Thine! Yet, tho' despised and go-ry, I joy to call Thee mine.
2. What Thou, my Lord, hast suffered Was all for sinners' gain: Mine, mine was the trans-gres-sion, But Thine the dead-ly pain. Lo, here I fall, my Sav-ior, 'T is I de-serve Thy place; Look on me with Thy fa-vor, Vouchsafe to me Thy grace.
3. What language shall I bor-row, To thank Thee, dearest Friend, For this, Thy dy-ing sor-row, Thy pit-y with-out end? Lord, make me Thine for-ev-er, Nor let me faithless prove: O let me nev-er, nev-er, A-buse such dy-ing love.
4. Be near when I am dy-ing, O show Thy cross to me, And for my suc-cor fly-ing, Come, Lord, and set me free. These eyes, new faith re-ceiv-ing, From Je-sus shall not move; For he who dies be-liev-ing, Dies safe-ly, thro' Thy love.
No. 301. My Jesus, as Thou Wilt.
Benjamin Schmolke.
Carl M. von Weber.
1. My Je-sus, as Thou wilt! Oh, may Thy will be mine; In-to Thy
2. My Je-sus, as Thou wilt! Tho' seen thro' many a tear, Let not my
3. My Je-sus, as Thou wilt! All shall be well for me; Each chang-ing

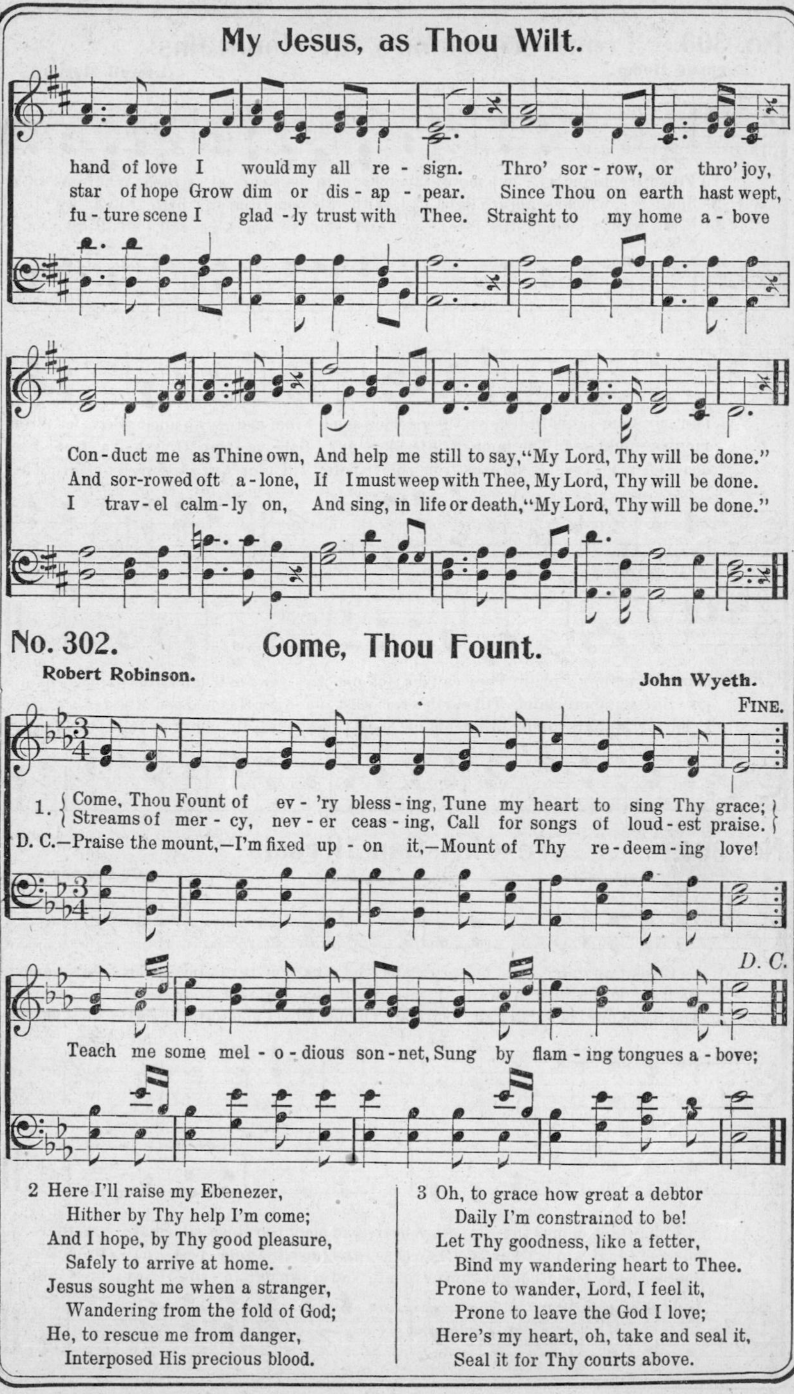
My Jesus, as Thou Wilt.
hand of love I would my all re - sign. Thro' sor - row, or thro' joy,
star of hope Grow dim or dis - ap - pear. Since Thou on earth hast wept,
fu - ture scene I glad - ly trust with Thee. Straight to my home a - bove
Con - duct me as Thine own, And help me still to say, "My Lord, Thy will be done."
And sor-rowed oft a - lone, If I must weep with Thee, My Lord, Thy will be done.
I trav - el calm - ly on, And sing, in life or death, "My Lord, Thy will be done."
No. 302. Come, Thou Fount.
Robert Robinson.
John Wyeth.
FINE.
1. Come, Thou Fount of ev - 'ry bless - ing, Tune my heart to sing Thy grace;
Streams of mer - cy, nev - er ceas - ing, Call for songs of loud - est praise.
D. C.—Praise the mount,—I'm fixed up - on it,—Mount of Thy re - deem - ing love!
D. C.
Teach me some mel - o - dious son - net, Sung by flam - ing tongues a - bove;
2 Here I'll raise my Ebenezer,
Hither by Thy help I'm come;
And I hope, by Thy good pleasure,
Safely to arrive at home.
Jesus sought me when a stranger,
Wandering from the fold of God;
He, to rescue me from danger,
Interposed His precious blood.
3 Oh, to grace how great a debtor
Daily I'm constrained to be!
Let Thy goodness, like a fetter,
Bind my wandering heart to Thee.
Prone to wander, Lord, I feel it,
Prone to leave the God I love;
Here's my heart, oh, take and seal it,
Seal it for Thy courts above.

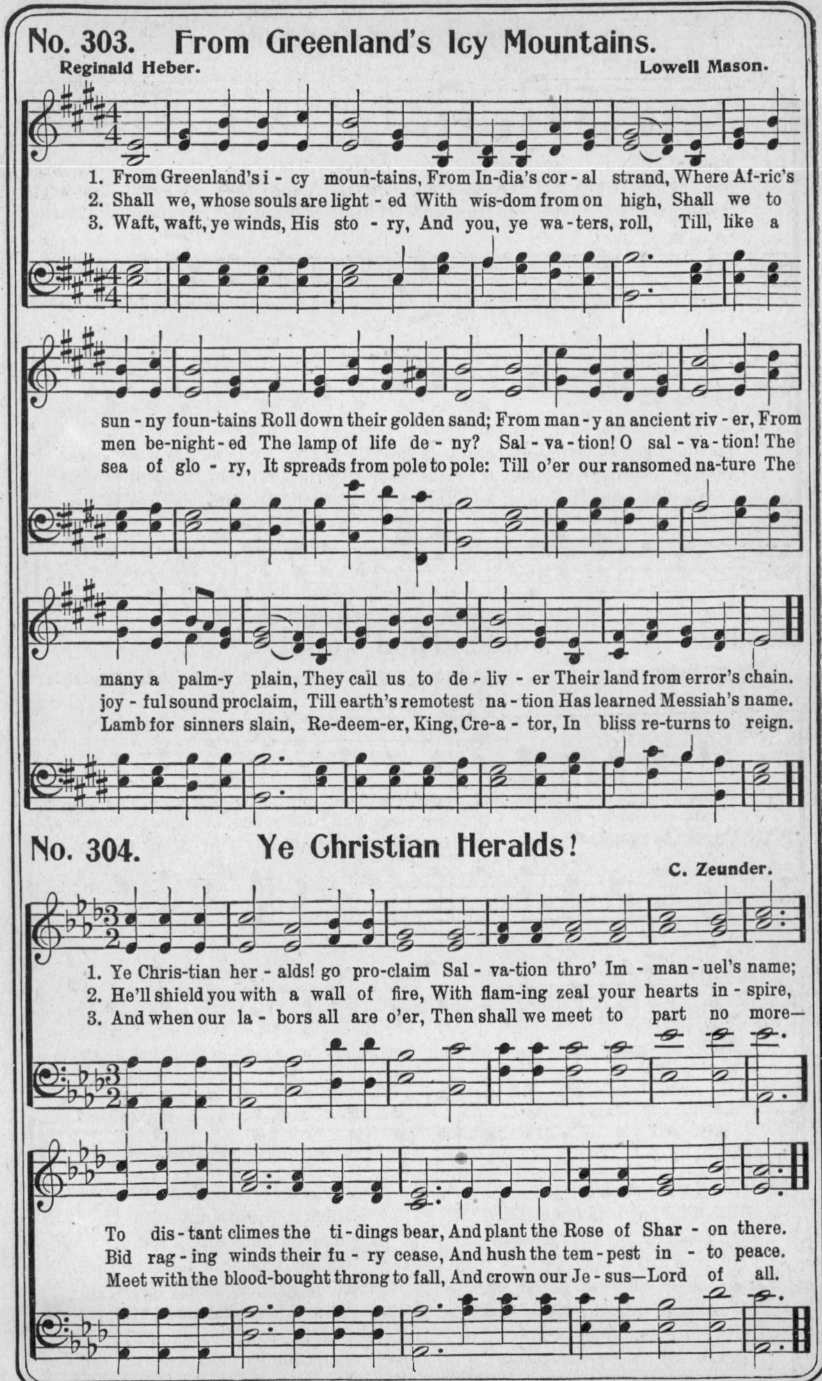
No. 303. From Greenland's Icy Mountains.
Reginald Heber.
Lowell Mason.
1. From Greenland's i - cy moun-tains, From In-dia's cor - al strand, Where Af-ric's
2. Shall we, whose souls are light - ed With wis-dom from on high, Shall we to
3. Waft, waft, ye winds, His sto - ry, And you, ye wa-ters, roll, Till, like a
sun - ny foun-tains Roll down their golden sand; From man - y an ancient riv - er, From
men be-night - ed The lamp of life de - ny? Sal - va - tion! O sal - va - tion! The
sea of glo - ry, It spreads from pole to pole: Till o'er our ransomed na-ture The
many a palm-y plain, They call us to de - liv - er Their land from error's chain.
joy - ful sound proclaim, Till earth's remotest na - tion Has learned Messiah's name.
Lamb for sinners slain, Re-deem-er, King, Cre-a - tor, In bliss re-turns to reign.
No. 304. Ye Christian Heralds!
C. Zeunder.
1. Ye Chris-tian her - alds! go pro-claim Sal - va-tion thro' Im - man - uel's name;
2. He'll shield you with a wall of fire, With flam-ing zeal your hearts in - spire,
3. And when our la - bors all are o'er, Then shall we meet to part no more—
To dis-tant climes the ti-dings bear, And plant the Rose of Shar - on there.
Bid rag - ing winds their fu - ry cease, And hush the tem - pest in - to peace.
Meet with the blood-bought throng to fall, And crown our Je - sus—Lord of all.

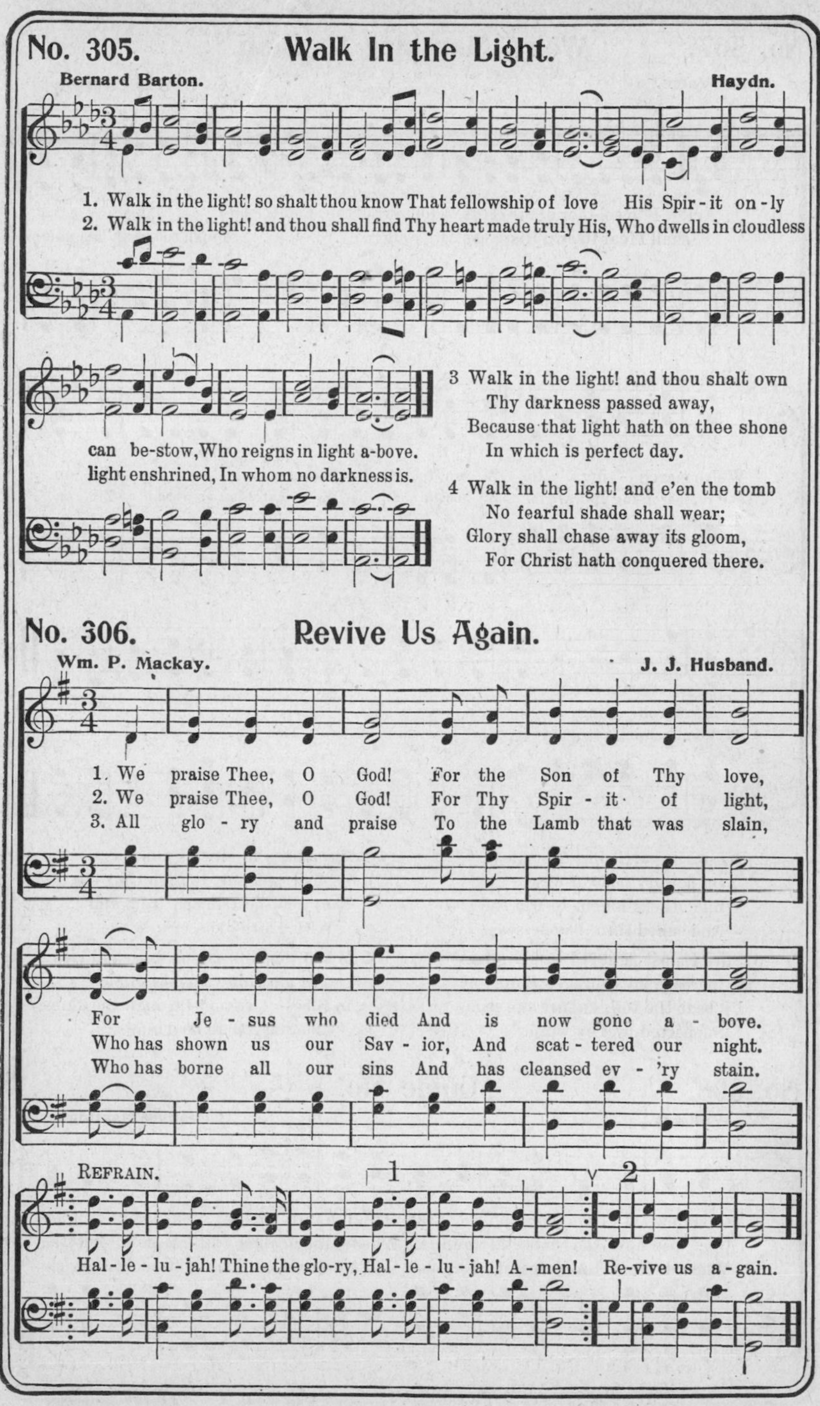
No. 305. Walk In the Light.
Bernard Barton.
Haydn.
1. Walk in the light! so shalt thou know That fellowship of love His Spir - it on - ly
2. Walk in the light! and thou shall find Thy heart made truly His, Who dwells in cloudless
can be-stow, Who reigns in light a-bove.
light enshrined, In whom no darkness is.
3 Walk in the light! and thou shalt own
Thy darkness passed away,
Because that light hath on thee shone
In which is perfect day.
4 Walk in the light! and e'en the tomb
No fearful shade shall wear;
Glory shall chase away its gloom,
For Christ hath conquered there.
No. 306. Revive Us Again.
Wm. P. Mackay.
J. J. Husband.
1. We praise Thee, O God! For the Son of Thy love,
2. We praise Thee, O God! For Thy Spir - it of light,
3. All glo - ry and praise To the Lamb that was slain,
For Je - sus who died And is now gone a - bove.
Who has shown us our Sav - ior, And scat - tered our night.
Who has borne all our sins And has cleansed ev - 'ry stain.
Refrain.
1
2
Hal - le - lu - jah! Thine the glo-ry, Hal - le - lu - jah! A - men! Re-vive us a - gain.

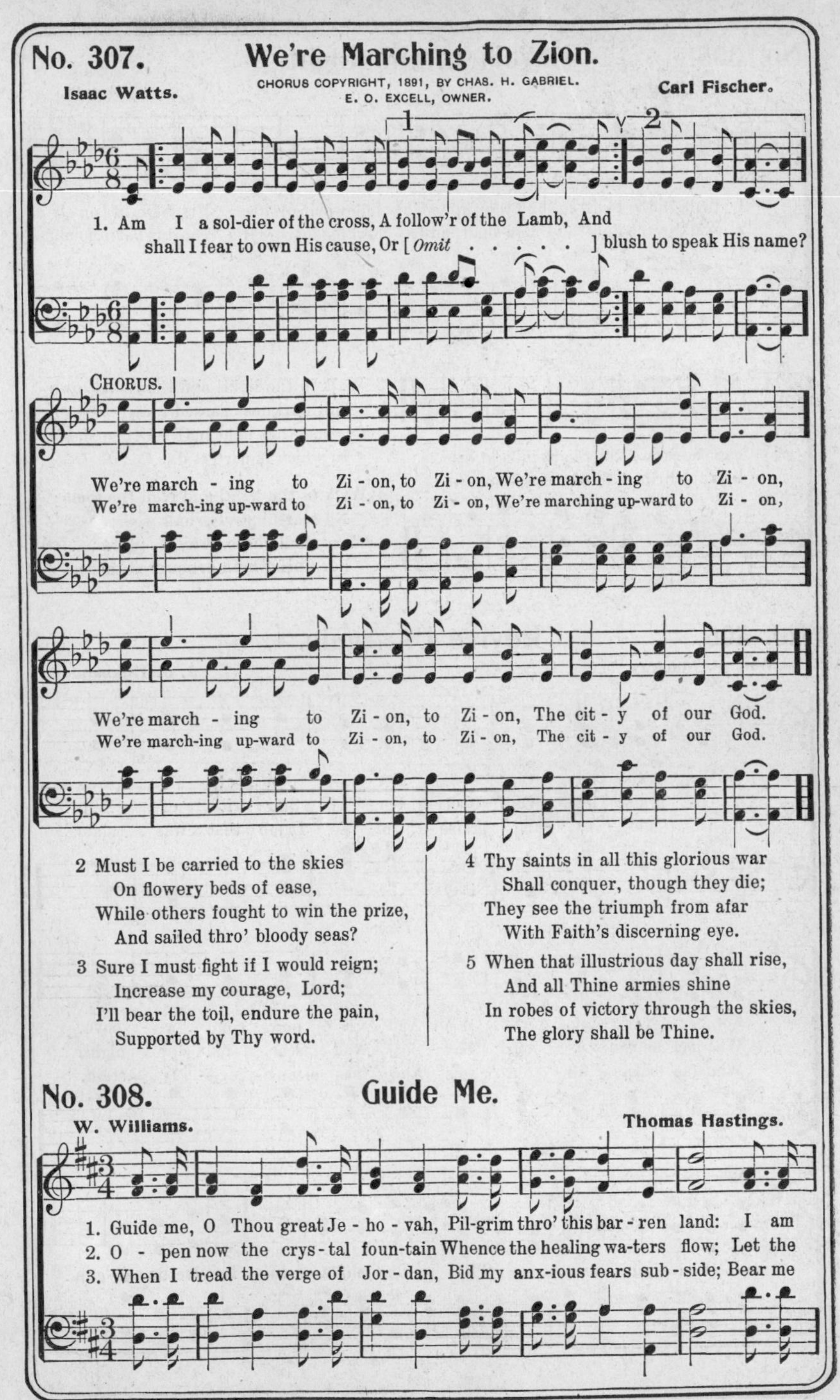
No. 307. We're Marching to Zion.
Isaac Watts.
CHORUS COPYRIGHT, 1891, BY CHAS. H. GABRIEL.
E. O. EXCELL, OWNER.
Carl Fischer.
1. Am I a sol-dier of the cross, A follow'r of the Lamb, And
shall I fear to own His cause, Or [Omit . . . . .] blush to speak His name?
CHORUS.
We're march - ing to Zi - on, to Zi - on, We're march - ing to Zi - on,
We're march-ing up-ward to Zi - on, to Zi - on, We're marching up-ward to Zi - on,
We're march - ing to Zi - on, to Zi - on, The cit - y of our God.
We're march-ing up-ward to Zi - on, to Zi - on, The cit - y of our God.
2 Must I be carried to the skies
On flowery beds of ease,
While others fought to win the prize,
And sailed thro' bloody seas?
3 Sure I must fight if I would reign;
Increase my courage, Lord;
I'll bear the toil, endure the pain,
Supported by Thy word.
4 Thy saints in all this glorious war
Shall conquer, though they die;
They see the triumph from afar
With Faith's discerning eye.
5 When that illustrious day shall rise,
And all Thine armies shine
In robes of victory through the skies,
The glory shall be Thine.
No. 308. Guide Me.
W. Williams.
Thomas Hastings.
1. Guide me, O Thou great Je - ho - vah, Pil-grim thro' this bar - ren land: I am
2. O - pen now the crys - tal foun-tain Whence the healing wa-ters flow; Let the
3. When I tread the verge of Jor - dan, Bid my anx-ious fears sub - side; Bear me

Guide Me.
weak but Thou art might-y, Hold me with Thy pow'r-ful hand; Bread of heav-en,
fier - y, cloud - y pil - lar Lead me all my jour-ney thro'; Strong De - liv-'rer,
thro' the swell-ing cur-rent; Land me safe on Ca-naan's side; Songs of prais-es
Feed me till I want no more; Bread of heav-en, Feed me till I want no more.
Be Thou still my strength and shield; Strong Deliv'rer, Be Thou still my strength and shield.
I will ev - er give to thee; Songs of praises I will ev - er give to Thee.
No. 309. O Day of Rest and Gladness.
Christopher Wordsworth.
Arr. by Lowell Mason.
1. { O day of rest and gladness, O day of joy and light,
O balm of care and sadness, Most beautiful, most brigth: } On thee, the high and lowly,
Thro' a - ges joined in tune, Sing "Ho-ly, ho - ly, ho - ly," To the great God Tri-une.
2 On thee, at the creation,
The light first had its birth;
On thee, for our salvation,
Christ rose from depths of earth;
On thee, our Lord victorious,
The Spirit sent from heaven;
And thus on thee, most glorious,
A triple light was given.
3 To-day on weary nations
The heavenly manna falls;
To holy convocations
The silver trumpet calls,
Where gospel light is glowing
With pure and radiant beams,
And living water flowing
With soul-refreshing streams.

No. 310. Whiter Than Snow.
James Nicholson.
USED BY PERMISSION OF WM. G. FISCHER.
Wm. G. Fischer.
1. Lord Je-sus, I long to be per-fect-ly whole; I want Thee for-ev-er to live in my soul, Break down ev-'ry i-dol, cast out ev-'ry foe; Now wash me, and
2. Lord Je-sus, look down from Thy throne in the skies, And help me to make a com-plete sac-ri-fice; I give up my-self and what-ev-er I know; Now wash me, and
3. Lord Je-sus, for this I most humbly en-treat, I wait, blessed Lord, at Thy cru-ci-fied feet; By faith, for my cleansing, I see Thy blood flow; Now wash me, and
FINE. CHORUS.
D. S.
I shall be whiter than snow. Whiter than snow, yes, whiter than snow; Now wash me, and
No. 311. Angels Ever Bright and Fair.
A. S. Sherwood.
Handel.
1. An-gels, ev-er bright and fair, Keep us all with-in thy care; Guard the al-tars of the home; Guide the steps that far may roam.
2 Round about encamping, stay
Near the loved ones far away;
Hover close to cheer and guide,
Whether joy or grief betide.
3 Angels, ever bright and fair,
In thy hands our dear ones bear;
Keep us all in memories sweet,
Till with joy again we meet.

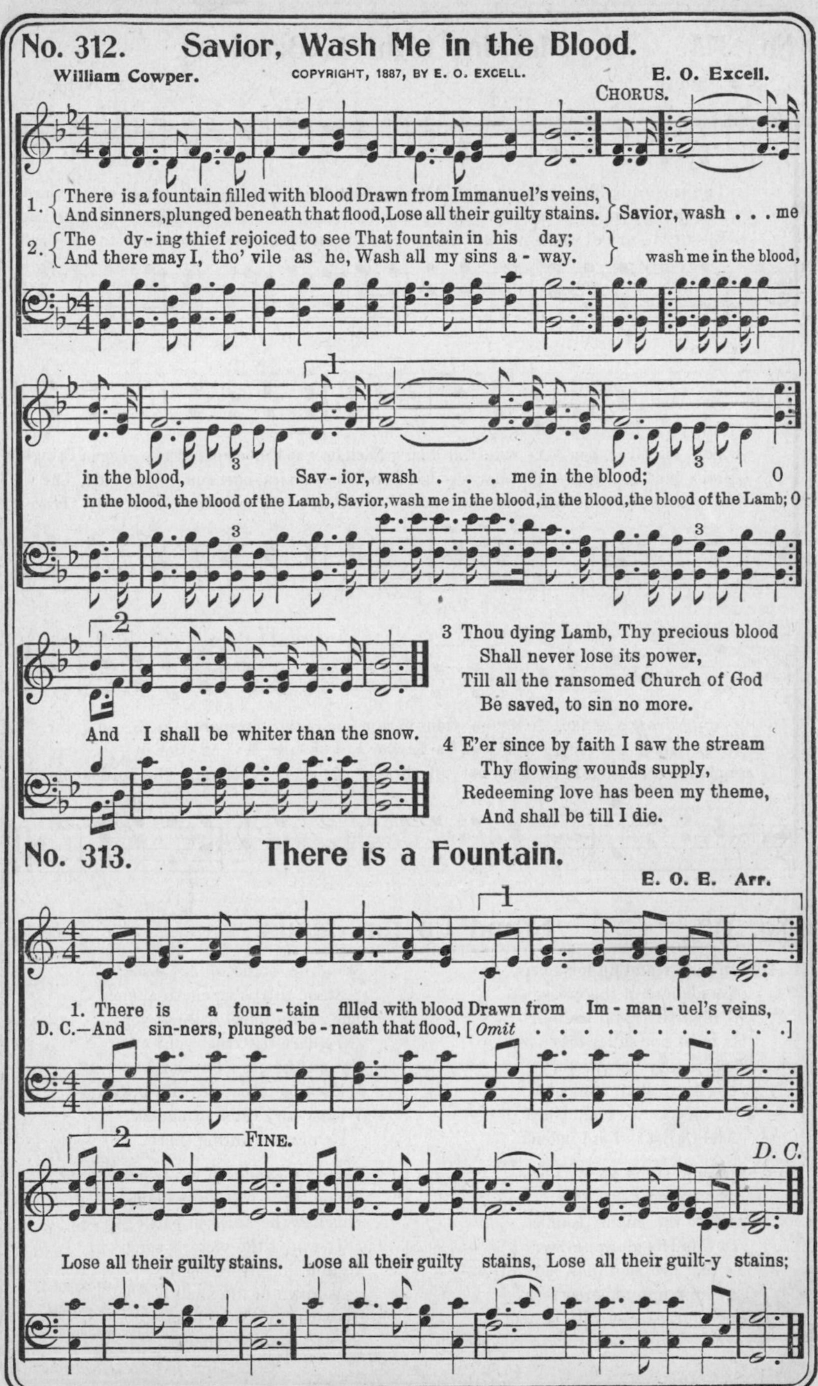
No. 312. Savior, Wash Me in the Blood.
William Cowper.
COPYRIGHT, 1887, BY E. O. EXCELL.
E. O. Excell.
CHORUS.
1. There is a fountain filled with blood Drawn from Immanuel's veins,
And sinners, plunged beneath that flood, Lose all their guilty stains.
2. The dy-ing thief rejoiced to see That fountain in his day;
And there may I, tho' vile as he, Wash all my sins a-way.
Savior, wash . . . me
wash me in the blood,
in the blood, Sav-ior, wash . . . me in the blood; O
in the blood, the blood of the Lamb, Savior, wash me in the blood, in the blood, the blood of the Lamb; O
And I shall be whiter than the snow.
3 Thou dying Lamb, Thy precious blood
Shall never lose its power,
Till all the ransomed Church of God
Be saved, to sin no more.
4 E'er since by faith I saw the stream
Thy flowing wounds supply,
Redeeming love has been my theme,
And shall be till I die.
No. 313. There is a Fountain.
E. O. E. Arr.
1. There is a foun-tain filled with blood Drawn from Im-man-uel's veins,
D. C.—And sin-ners, plunged be-neath that flood, [Omit . . . .]
FINE.
D. C.
Lose all their guilty stains. Lose all their guilty stains, Lose all their guilt-y stains;

No. 314. The Morning Light is Breaking.

S. F. Smith. G. J. Webb.

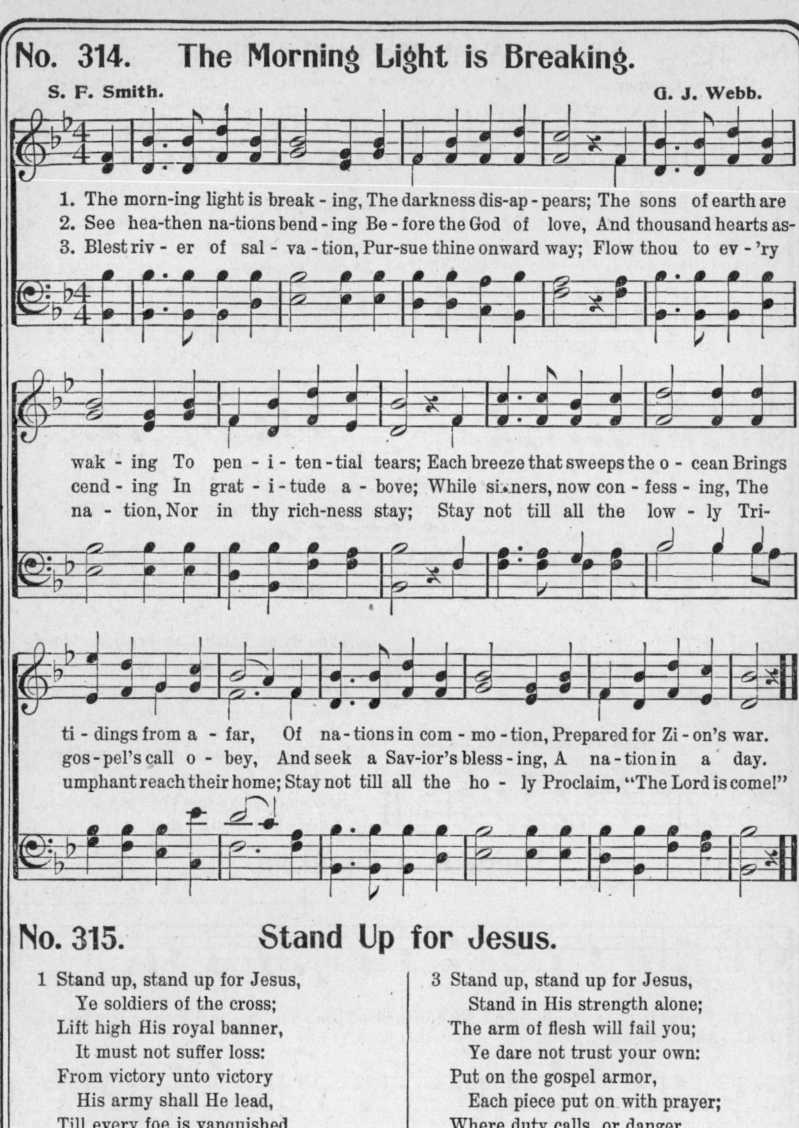

No. 315. Stand Up for Jesus.

1 Stand up, stand up for Jesus,
Ye soldiers of the cross;
Lift high His royal banner,
It must not suffer loss:
From victory unto victory
His army shall He lead,
Till every foe is vanquished
And Christ is Lord indeed.

2 Stand up, stand up for Jesus,
The trumpet call obey;
Forth to the mighty conflict,
In this His glorious day:
"Ye that are men, now serve Him,"
Against unnumbered foes;
Your courage rise with danger,
And strength to strength oppose.

3 Stand up, stand up for Jesus,
Stand in His strength alone;
The arm of flesh will fail you;
Ye dare not trust your own:
Put on the gospel armor,
Each piece put on with prayer;
Where duty calls, or danger,
Be never wanting there.

4 Stand up, stand up for Jesus,
The strife will not be long;
This day the noise of battle,
The next the victor's song:
To him that overcometh,
A crown of life shall be;
He with the King of glory
Shall reign eternally.

—George Duffield.

Responsive Readings.

No. 316. Morning Praise.

1. Hymn No. 263.

My faith looks up to Thee.

2. Responsive Reading.

LEADER—O Lord, thou hast searched me, and known me.

RESPONSE—Thou knowest my downsitting and mine uprising; thou understandest my thought afar off.

Thou compassest my path and my lying down, and art acquainted with all my ways.

For there is not a word in my tongue, but, lo, O Lord, thou knowest it altogether.

Whither shall I go from thy Spirit? Or whither shall I flee from thy presence?

If I ascend up into heaven, thou art there; if I make my bed in hell, behold, thou art there.

If I take the wings of the morning, and dwell in the uttermost parts of the sea;

Even there shall thy hand lead me and thy right hand shall hold me.

If I say, Surely the darkness shall cover me; even the night shall be light about me.

Yea, the darkness hideth not from thee; but the night shineth as the day: the darkness and the light are both alike to thee.

Search me, O God, and know my heart: try me, and know my thoughts.

And see if there be any wicked way in me, and lead me in the way everlasting.

How precious also are thy thoughts unto me, O God! How great is the sum of them!

If I should count them they are more in number than the sand: when I awake, I am still with thee.

3. Hymn No. 134.

When upon life's billows you are tempest-tossed.

No. 317. Prayer.

1. Hymn No. 267.

Sweet hour of prayer, etc.

2. Responsive Reading.

LEADER—If any man lack wisdom, let him ask of God, that giveth to all men liberally and upbraideth not, and it shall be given him.

RESPONSE—Confess your faults one to another, and pray one for another, that ye may be healed. The effectual fervent prayer of the righteous man availeth much.

Whatsoever ye ask the Father in my name, he will give it you; hitherto have ye asked nothing in my name: Ask, and ye shall receive, that your joy may be full.

Let us, therefore, come boldly unto the throne of grace, that we may obtain mercy, and find grace to help in time of need.

Praying always with all prayer and supplication in the Spirit, and watching thereunto with all perseverance and supplication for all saints.

Likewise the Spirit also helpeth our infirmities: for we know not what we should pray for as we ought: but the Spirit itself maketh intercession for us with groanings which cannot be uttered.

3. Hymn No. 265.

What a Friend we have in Jesus.

Responsive Readings.

No. 318. Evensong.

1. Hymn No. 106.

Day is dying in the west.

LEADER—O come, let us sing unto the Lord; let us come before his presence with singing; let us worship and bow down; let us kneel before the Lord, our Maker.

RESPONSE—Thou wilt keep him in perfect peace, whose mind is stayed on thee because he trusteth in thee.

2. Hymn No. 30.

When earthly cares and sorrows roll.

3. Responsive Reading.

LEADER—If any man thirst, let him come unto me, and drink. Whosoever drinketh of the water that I shall give him shall never thirst.

RESPONSE—I will call upon God and the Lord will save me; evening and morning and at noon will I pray and cry aloud and he will hear my voice.

It shall come to pass, that before they call, I will answer; and while they are yet speaking, I will hear.

My voice shalt thou hear in the morning, O Lord; in the morning will I direct my prayer unto thee and will look up.

O taste and see that the Lord is good; blessed is the man that trusteth in him.

O Lord, thou art my God, early will I seek thee; my soul thirsteth for thee.

Yea, I have loved thee with an everlasting love: therefore with loving-kindness have I drawn thee.

Because thy loving-kindness is better than life, my lips shall praise thee.

4. Hymn No. 270.

Abide with me! fast falls, etc.

No. 319. Promises.

1. Responsive Reading.

LEADER—Call upon me in the day of trouble: I will deliver thee, and thou shalt glorify me.

RESPONSE—And him that cometh to me, I will in no wise cast out.

I will instruct thee, and teach thee in the way which thou shalt go: I will guide thee with mine eye.

He is a shield unto them that put their trust in him.

The Lord is thy keeper: the Lord shall preserve thee from all evil: he shall preserve thy soul.

Before they call, I will answer; and while they are yet speaking, I will hear.

No good thing will he withhold from them that walk uprightly.

Commit thy works unto the Lord, and thy thoughts shall be established.

I will be with thy mouth, and teach thee what thou shalt say:

I will never leave thee, nor forsake thee.

2. Hymn No. 103.

Sweet is the promise.

No. 320. Praise.

1. Hymn No. 306.

We praise Thee, O God.

2. Responsive Reading.

LEADER—Praise ye the Lord, for it is good to sing praises unto our God, for it is pleasant, and praise is comely.

RESPONSE—I will praise thee, O Lord, with my whole heart; I will show forth all thy marvelous works.

Sing forth the honor of his name; make his praise glorious.

I will be glad and rejoice in thee; I will sing praise to thy name, O thou Most High.

Sing unto the Lord with thanksgiving; sing praise upon the harp unto our God.

I will bless the Lord at all times; his praise shall continually be in my mouth.

Because thy loving-kindness is better than life, my lips shall praise thee.

Sing unto the Lord, bless his name, show forth his salvation from day to day.

Every day will I bless thee, and I will praise thy name forever and ever.

O give thanks unto the Lord, for he is good, because his mercy endureth forever.

O that men would praise the Lord for his goodness, and for his wonderful works to the children of men.

He healeth the broken in heart, and bindeth up their wounds.

He giveth to the beast his food, and the young ravens which cry.

Great is the Lord, and greatly to be praised.

3. Hymn No. 299.

Jesus shall reign.

No. 321. Heaven.

1. Responsive Reading.

LEADER—For we know that if our earthly house of this tabernacle were dissolved, we have a building of God, an house not made with hands, eternal in the heavens.

RESPONSE—In my Father's house are many mansions: if it were not so, I would have told you. I go to prepare a place for you, that where I am, there ye may be also.

And one of the elders answered, saying unto me, What are these which are arrayed in white robes? and whence came they?

And he said unto me, These are they which came out of great tribulation, and have washed their robes, and made them white in the blood of the Lamb.

Therefore are they before the throne of God, and serve him day and night in his temple; and he that sitteth on the throne shall dwell among them.

They shall hunger no more, neither thirst any more; neither shall the sun light on them, nor any heat.

For the Lamb which is in the midst of the throne shall feed them, and shall lead them unto living fountains of waters: and God shall wipe away all tears from their eyes.

To him that overcometh will I give to eat of the tree of life in the paradise of God.

2. Hymn No. 277.

There's a land that is fairer, etc.

No. 322. Atonement.

1. Hymn No. 168.

I love to tell the story.

2. Responsive Reading.

LEADER—Greater love hath no man than this, that a man lay down his life for his friends.

RESPONSE—Hereby perceive we the love of God, because he laid down his life for us.

Even the son of man came not to be ministered unto, but to minister, and to give his life a ransom for many.

This is a faithful saying and worthy of all acceptation, that Christ Jesus came into the world to save sinners.

He that spared not his own Son, but delivered him up for us all, how shall he not with him also freely give us all things?

For he hath made him to be sin for us, who knew no sin; that we might be made the righteousness of God in him.

Christ hath redeemed us from the curse of the law, being made a curse for us; for it is written, Cursed is every one that hangeth on a tree.

For Christ also hath once suffered for sins, the just for the unjust, that he might bring us to God, being put to death in the flesh, but quickened by the Spirit.

But we see Jesus, who was made a little lower than the angels for the suffering of death, crowned with glory and honor; that he by the grace of God should taste death for every man.

How shall we escape, if we neglect so great salvation?

3. Hymn No. 294.

I hear Thy welcome voice.

Responsive Readings.

No. 323. The Name of Jesus.

Compiled by Marion Lawrance.

Superintendent—Stand up and bless the Lord your God for ever and ever; and blessed be thy glorious name.

1. Hymn No. 284. (3d verse.) *Rise.*

Jesus! the name that charms all fears.

Supt.—By how many names and titles is our Savior mentioned in the Bible?

School—Over two hundred and fifty.

Supt.—What are some of the names given to him hundreds of years before he was born?

School—For unto us a Child is born, unto us a Son is given; . . . . and his name shall be called Wonderful, Counselor, The Mighty God, The Everlasting Father, The Prince of Peace.

Supt.—God has highly exalted him, and given him a name which is above every name.

Pastor—He is the Lord of lords, and the King of kings.

Officers—Chiefest among ten thousand.

Senior Dept —Son of the Living God.

Young Men's Dept.—Lion of the tribe of Judah.

Young Women's Dept.—The Bright and Morning Star

Intermediate Dept.—The Light of the World.

Junior Dept.—The Good Shepherd.

Supt.—Which of all his names is the sweetest?

School—JESUS.

2. Hymn No. 292. (Refrain.)

Sweetest note in seraph song.

Supt.—Why was he called Jesus?

School—Thou shalt call his name JESUS; for he shall save his people from their sins.

Pastor—Neither is there salvation in any other; for there is none other name under heaven given among men whereby we must be saved.

Supt.—He is the Captain of our Salvation.

Officers—The Author and Finisher of our Faith.

Senior Dept.—The Head of the Church.

Young Men's Dept.—He is the Way, the Truth, and the Life.

Young Women's Dept.—The Precious Corner Stone.

Intermediate Dept.—The Friend of Sinners.

Junior Dept.—The Man of Sorrows.

Supt —But of all his names, which is the sweetest?

School—JESUS

3. Hymn No. 292. (Refrain.)

Sweetest note in seraph song.

4. Prayer.

Supt.—Oh, magnify the Lord with me, and let us exalt his name together.

5. Hymn No. 243, or No. 1.

All hail the power of Jesus' name.

No. 324. Value of the Word.

1. Responsive Reading.

LEADER—All scripture is given by inspiration of God, and is profitable for doctrine, for reproof, for correction, for instruction in righteousness;

RESPONSE—That the man of God be perfect, thoroughly furnished unto all good works.

Knowing this first, that no prophecy of the scripture is of any private interpretation. For the prophecy came not in old time by the will of man: But holy men of God spake as they were moved by the Holy Ghost.

Blessed is he that readeth, and they that hear the words of this prophecy, and keep those things which are written therein.

The word of the Lord in thy mouth is truth.

Be ye doers of the word and not hearers only.

Search the scriptures; for in them ye think ye have eternal life;

And they are they which testify of me.

Wherewithal shall a young man cleanse his way?

By taking heed thereto according to thy word.

Study to show thyself approved unto God,

A workman that needeth not to be ashamed, rightly divining the word of truth.

2. Hymn No. 114.

Holy Bible, Book divine.

Selected Psalms

No. 325. PSALM 1.

1 Blessed is the man that walketh not in the counsel of the ungodly, nor standeth in the way of sinners, nor sitteth in the seat of the scornful.

2 But his delight is in the law of the Lord; and in his law doth he meditate day and night.

3 And he shall be like a tree planted by the rivers of water, that bringeth forth his fruit in his season; his leaf also shall not wither, and whatsoever he doeth shall prosper.

4 The ungodly are not so; but are like the chaff which the wind driveth away.

5 Therefore the ungodly shall not stand in the judgment, nor sinners in the congregation of the righteous.

6 For the Lord knoweth the way of the righteous: but the way of the ungodly shall perish.

Hymn No. 310.

Lord Jesus, I long to be perfectly whole.

No. 326. PSALM 5.

1 Give ear to my words, O Lord consider my meditation.

2 Hearken unto the voice of my cry, my King and my God; for unto thee will I pray.

3 My voice shalt thou hear in the morning, O Lord; in the morning will I direct my prayer unto thee, and will look up.

4 For thou art not a God that hath pleasure in wickedness: neither shall evil dwell with thee.

5 The foolish shall not stand in thy sight: thou hatest all workers of iniquity.

6 Thou shalt destroy them that speak leasing: the Lord will abhor the bloody and deceitful man.

7 But as for me, I will come into thy house in the multitude of thy mercy: and in thy fear will I worship toward thy holy temple.

8 Lead me, O Lord, in thy righteousness because of mine enemies; make thy way straight before my face.

Hymn No. 308.

Guide me, O Thou great Jehovah.

No. 327. PSALM 8.

1 O Lord, how excellent is thy name in all the earth! who hast set thy glory above the heavens.

2 Out of the mouths of babes and sucklings hast thou ordained strength, because of thine enemies, that thou mightest still the enemy and the avenger.

3 When I consider thy heavens, the work of thy fingers, the moon and the stars, which thou hast ordained;

4 What is man, that thou art mindful of him? and the son of man, that thou visitest him?

5 For thou hast made him a little lower than the angels, and hast crowned him with glory and honor.

6 Thou madest him to have dominion over the works of thy hands; thou hast put all things under his feet:

7 All sheep and oxen, yea, and the beasts of the field;

8 The fowl of the air, and the fish of the sea, and whatsoever passeth through the paths of the seas,

9 O Lord, our Lord, how excellent is thy name in all the earth!

Hymn No. 284.

Oh, for a thousand tongues, to sing.

No. 328. PSALM 15

1 Lord, who shall abide in thy tabernacle? who shall dwell in thy holy hill?

2 He that walketh uprightly, and worketh righteousness, and speaketh the truth in his heart.

3 He that backbiteth not with nis tongue, nor doeth evil to his neighbor, nor taketh up a reproach against his neighbor.

4 In whose eyes a vile person is contemned; but he honoreth them that fear the Lord. He that sweareth to his own hurt, and changeth not.

5 He that putteth not out his money to usury, nor taketh reward against the innocent. He that doeth these things shall never be moved.

Hymn No. 271.

My Jesus, I love Thee.

Selected Psalms.

No. 329. PSALMS 17.

1 Hear the right, O Lord, attend unto my cry; give ear unto my prayer, that goeth not out of feigned lips.

2 Let my sentence come forth from thy presence; let thine eyes behold the things that are equal.

3 Thou hast proved mine heart; thou hast visited me in the night; thou hast tried me, and shalt find nothing: I am purposed that my mouth shall not trangress.

4 Concerning the works of men, by the word of thy lips I have kept me from the paths of the destroyer.

5 Hold up my goings in thy paths, that my footsteps slip not.

6 I have called upon thee, for thou wilt hear me, O God: incline thine ear unto me, and hear my speech.

Hymn No. 281.

O Love, that wilt not let me go

No. 330. PSALM 19.

1 The law of the Lord is perfect, converting the soul: the testimony of the Lord is sure, making wise the simple.

2 The statutes of the Lord are right, rejoicing the heart; the commandment of the Lord is pure enlightening the eyes.

3 The fear of the Lord is clean, enduring forever: the judjments of the Lord are true and righteous altogether.

4 More to be desired are they than gold, yea, than much fine gold: sweeter also honey and the honeycomb.

5 Morevover by them is thy servant warned; and in keeping of them there is great reward.

6 Who can understand his errors? cleanse thou me from secret faults.

7 Keep back thy servant also from presumptuous sins; let them not have dominion over me: then shall I be upright, and I shall be innocent from the great transgression.

8 Let the words of my mouth, and the meditation of my heart, be acceptable in thy sight, O Lord, my strength, and my Redeemer.

Hymn No. 288.

Break Thou the Bread of Life.

No 331. PSALM 23.

1 The Lord is my Shepherd; I shall not want.

2 He maketh me to lie down in green pastures: he leadeth me beside the still waters.

3 He restoreth my soul: he leadeth me in the paths of righteousness for his name's sake.

4 Yea, though I walk through the valley of the shadow of death, I will fear no evil: for thou art with me; thy rod and thy staff they comfort me.

5 Thou preparest a table before me in the presence of mine enemies: thou anointest my head with oil; my cup runneth over.

Hymn No 285.

Savior, like a shepherd lead us.

No. 332. PSALM 24.

1 The earth is the Lord's, and the fullness thereof; the world, and they that dwell therein.

2 For he hath founded it upon the seas, and established it upon the floods.

3 Who shall ascend into the hill of the Lord? or who shall stand in his holy place?

4 He that hath clean hands, and a pure heart; who hath not lifted his soul unto vanity, nor sworn deceitfully.

5 He shall receive the blessing from the Lord, and righteousness from the God of his salvation.

6 This is the generation of them that seek him, that seek thy face, O Jacob. Selah.

7 Lift up your heads, O ye gates; and be ye lifted up ye everlasting doors; and the King of glory shall come in.

8 Who is this King of glory? The Lord strong and mighty, the Lord mighty in battle.

9 Lift up your heads, O ye gates; even lift them up, ye everlasting doors; and the King of glory shall come in.

10 Who is this King of glory? The Lord of hosts, he is the King of glory. Selah.

Hymn No. 251.

O worship the King all-glorious above.

Selected Psalms.

No. 333. PSALM 27.

1 The Lord is my light and my salvation; whom shall I fear? the Lord is the strength of my life; of whom shall I be afraid?

2 When the wicked, even mine enemies and my foes, came upon me to eat up my flesh, they stumbled and fell.

3 Though a host should encamp against me, my heart shall not fear; though war should rise against me, in this will I be confident.

4 One thing have I desired of the Lord, that will I seek after; that I may dwell in the house of the Lord all the days of my life, to behold the beauty of the Lord, and to inquire in his temple.

5 For in the time of trouble he shall hide me in his pavilion; in the secret of his tabernacle shall he hide me; he shall set me up upon a rock.

6 And now shall mine head be lifted up above mine enemies round about me; therefore will I offer in his tabernacle sacrifices of joy; I will sing, yea, I will sing praises unto the Lord.

7 Hear, O Lord, when I cry with my voice: have mercy also upon me, and answer me.

Hymn No. 287.

Come, Thou Almighty King.

No. 334. PSALM 32.

1 Blessed is he whose transgression is forgiven, whose sin is covered.

2 Blessed is the man unto whom the Lord imputeth not iniquity, and in whose spirit there is no guile.

3 When I kept silence, my bones waxed old through my roaring all the day long.

4 For day and night thy hand was heavy upon me; my moisture is turned into the drought of summer. Selah.

5 I acknowledged my sin unto thee, and mine iniquity have I not hid. I said, I will confess my transgressions unto the Lord; and thou forgavest the iniquity of my sin. Selah.

6 For this shall every one that is godly pray unto thee in a time when thou mayest be found; surely in the floods of great waters they shall not come nigh unto him.

7 Thou art my hiding place; thou shalt preserve me from trouble; thou shalt compass me above with songs of deliverance. Selah.

Hymn No. 254.

Rock of Ages, cleft for me.

No. 335. PSALM 34.

1 I will bless the Lord at all times; His praise shall continually be in my mouth.

2 My soul shall make her boast in the Lord: the humble shall hear thereof, and be glad.

3 O magnify the Lord with me, and let us exalt his name together.

4 I sought the Lord, and he heard me, and delivered me from all my fears.

5 They looked unto him, and were lightened: and their faces were not ashamed.

6 This poor man cried, and the Lord heard him, and saved him out of all his troubles.

7 The angel of the Lord encampeth round about them that fear him, and delivereth them.

8 O taste and see that the Lord is good; blessed is the man that trusteth in Him.

Hymn No. 263.

My faith looks up to Thee.

No. 336. PSALM 51.

1 Have mercy upon me, O God according to thy loving-kindness: according unto the multitude of thy tender mercies blot out my transgressions.

2 Wash me thoroughly from mine iniquity, and cleanse me from my sin.

3 For I acknowledge my transgressions: and my sin is ever before me.

4 Against thee, thee only, have I sinned, and done this evil in thy sight: that thou mightest be justified when thou speakest, and be clear when thou judgest.

5 Behold, I was shapen in iniquity; and in sin did my mother conceive me.

6 Behold, thou desireth truth in the inward parts: and in the hidden part thou shalt make me to know wisdom.

7 Purge me with hyssop, and I shall be clean: wash me, and I shall be whiter than snow.

8 Make me to hear joy and gladness, that the bones which thou hast broken may rejoice.

9 Hide thy face from my sins, and blot out all my iniquities.

10 Create in me a clean heart, O God; and renew a right spirit within me.

Hymn No. 310.

Lord Jesus, I long to be perfectly whole.

Selected Psalms.

No. 337. PSALM 61.

1 Hear my cry, O God; attend unto my prayer.

2 From the end of the earth will I cry unto thee, when my heart is overwhelmed; lead me to the rock that is higher than I.

3 For thou hast been a shelter for me, and a strong tower from the enemy.

4 I will abide in thy tabernacle forever: I will trust in the covert of thy wings.

5 For thou, O God, hast heard my vows; thou hast given me the heritage of them that fear thy name.

6 Thou wilt prolong the king's life: and his years as many generations.

7 He shall abide before God forever; O prepare mercy and truth, which may preserve him.

8 So will I sing praise unto thy name forever, that I may daily perform my vows.

Hymn No. 306.

We Praise Thee, O God.

No. 338. PSALM 63.

1 O God, thou art my God; early will I seek thee; my soul thirsteth for thee, my flesh longeth for thee in a dry and thirsty land, where no water is;

2 To see thy power and thy glory, so as I have seen thee in the sanctury.

3 Because thy loving kindness is better than life, my lips shall praise thee.

4 Thus will I bless thee while I live; I will lift up my hands in thy name.

5 My soul shall be satisfied as with marrow and fatness; and my mouth shall praise thee with joyful lips:

6 When I remember thee upon my bed, and meditate on thee in the night watches.

7 Because thou hast been my help, therefore in the shadow of thy wings will I rejoice.

8 My soul followeth hard after thee; thy right hand upholdeth me.

9 But those that seek my soul, to destroy it, shall go into the lower parts of the earth.

10 They shall fall by the sword: they shall be a portion for foxes.

11 But the king shall rejoice in God; every one that sweareth by him shall glory: but the mouth of them that speak lies shall be stopped.

Hymn No. 274.

My soul, be on thy guard.

No. 339. PSALM 65

1 Praise waiteth for thee, O God in Zion: and unto thee shall the vow be performed.

2 O thou that hearest prayer, unto thee shall all flesh come.

3 Iniquities prevail against me; as for our transgressions, thou shalt purge them away.

4 Blessed is the man whom thou chooseth, and causest to approach unto thee, that he may dwell in thy courts, we shall be satisfied with the goodness of thy house, even thy holy temple.

5 By terrible things in righteousness wilt thou answer us, O God of our salvation: who are the confidence of all the ends of the earth, and of them that are afar off upon the sea.

6 Which by his strength setteth fast the mountains; being girded with power.

7 Which stilleth the noise of the seas, the noise of their waves, and the tumult of the people.

8 They also that dwell in the uttermost parts are afraid at thy tokens: thou makest the outgoings of the morning and evening rejoice.

9 Thou visitest the earth, and waterest it: thou greatly enrichest it with the river of God, which is full of water: thou preparest them corn, when thou hast so provided for it.

Hymn No. 244.

Glorious things of thee are spoken.

No. 340. PSALM 67.

1 God be merciful unto us, and bless us and cause his face to shine upon us. Selah.

2 That thy way may be known upon earth, thy saving health among all nations.

3 Let the people praise thee, O God; let all the people praise thee.

4 O let the nations be glad and sing for joy: for thou shalt judge the people righteously, and govern the nations upon earth. Selah.

5 Let the people praise thee, O God; let all the people praise thee.

6 Then shall the earth yield her increase. and God, even our own God, shall bless us.

7 God shall bless us; and all the ends of the earth shall fear him.

Hymn No. 134.

When upon life's billows you are, etc.

Selected Psalms.

No. 341. PSALL 84.

1 How amiable are thy tabernacles, O Lord of hosts!

2 My soul longeth, yea, even fainteth for the courts of the Lord: my heart and my flesh crieth out for the living God.

3 Yea, the sparrow hath found an house, and the swallow a nest for herself, where she may lay her young, even thine altars, O Lord of hosts, my King, and my God.

4 Blessed are they that dwell in thy house: they will be still praising thee. Selah.

5 Blessed is the man whose strength is in thee; in whose heart are the ways of them.

6 Who passing through the valley of Baca make it a well: the rain also filleth the pools.

7 They go from strength to strength, every one of them in Zion appeareth before God.

8 O Lord God of hosts, hear my prayer: give ear, O God of Jacob. Selah.

9 Behold, O God, our shield, and look upon the face of thine anointed.

10 For a day in thy courts is better than a thousand. I had rather be a doorkeeper in the house of my God, than to dwell in the tents of wickedness.

11 For the Lord God is a sun and shield: the Lord will give grace and glory: no good thing will he withhold from them that walk uprightly.

12 O Lord of hosts, blessed is the man that trusteth in thee.

Hymn No. 244.

Glorious things of thee are spoken.

No. 342. PSALM 91.

1 He that dwelleth in the secret place of the Most High shall abide under the shadow of the Almighty.

2 I will say of the Lord, he is my refuge and my fortress: my God; in him will I trust.

3 Surely he shall deliver thee from the snare of the fowler, and from the noisome pestilence.

4 He shall cover thee with his feathers, and under his wings shalt thou trust: his truth shall be thy shield and buckler.

5 Thou shalt not be afraid for the terror by night; nor for the arrow that flieth by day;

6 Nor for the pestilence that walketh in the darkness: nor for the destruction that wasteth at noonday.

7 A thousand shall fall at thy side, and ten thousand at thy right hand; but it shall not come nigh thee.

8 Only with thine eyes shalt thou behold and see the reward of the wicked.

9 Because thou hast made the Lord which is my refuge, even the Most High, thy habitation.

Hymn No. 297.

Jesus, Lover of my soul.

No. 343. PSALM 93.

1 The Lord reigneth, he is clothed with majesty; the Lord is clothed with strength, wherewith he hath girded himself: the world also is established, and cannot be moved.

2 Thy throne is established of old; thou art from everlasting.

3 The floods have lifted up, O Lord, the floods have lifted up their voice; the floods lift up their waves.

4 The Lord on high is mightier than the noise of many waters, yea, than the mighty waves of the sea.

5 The testimonies are very sure: holiness becometh thine house, O Lord, for ever.

Hymn No. 291.

Holy, holy, holy, Lord God Almighty.

No. 344. PSALM 95.

1 O come, let us sing unto the Lord; let us make a joyful noise to the Rock of our salvation.

2 Let us come before his presence with thanksgiving, and make a joyful noise unto him with psalms.

3 For the Lord is a great God, and a great King above all gods.

4 In his hand are the deep places of the earth: the strength of the hills is his also.

5 The sea is his, and he made it; and his hand formed the dry land.

6 O come, let us worship and bow down: let us kneel before the Lord, our Maker.

7 For he is our God; and we are the people of his pasture, and the sheep of his hand.

Hymn No. 251.

O worship the King all-glorious above.

Selected Psalms,

No. 345. PSALM 98.

1 O sing unto the Lord a new song; for he hath done marvelous things; his right hand, and his holy arm, hath gotten him the victory.

2 The Lord hath made known his salvation: his righteousness hath he openly showed in the sight of the heathen.

3 He hath remembered his mercy and his truths toward the house of Israel: all the ends of the earth have seen the salvation of our God.

4 Make a joyful noise unto the Lord, all the earth; make a loud noise, and rejoice, and sing praise.

5 Sing unto the Lord with the harp; with the harp, and the voice of a psalm.

6 With trumpets and sound of cornet make a joyful noise before the Lord, the King.

7 Let the sea roar, and the fullness thereof; the world, and they that dwell therein.

8 Let the floods clap their hands: let the hills be joyful together.

9 Before the Lord; for he cometh to judge the earth: with righteousness shall he judge the world, and the people with equity.

Hymn No. 1.

All hail the power of Jesus' name.

No 346. PSALM 103.

1 Bless the Lord, O my soul: and all that is within me, bless his holy name.

2 Bless the Lord, O my soul, and forget not all his benefits.

3 Who forgiveth all thine iniquities; who healeth all thy diseases;

4 Who redeemeth thy life from destruction; who crowneth thee with loving kindness and tender mercies;

5 Who satisfieth thy mouth with good things; so that thy youth is renewed like the eagle's.

6 The Lord executeth righteousness and judgment of all that are oppressed.

7 He made known his ways unto Moses, his acts unto the children of Israel.

8 The Lord is merciful and gracious, slow to anger, and plenteous in mercy.

9 He will not always chide: neither will he keep his anger forever.

10 He hath not dealt with us after our sins; nor rewarded us according to our iniquities.

11 For as the heaven is high above the earth, so great is his mercy toward them that fear him.

12 As far as the east is from the west, so far hath he removed our transgressions from us.

Hymn No. 276.

O happy day, that fixed my choice.

No. 347. PSALM 119.

1 Blessed are the undefiled in the way, who walk in the law of the Lord.

2 Blessed are they that keep his testimonies, and that seek him with the whole heart.

3 They also do no iniquity: they walk in his ways.

4 Thou hast commanded us to keep thy precepts diligently.

5 O that my ways were directed to keep thy statutes.

6 Then shall I not be ashamed, when I have respect unto all thy commandments.

7 I will praise thee with uprightness of heart, when I shall have learned thy righteous judgments.

8 I will keep thy statutes: O forsake me not utterly.

Hymn No. 262.

Nearer, my God, to Thee.

No. 348. PSALM 122.

1 I was glad when they said unto me, Let us go into the house of the Lord.

2 Our feet shall stand within thy gates, O Jerusalem.

3 Jerusalem is builded as a city that is compact together.

4 Whither the tribes go up, the tribes of the Lord, unto the testimony of Israel, to give thanks unto the name of the Lord.

5 For there are set thrones of judgment, the thrones of the house of David.

6 Pray for the peace of Jerusalem: they shall prosper that love thee.

7 Peace be within thy walls, and prosperity within thy palaces.

8 For my brethren and companions' sakes, I will now say, Peace be within thee.

9 Because of the house of the Lord our God I will seek thy good.

Hymn No. 286.

I love Thy kingdom, Lord.

Patriotic Songs

No. 349. Home, Sweet Home.

John Howard Payne. H. R. Bishop.

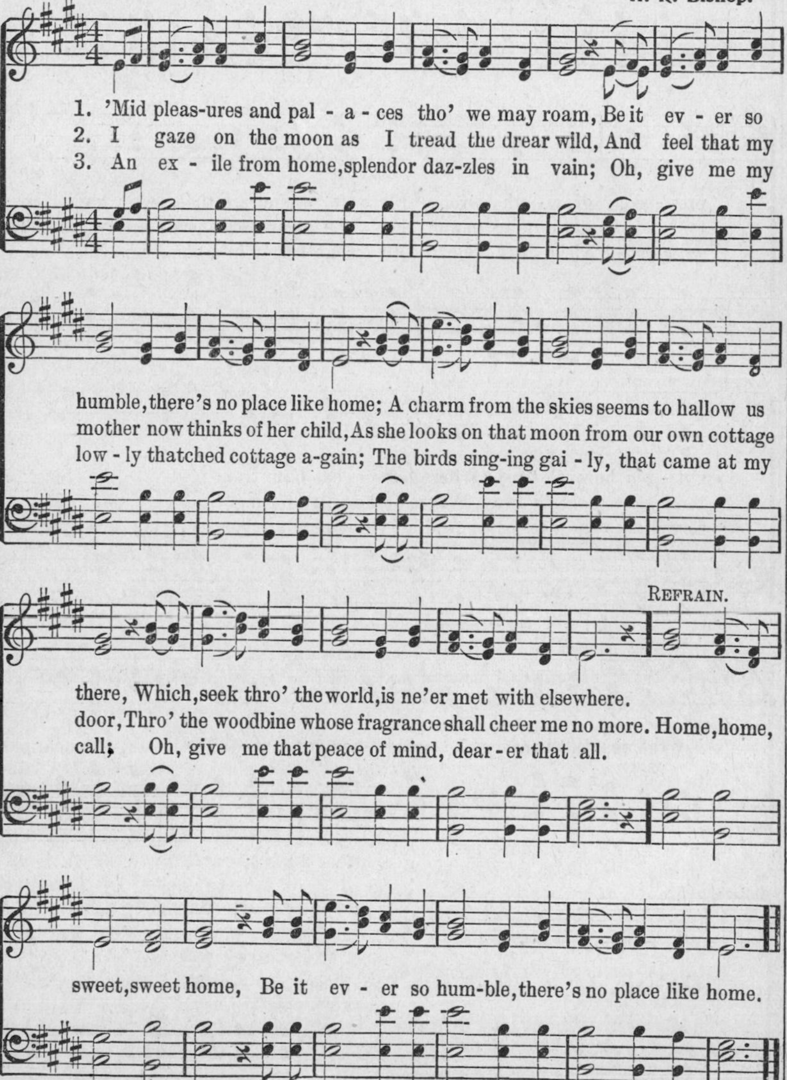

1. 'Mid pleas-ures and pal - a - ces tho' we may roam, Be it ev - er so
2. I gaze on the moon as I tread the drear wild, And feel that my
3. An ex - ile from home, splendor daz-zles in vain; Oh, give me my

humble, there's no place like home; A charm from the skies seems to hallow us
mother now thinks of her child, As she looks on that moon from our own cottage
low - ly thatched cottage a-gain; The birds sing-ing gai - ly, that came at my

there, Which, seek thro' the world, is ne'er met with elsewhere.
door, Thro' the woodbine whose fragrance shall cheer me no more. Home, home,
call; Oh, give me that peace of mind, dear-er that all.

REFRAIN.

sweet, sweet home, Be it ev - er so hum-ble, there's no place like home.

No. 350. Fly the Dear Old Banner.
Mrs. Frank A. Breck.
COPYRIGHT, 1906, BY CHAS. H. GABRIEL. E. O. EXCELL, OWNER.
Chas. H. Gabriel.
1. Fly the dear old ban-ner wher-ev-er dwelleth wrong; Fly it where op-
2. Fly the dear old ban-ner where dwelleth grief and shame, Un-til lib-er-
3. Fly the dear old ban-ner, yea, with an arm of might; Fly it till the
pres-sion grow-eth strong; Fly it where are those who have for-
ty is more than name; Fly the dear old ban-ner where in-
wrong shall yield to right; Fly dear free-dom's ban-ner till en-
got-ten how to trust, Where hon-or has been tram-pled in the dust.
temp'rance holdeth sway, Where orphans cry for hun-ger day by day.
slaved ones know re-lease, And ev-'ry-where are plen-ty, joy, and peace.
CHORUS.
Fly the dear old ban-ner, 't is good e-nough for me (for me)! Fly the dear old
ban-ner, the en-sign of the free! 'T is good e-nough for me, it is

Fly the Dear Old Banner.

No. 351. Hurrah for the Red, White and Blue.

E. L. McCord. USED BY PERMISSION. W. W. Gilchrist.

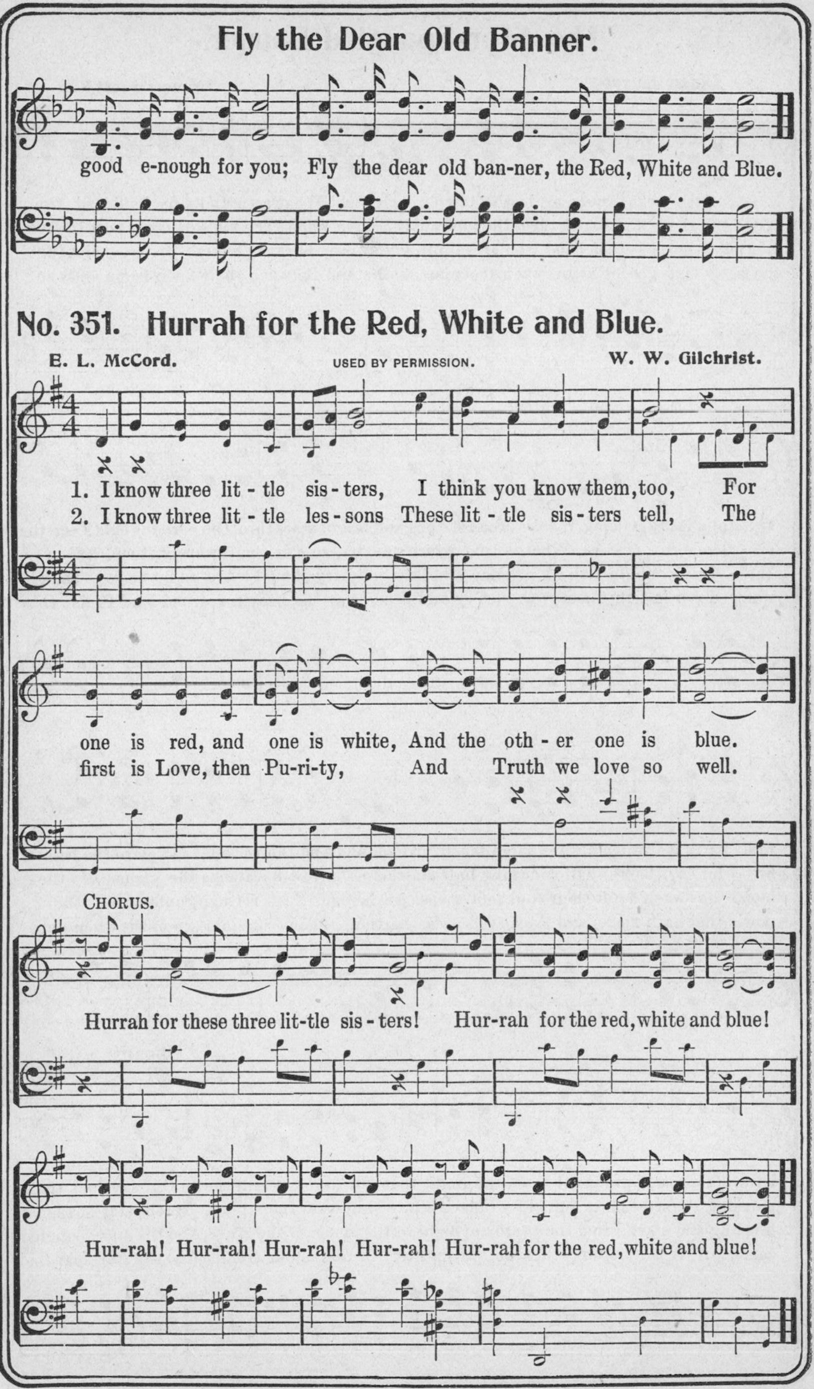

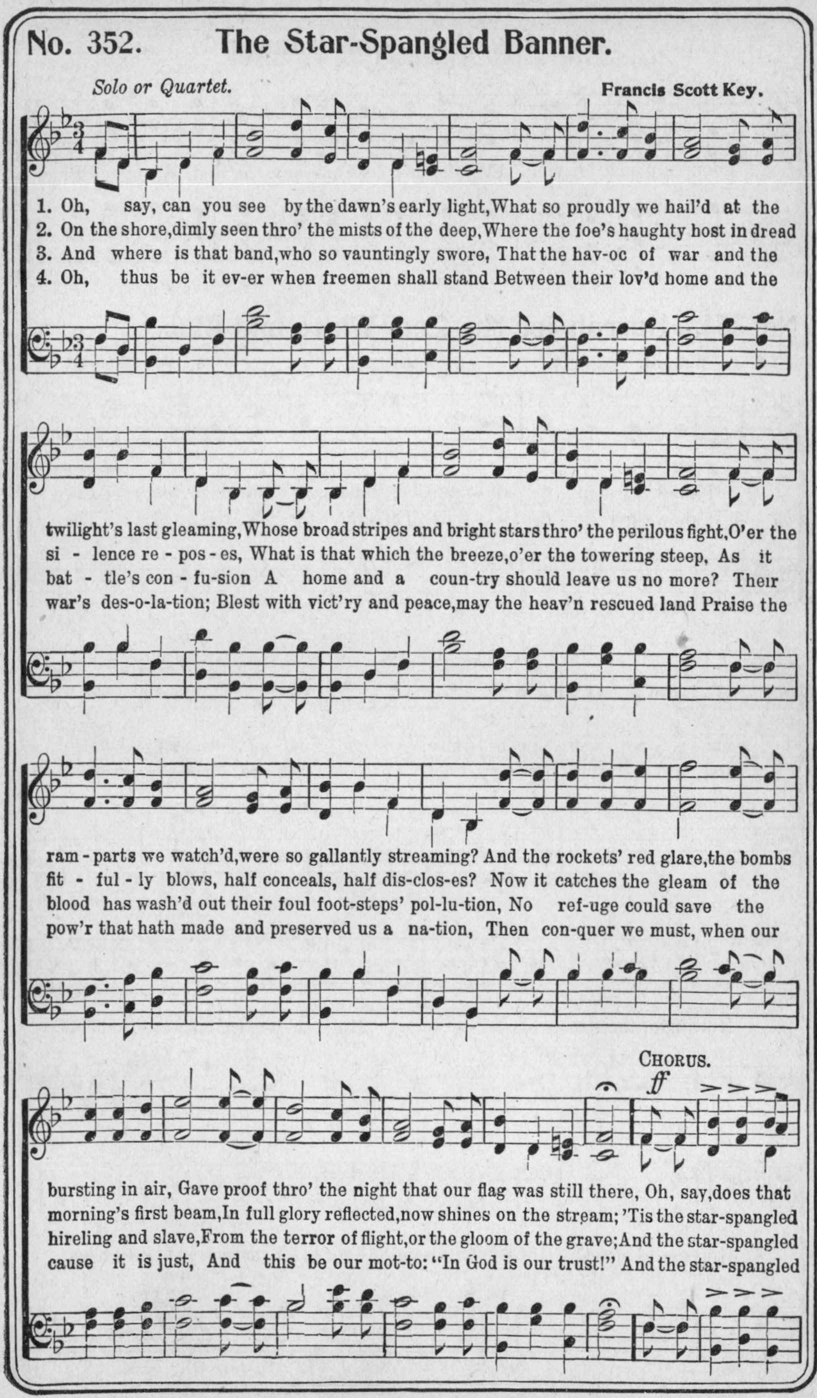
No. 352. The Star-Spangled Banner.
Solo or Quartet.
Francis Scott Key.
1. Oh, say, can you see by the dawn's early light, What so proudly we hail'd at the
2. On the shore, dimly seen thro' the mists of the deep, Where the foe's haughty host in dread
3. And where is that band, who so vauntingly swore, That the hav-oc of war and the
4. Oh, thus be it ev-er when freemen shall stand Between their lov'd home and the
twilight's last gleaming, Whose broad stripes and bright stars thro' the perilous fight, O'er the
si - lence re - pos - es, What is that which the breeze, o'er the towering steep, As it
bat - tle's con - fu-sion A home and a coun-try should leave us no more? Their
war's des-o-la-tion; Blest with vict'ry and peace, may the heav'n rescued land Praise the
ram - parts we watch'd, were so gallantly streaming? And the rockets' red glare, the bombs
fit - ful - ly blows, half conceals, half dis-clos-es? Now it catches the gleam of the
blood has wash'd out their foul foot-steps' pol-lu-tion, No ref-uge could save the
pow'r that hath made and preserved us a na-tion, Then con-quer we must, when our
CHORUS.
ff
bursting in air, Gave proof thro' the night that our flag was still there, Oh, say, does that
morning's first beam, In full glory reflected, now shines on the stream; 'Tis the star-spangled
hireling and slave, From the terror of flight, or the gloom of the grave; And the star-spangled
cause it is just, And this be our mot-to: "In God is our trust!" And the star-spangled

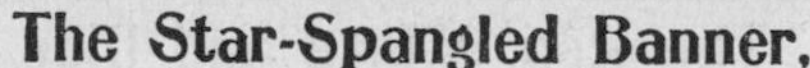

The Star-Spangled Banner.

star-spangled ban-ner yet wave O'er the land of the free, and the home of the brave?
ban-ner; oh, long may it wave O'er the land of the free, and the home of the brave?
ban-ner in tri-umph doth wave O'er the land of the free, and the home of the brave?
ban-ner in tri-umph shall wave O'er the land of the free, and the home of the brave?

No. 353. America.

S. F. Smith. The National Song of America. English.

1. My country! 'tis of thee, Sweet land of lib - er - ty, Of thee I sing; Land where my
2. My na - tive coun-try, thee, Land of the no - ble, free, Thy name I love; I love thy
3. Let music swell the breeze, And ring from all the trees Sweet freedom's song: Let mortal
4. Our father's God! to Thee, Au-thor of lib - er - ty, To Thee we sing; Long may our

fathers died, Land of the pilgrim's pride, From ev'ry mountain side, Let free-dom ring!
rocks and rills, Thy woods and templed hills; My heart with rapture thrills Like that above.
tongues awake, Let all that breathe partake, Let rocks their sil ence break, The sound prolong.
land be bright With freedom's holy light; Protect us by Thy might, Great God, our King!

No. 354. God Save the King.

The National Song of Britain.

1.

God save our gracious King,
Long live our noble King,
God save the King;
Send him victorious,
Happy and glorious,
Long to reign over us,
God save the King.

2.

Thro' every changing scene,
O Lord, preserve our King,
Long may he reign;
His heart inspire and move
With wisdom from above,
And in a nation's love
His throne maintain.

3.

Thy choicest gifts in store,
On him be pleased to pour,
Long may he reign;
May he defend our laws,
And ever give us cause,
To sing with heart and voice,
God save the King.

No. 355. The Red, White and Blue.
1. O Co-lum-bia! the gem of the o-cean, The home of the brave and the free;
2. When war wing'd its wide des-o-la-tion, And threaten'd the land to de-form,
3. Then sons of Co-lum-bia, come hither, And join in our nation's sweet hymn;
The shrine of each patriot's de-vo-tion, A world offers homage to thee,
The ark then of freedom's foundation, Columbia rode safe thro' the storm;
May the wreaths they have won never wither, Nor the stars of their glory grow dim!
Thy mandates make heroes as-sem-ble, When lib-er-ty's form stands in view;
With her garlands of vict'ry around her; When so proudly she bore her brave crew,
May the serv-ice u-ni-ted, ne'er sev-er, But they to their colors prove true!
FINE.
Thy banners make tyr-an-ny tremble, When borne by the red, white and blue.
With her flag proudly waving before her, The boast of the red, white and blue.
The Ar-my and Na-vy for-ev-er, Three cheers for the red, white and blue.
CHORUS.
When borne by the red, white and blue, When borne by the red, white and blue.
The boast of the red, white and blue, The boast of the red, white and blue.
Three cheers for the red, white and blue, Three cheers for the red, white and blue.
D. S.

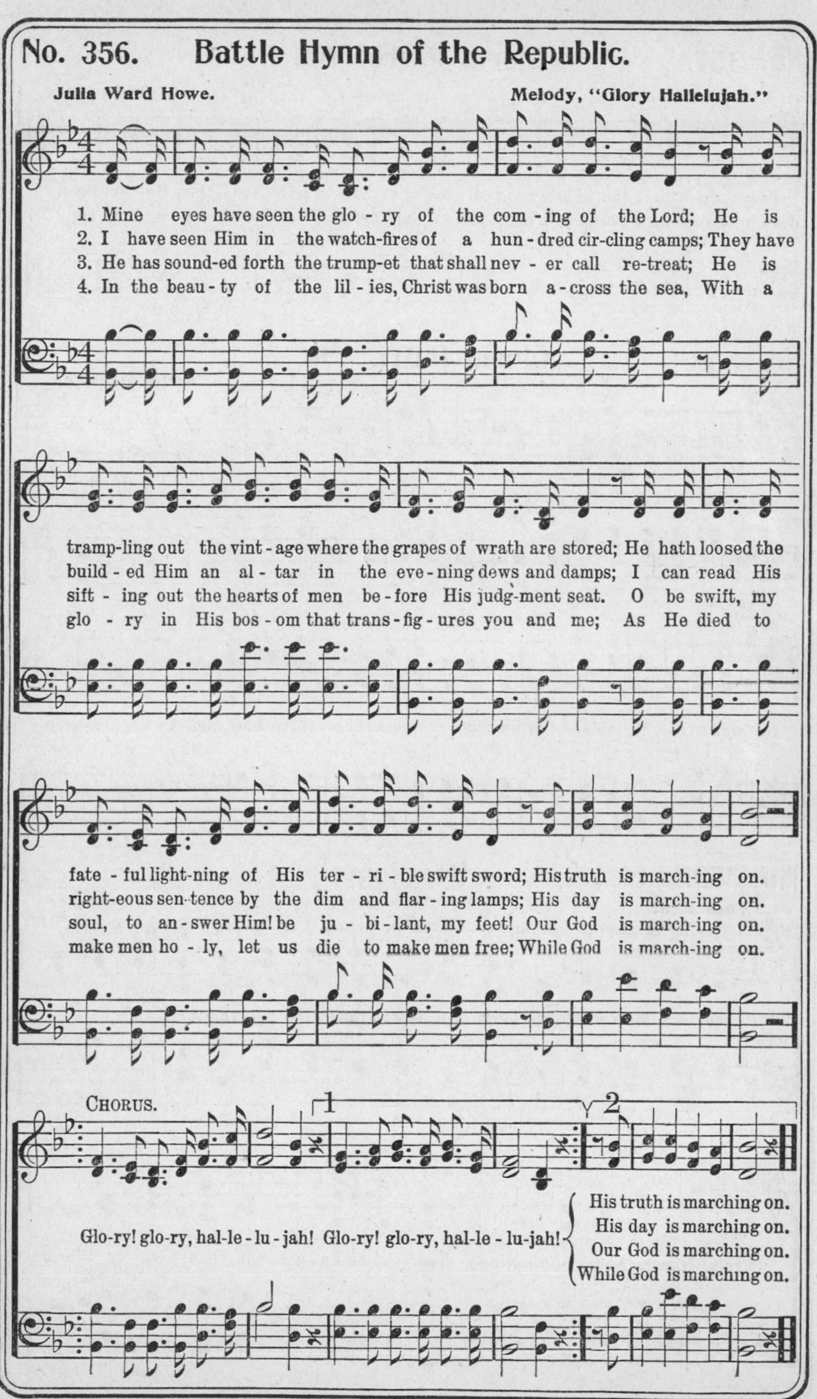
No. 356. Battle Hymn of the Republic.
Julia Ward Howe.
Melody, "Glory Hallelujah."
1. Mine eyes have seen the glo - ry of the com - ing of the Lord; He is
2. I have seen Him in the watch-fires of a hun - dred cir-cling camps; They have
3. He has sound-ed forth the trump-et that shall nev - er call re-treat; He is
4. In the beau - ty of the lil - ies, Christ was born a - cross the sea, With a
tramp-ling out the vint - age where the grapes of wrath are stored; He hath loosed the
build - ed Him an al - tar in the eve - ning dews and damps; I can read His
sift - ing out the hearts of men be - fore His judg-ment seat. O be swift, my
glo - ry in His bos - om that trans - fig - ures you and me; As He died to
fate - ful light-ning of His ter - ri - ble swift sword; His truth is march-ing on.
right-eous sen-tence by the dim and flar - ing lamps; His day is march-ing on.
soul, to an - swer Him! be ju - bi - lant, my feet! Our God is march-ing on.
make men ho - ly, let us die to make men free; While God is march-ing on.
CHORUS.
1
2
Glo-ry! glo-ry, hal-le - lu - jah! Glo-ry! glo-ry, hal-le - lu-jah!
His truth is marching on.
His day is marching on.
Our God is marching on.
While God is marching on.

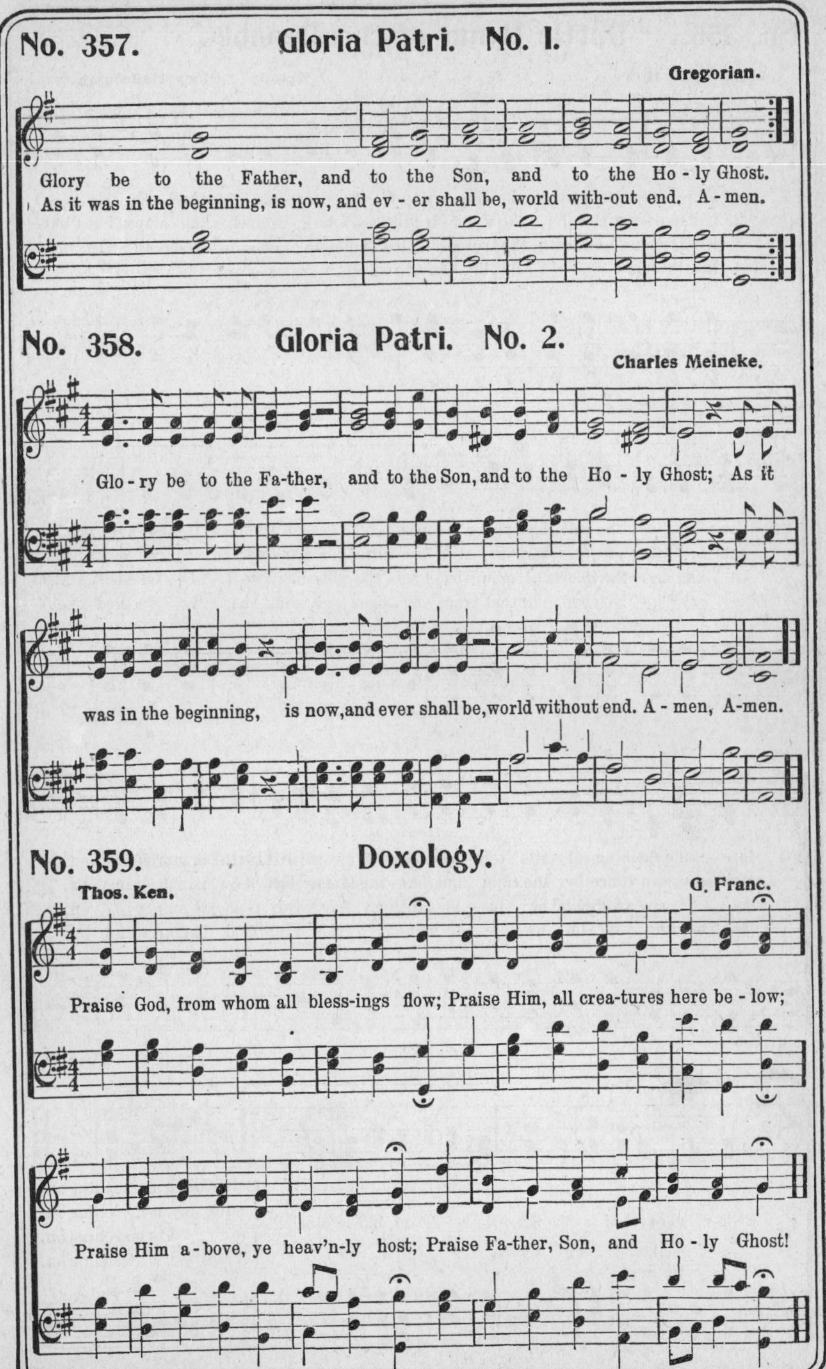
No. 357. Gloria Patri. No. 1.
Gregorian.
Glory be to the Father, and to the Son, and to the Ho-ly Ghost.
As it was in the beginning, is now, and ev - er shall be, world with-out end. A-men.
No. 358. Gloria Patri. No. 2.
Charles Meineke.
Glo-ry be to the Fa-ther, and to the Son, and to the Ho - ly Ghost; As it
was in the beginning, is now, and ever shall be, world without end. A - men, A-men.
No. 359. Doxology.
Thos. Ken.
G. Franc.
Praise God, from whom all bless-ings flow; Praise Him, all crea-tures here be - low;
Praise Him a-bove, ye heav'n-ly host; Praise Fa-ther, Son, and Ho - ly Ghost!

Index.

INDEX.

INDEX.

INDEX.

INDEX.

Responsive Readings.

Selected Psalms.